D1239397

Introduction to
MASS SPECTROMETRY
and Its Applications

PRENTICE-HALL INTERNATIONAL SERIES IN CHEMISTRY

PRENTICE-HALL, INC.
PRENTICE-HALL INTERNATIONAL, INC., UNITED KINGDOM AND EIRE
PRENTICE-HALL OF CANADA, LTD., CANADA

J. S. Griffith:

THE IRREDUCIBLE TENSOR METHOD FOR
MOLECULAR SYMMETRY GROUPS

J. H. Hildebrand and R. L. Scott:

REGULAR SOLUTIONS

E. K. Hyde, I. Perlman, and G. T. Seaborg:

THE NUCLEAR PROPERTIES OF THE HEAVY ELEMENTS
Volume I: Systematics of Nuclear Structure and Radioactivity

E. K. Hyde, I. Perlman, and G. T. Seaborg:

THE NUCLEAR PROPERTIES OF THE HEAVY ELEMENTS
Volume II: Detailed Radioactivity Properties

E. K. Hyde:

THE NUCLEAR PROPERTIES OF THE HEAVY ELEMENTS
Volume III: Fission Phenomena

R. W. Kiser:

INTRODUCTION TO MASS SPECTROMETRY
AND ITS APPLICATIONS

W. T. Simpson:

THEORIES OF ELECTRONS IN MOLECULES

Introduction to MASS SPECTROMETRY and Its Applications

ROBERT W. KISER

Associate Professor
Department of Chemistry
Kansas State University

PRENTICE-HALL, INC.

Englewood Cliffs, N.J.

PRENTICE-HALL INTERNATIONAL, INC., *London*
PRENTICE-HALL OF AUSTRALIA, PTY., LTD., *Sydney*
PRENTICE-HALL OF CANADA, LTD., *Toronto*
PRENTICE-HALL OF INDIA (PRIVATE) LTD., *New Delhi*
PRENTICE-HALL OF JAPAN, INC., *Tokyo*

Library of Congress Catalog Card Number 65-18387
Printed in the United States of America
48745C

To

MARK

SCOTT

ANN

PREFACE

In this brief *Introduction to Mass Spectrometry*, I have attempted to accomplish one specific purpose: to teach mass spectrometry to those who know very little or nothing about it, by using numerous examples to illustrate both principles and applications. Such an undertaking requires a few additional comments.

The mass spectrometer is unquestionably among the most versatile of all modern instruments, and its applications are extraordinarily diverse. These points will become self-evident during the reading of this volume. Yet, many chemists, and some other scientists as well, have little knowledge of mass spectrometry, including particularly the principles and many of the possible applications. For these reasons, I believe it worthwhile to provide an "Introduction to Mass Spectrometry" which will enable interested chemists and others to learn easily and readily of this area.

A basic course in physics, rudimentary preparation in mathematics, and Freshman chemistry provide a reasonably satisfactory background for beginning this study. The discussion of the applications of mass spectrometry to various chemical problems and systems will only occasionally involve a somewhat advanced knowledge of chemistry and chemical problems. For certain discussions in later sections, some advanced mathematics is used.

In the discussions of the principles, an attempt has been made to cover the important theoretical principles of the various types of mass spectrometers and their operation. Additionally, some commercially-available instruments are described. The applications of the mass spectrometer to problems of organic, inorganic, analytical, physical, and biochemical problems, and to certain physical, geophysical, and geological problems are treated in some detail utilizing many examples.

For those desiring information beyond the scope of this volume, I have included fairly extensive literature references in addition to a General

Bibliography (in Appendix V) which lists most of the thorough discussions of mass spectrometry available either in book form or as review articles.

Much of the material presented in this *Introduction to Mass Spectrometry* was delivered in an experimental form in the "Fall Lecture Series" before the Kansas City Section of the American Chemical Society in October of 1962. Indeed, the reception of these lectures was influential in my decision to expand and complete this introductory work. In this way, and in others, the members of the Kansas City Section of the American Chemical Society have aided significantly, and I wish to indicate here my sincere gratitude and deep appreciation for all of their comments, criticisms, and kindnesses.

The author also wishes to express his appreciation to Mrs. Paula Lapp, who for many long hours had as her task the conversion of the author's first drafts to readable form. She indeed did a skillful and admirable job. Miss Linda Claydon transformed with a sensitive touch the numerous revisions into the present manuscript. Also, the author would be remiss if the did not thank all of the students in his laboratory at Kansas State University, and particularly Dr. Brice G. Hobrock and Dr. Thomas W. Lapp, for their assistance in various parts and revisions of the manuscript.

Three men deserve special mention. Dr. Vernon L. Dibeler and Professor J. L. Franklin read the manuscript prior to publication and provided me with valuable comments and criticisms. As a result of a suggestion made by Professor Franklin, Chapter 11 has been included in order to indicate new and active fields of research involving mass spectrometry. It is a particular pleasure for me to acknowledge their fine aid. However, these two scientists are not responsible for any remaining shortcomings. The responsibility for any errors rests with the author.

The third man, Sir J. J. Thomson, is (through his printed work) the person most responsible for my interest in and enthusiasm for mass spectrometry. By way of thanking him for his influence, I can only request that the readers of this volume also will take the opportunity to read his significant early contributions at first hand.

Certainly the author is indebted to the staff of Prentice-Hall, and to James J. Walsh, Albert J. Belski, and Ken Cashman, for their cooperation and invaluable editorial aid. The granting of permissions to use illustrations and other material, the origins of which are indicated in the appropriate captions, is gratefully acknowledged.

The long hours away from my wife, Barbara, and our family during the preparation of this manuscript were only possible through Barbara's extra efforts and continued understanding. In her way, she has contributed materially to this work.

Manhattan, Kansas

ROBERT W. KISER

CONTENTS

CHAPTER 1

INTRODUCTION

Mass spectrographs and mass spectrometers are electronic instruments that analyze substances according to the mass-to-charge ratio of the constituent atoms, groups of atoms, or molecules present. Mass spectrographs and mass spectrometers are two distinct types of instruments. The name *mass spectrograph*, first introduced by F. W. Aston in 1920, is generally restricted to mass-sensitive instruments that produce a focused mass spectrum on a photographic plate. The name *mass spectrometer*, first used by Smythe and Mattauch about 1926, is applied to those instruments which bring a focused beam of ions to a fixed collector, where the ion current is detected electrically; commonly, the signal from the detector is further amplified electronically before it is used to drive a recorder trace. The term *mass spectroscopy* is used in a loose sense to include the use of both types of instruments, including studies of isotope abundance, precise mass determinations, analytical chemical uses, appearance potential studies, and others.

Nearly all mass spectrometers accelerate and detect only the positively charged ions, although negative ions are produced as well in the mass spectrometer ion source (but to a lesser extent than the positive ions). We shall restrict our discussion to the mass spectroscopy of positive ions for the most part, except in those sections dealing specifically with negative ions.

In general, the instruments consist of three major components, as shown in Figure 1–1: an ion source for producing a beam of gaseous ions from the

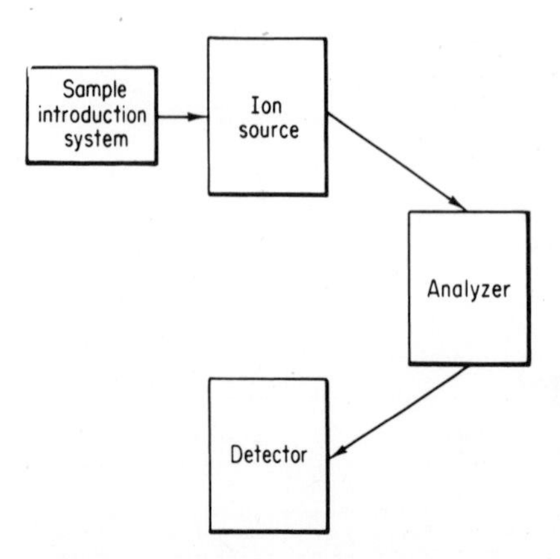

Fig. 1-1. Schematic representation of the principal features of a mass spectrometer or a mass spectrograph.

substance or substances being studied; an analyzer for resolving the ion beam into its characteristic mass components according to the mass-to-charge ratios of the ions present; and a detector system for recording the relative abundance or intensity of each of the resolved ionic species present. In addition, a sample introduction system is necessary in order to admit to the ion source the samples to be studied in whatever form is desired.

In Chapter 2 we shall first discuss the basic ideas and development of mass spectrometers and spectrographs, so that an overall view of the instrumentation can be obtained. Then in Chapter 3 we shall return to a detailed discussion of the three major components of mass spectrometers. The discussion of sample introduction shall be taken up in Chapter 9.

There are a great number of new terms to face in our study of mass spectrometry. Because it is apparently less painful to learn these new terms a few at a time, and when they are used in situations wherein their meaning becomes still clearer, we shall not here present a long tabulation of these terms; rather, the various terms will be introduced as we proceed in our study.

We shall go well beyond the description of mass spectrometers and spectrographs and the discussions of the principles of their operation, for we also wish to examine the usefulness of these instruments. In so doing, we will find that a variety of intriguing ions may be formed and detected with the mass spectrometer, and that these will prove to present additional interesting studies.

The chemist finds that the mass spectrometer can be used to solve or analyze a wide range of problems. There are many examples which provide ample illustration of this extreme versatility: rapid analyses of hydrocarbon mixtures; use of stable isotope tracers in biological, chemical, and metallurgical problems; lead detection; routine controlling of industrial processes and plants; age determinations (of the elements, the earth, etc.); outgassing studies; radioactive half-life determinations; ionization and dissociation phenomena; thermochemical information; free radical phenomena; solids analyses; packing fractions; isotope existence and abundance determinations; and many more. We will examine a great number of these applications in detail and with examples. But to do so, we must first understand more fully some of the basic chemistry and physics underlying the presentation of mass spectra by these instruments. For this reason we will encounter in our studies discussions of the theory of mass spectra and of the energetics of electron impact processes.

Beynon's book on mass spectrometry (see Appendix V, General Bibliography) lists more than 2200 references to papers, articles, reviews, and books dealing with various aspects of mass spectroscopy. The two volumes of *Advances in Mass Spectrometry* edited by Waldron and Elliott (see Appendix V) give a detailed bibliography of mass spectrometry from 1938 through 1960. In our short introductory treatment we shall not be so thorough as to cover the entire literature of mass spectroscopy, but we will cover all of the more essential points and principles of mass spectroscopy, and we will develop and illustrate many features with detailed examples.

CHAPTER 2

HISTORY

The principal purpose in presenting a brief discussion of the history of mass spectroscopy is to provide a background of the developments in this interesting field. Thus, the treatment is not an end unto itself; rather, its purpose is to explain the development of an art and the growth of the science, to show how the major ideas and advances appeared, and then to apply certain of these features to our subsequent discussions. We shall not dwell at length on each and every point in the historical development of mass spectroscopy, but instead, we will examine briefly a number of specific instances or major turning points.

Fig. 2-1. Sir J. J. Thomson. (Photograph by James J. Stokley; Courtesy of Dr. Vernon H. Dibeler.)

Two very significant discoveries are due to mass spectroscopic studies. First, J. J. Thomson (1) discovered that neon consisted of a mixture of two different isotopes (masses 20 and 22) rather than only a single isotope. This observation of the existence of stable isotopes is perhaps the greatest achievement that can be claimed by mass spectroscopy. Later studies showed that there are three stable isotopes of neon. Since Thomson's early work many other isotopes have been discovered and studied by mass spectroscopy. The consequence of this discovery was the realization that the chemical properties of an element are determined by the atomic number rather than by the atomic weight of the element, as was beautifully shown also by H. G. J. Moseley's classic (2) X-ray line spectra investigations. The second significant discovery due to mass spectrographic studies was made by F. W. Aston (3). He observed that the masses of all isotopes are not simple multiples of a fundamental unit, but rather, that they are characterized by a mass defect; i.e., isotopes do not have integral masses. (It is interesting to note that in this paper, Aston reports two new isotopes of xenon—xenon-124 and xenon-126—present to about 0.1% each in natural xenon, and shows that

Fig. 2-2. H. G. J. Moseley. (Reproduced from "Discovery of the Elements" by Mary Elvira Weeks, *Journal of Chemical Education*, by permission of the publishers.)

Fig. 2-3. F. W. Aston. (Courtesy of Dr. Edward Wichers.)

chlorine-39 is not present in natural chlorine.) The divergences of atomic masses from whole numbers can be summarized in a packing fraction curve (see Chapter 10), and the great significance of these results lies in nuclear transformation studies. Along these same lines, K. T. Bainbridge (4) experimentally demonstrated the equivalence of mass and energy through precise comparisons of the masses of light particles involved in nuclear disintegrations (e.g., carbon-14 $\longrightarrow$ nitrogen-14 + β^-; this particular example will be discussed at greater length in Chapter 10). These two results serve to illustrate the important influence that mass spectroscopy has had upon chemistry and physics.

One should hasten to point out that F. Soddy (5) suggested the name *isotopes* for different radioactive forms of the same chemical species since they would occupy identical positions in the periodic table. Although the ion of mass 22 observed by Thomson was believed to be a stable isotope of neon, it was not until 1919 that Aston (6) proved this conclusively.

2.1 HISTORICAL DEVELOPMENT OF MASS SPECTROSCOPY

The discovery of positively charged electrical entities was made in 1886 by E. Goldstein (7), when he observed that an electrical discharge at low pressures caused a slightly divergent discharge to stream through the openings in a perforated cathode. Later, W. Wien (8), Nobel Laureate of 1911, showed that the rays of Goldstein were deflected in a magnetic field and then established that these rays carried a positive electrical charge.

Upon introducing such polyatomic molecules as $COCl_2$ and hydrocarbons into the discharge tube of the parabola mass spectrograph, Thomson noted the formation of many parabolas, revealing the formation of a variety

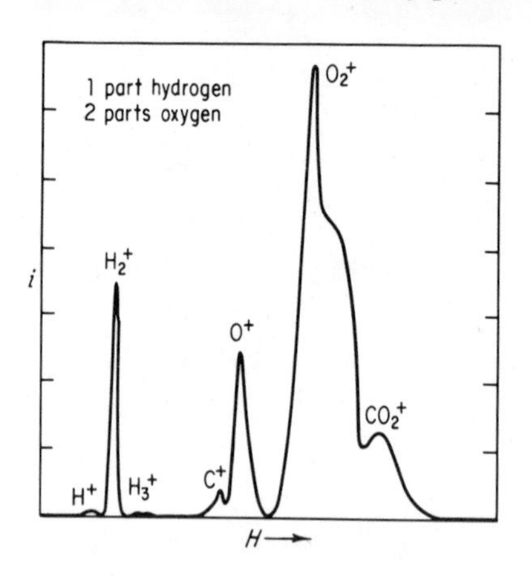

Fig. 2-4. Mass spectrum of a hydrogen-oxygen mixture. (Thomson, *Phil. Mag.* **24**, 209 (1912).)

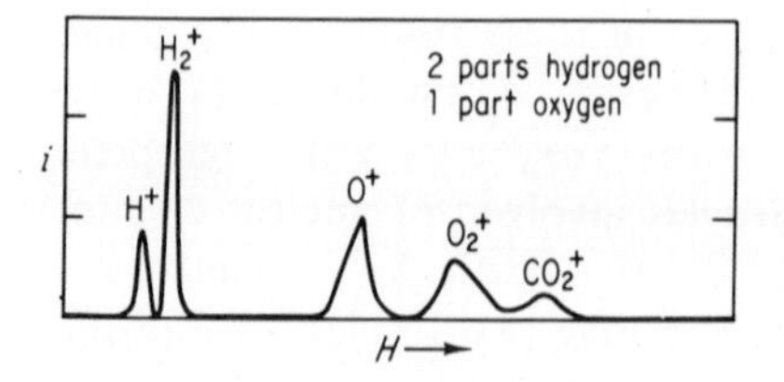

Fig. 2-5. Mass spectrum of a hydrogen-oxygen mixture. (Thomson, *Phil. Mag.* **24**, 209 (1912).)

of positively charged fragments (e.g., those corresponding to $COCl_2^+$, CO^+, C^+, O^+, etc., from the $COCl_2$). But, since the photographic plate has different sensitivities for the various ions, quantitative measurements of the relative intensities of the ions were not possible. Therefore Thomson replaced his photographic plate with a Wilson tilted electroscope and Faraday cylinder behind a parabolic slit. By changing the magnetic field and taking 10-sec measurements, Thomson was then able to measure the current corresponding to the various positive ions as they were brought over the slit, and thereby obtained the first mass spectrum: a plot of the ion current as a function of the mass-to-charge (m/e) ratio (see Figures 2–4 to 2–8). However, it was not until 1920 that F. W. Aston first introduced the term "mass spectrum."

Thomson pointed out [see p. 60 of reference (1)] that for mixtures of hydrogen and oxygen, varying in composition over wide ranges, there was little difference in the intensities of the H_2^+ and O_2^+ ions on the photographic plate. By means of the electrical detection system, he was able to achieve a much more quantitative measure of the relative proportions of hydrogen and oxygen present in a given mixture, as is shown by Figures 2–4 and 2–5. Thus, as well as being credited with the invention of the first mass spectrograph, Thomson must also be credited with the invention of the mass spectrometer.

Figures 2–6 and 2–7 show the first mass spectra of carbon monoxide and carbon dioxide taken using an electric field of 320 volts. Some of the ions observed are obviously due to impurities from the poor vacuum conditions. Figure 2-8 shows the mass spectrum of phosgene, referred to above. Note here that Thomson also studied the negative ions, finding C^-, O^-, and Cl^- in the products of the discharge in $COCl_2$. From photographic detection, Thomson noted that the relative intensities of O^- and Cl^- were about the

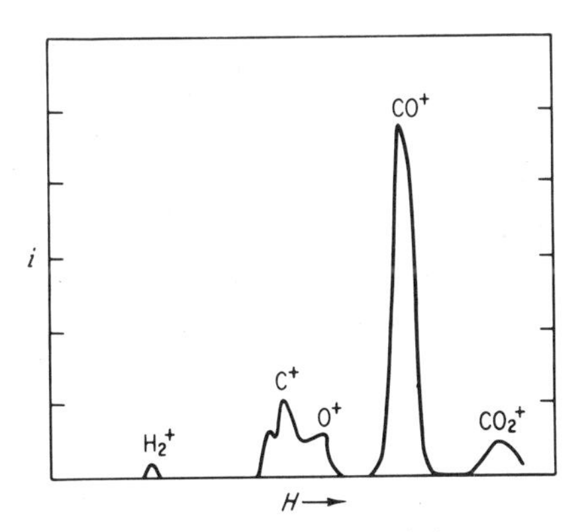

Fig. 2-6. Mass spectrum of carbon monoxide (at high pressure). (Thomson, *Phil. Mag.* **24**, 209 (1912).)

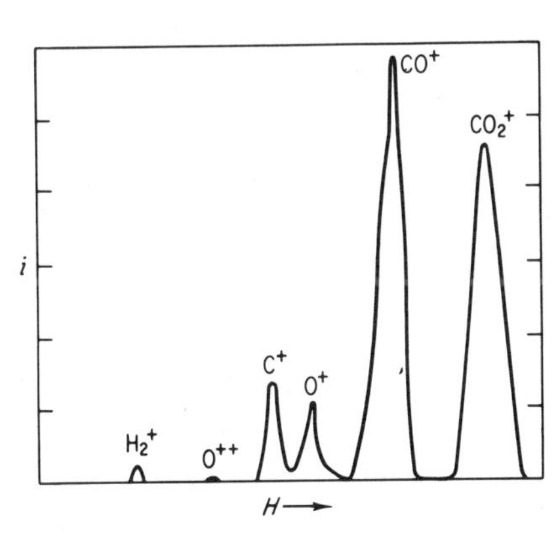

Fig. 2-7. Mass Spectrum of carbon dioxide (at high pressure). (Thomson, *Phil. Mag.* **24**, 209 (1912).)

same, but the electrical detection shows conclusively that the intensity due to Cl^- is much greater than that due to O^-. Interestingly, Thomson considered the possibility that both positive and negative ions might actually exist in the $COCl_2$ molecule and reasoned that such would not be the case.

Thomson also often observed a beaded appearance of his photographically recorded parabolas and suggested that this effect might be caused by spontaneous dissociation of ions in flight, an effect which we now refer to as *metastable transitions* (see Chapter 6). By utilizing two consecutive parabola mass spectrographs, Thomson showed that these spontaneous dissociations were observed in several instances and were responsible for the beaded effect.

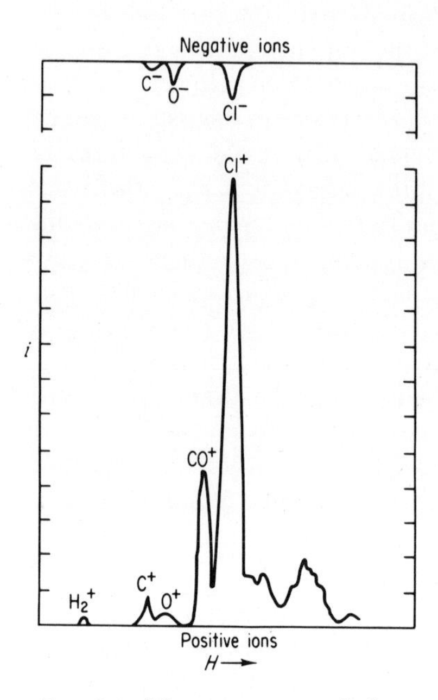

Fig. 2-8. Mass spectrum of phosgene (at high pressure). (Thomson, *Phil. Mag.* **24**, 209 (1912).)

In a very interesting paper, Thomson (9) discusses multiply charged ions. He observed up to eight electronic charges on mercury, up to four or five for krypton, three for argon, two or three for nitrogen and oxygen, two for helium and neon, but only one electronic charge on hydrogen, a "very suggestive exception. . . " [p. 53 of reference (1)]. He noted that the greater the number of charges the fainter the corresponding parabola on the photographic plate. He suggested the interesting hypothesis that the mercury atoms lose eight electrons and then regain one to six electrons to give Hg^{++} to Hg^{8+}. Hg^+, resulting from the loss of a single electron, was the exception. Bleakney (10) in his study of the multiply charged ions of mercury, was just able to resolve Hg^+ from Hg^{++}, Hg^{++} from Hg^{+++}, and so on, with his mass spectrometer. Although Thomson had studied a number of molecules with his parabola instrument, he reported that he had not yet been able to find a case of a molecule carrying a double charge. By way of comparison, S. Meyerson, with the much greater sensitivity now available, has recently reported (11) the existence of a fairly large number of cases of multiply charged molecular ions.

Thomson, Wien, and other early workers were plagued with many other complications because they lacked the high-vacuum technique we possess today. Many effects present at the excessive pressures of the early instruments are eliminated in our modern instrumentation employing high vacuum. Yet there are underway today some highly exciting studies of reactions in high-pressure mass spectrometer ion sources. It is interesting to note that Thomson first observed and reported on an ion of $m/e = 3$ in hydrogen. Thomson (1, 12) reasoned that this ion was due to H_3^+ and not C^{4+}, since many carbon compounds (CO, C_2H_2, C_2H_4, $COCl_2$, CCl_4) gave no C^{4+} and since when $m/e = 3$ was observed, he also had a large H_2^+ ion intensity. A. J. Dempster (13) examined H_2 and observed $m/e = 1, 2$, and 3 at higher pressures, but at much lower pressures he noted that the ions of $m/e = 3$ very nearly disappeared. It was not, however, until 1920 that this ion at $m/e = 3$ was shown to be H_3^+. We should note that Thomson reported on N_3^+ and HO_2^+ in addition to his discussion of H_3^+. Some of the present work in this exciting field of ion-molecule reactions is described in Chapter 6.

One can readily see from these few paragraphs that the making of the history of mass spectroscopy has involved many scientists. However, a very important point remains: one cannot be unimpressed by the tremendous contributions made by Thomson, Nobel Laureate of 1906 and the father of mass spectroscopy.

From about 1915–1920 on, mass spectrometry developed along two main lines: one concerned with the precise determinations of masses, and the other concerned with measuring the relative abundances of ionic species. The mass spectrograph which Aston used in many of his studies of stable isotopes was readily adapted to measurements of isotopic mass to a precision of 0.1%, but it was not suited to accurate determinations of the relative abundances of these isotopes, because of the photographic recording.

In 1918, A. J. Dempster (14) reported the construction of an electron bombardment ion source mass spectrometer of simpler design than Aston's mass spectrograph. Dempster's mass spectrometer could not be used for precise mass measurements, but it was better suited than Aston's mass spectrograph for measuring the relative abundances of the ionic species and was suitable for studying electron impact processes in gases.

Thus, by 1920, the early instruments were capable of the three types of measurements which can be made in mass spectroscopy: (a) precise mass determinations, (b) measurement of relative abundances of ions, and (c) electron impact studies. However, the full potentialities of the methods of mass spectroscopy were not realized with the early instruments, and not until 1942 was the first commercial instrument built by Consolidated Engineering Corporation and delivered to the Atlantic Refining Corporation. Today there are a number of industrial organizations producing a wide variety of instruments. (See Chapter 5).

The instability of the discharge tube, which was used in the early investigations of Thomson and others, and the associated high pressure of the discharge caused it to be a relatively unsatisfactory ion source. C. T. Knipp in 1911 first used an ion source in which ionization was accomplished by means of electron bombardment. H. D. Smyth (15) made the first attempt to combine a low-energy ion source with a positive ion mass analyzer in order to identify positively charged products and to establish energetic requirements. However, Thomson had pointed out earlier that the ionic products observed with the mass spectrograph arose both through ionization and dissociation, and Dempster's instrument, in which Dempster introduced an electron bombardment ion source, was suitable for such studies.

Fig. 2-9. A. J. Dempster.

D. D. Taylor (16) used a modified Aston-type mass spectrometer together with an electrometer amplifier to investigate the ionization of molecules.

The problems at this point were largely of three types: (a) to study the nature of the ions produced, (b) to elucidate whether or not the ions observed were produced by primary processes, and (c) to determine the minimum electron energies required for the production of various ions. By 1930, it was apparent that transitions between one electronic state and another, effected by electron impact, followed the *Franck-Condon principle*. (See Chapter 6.)

If the ion current of a given m/e is plotted as a function of the energy of the ionizing electron beam, an *ionization efficiency* curve results. Although we shall not discuss ionization efficiency curves in detail until Chapter 8, several observations noted many years ago should be pointed out. In the low-pressure (about 10^{-7} mm) investigations of W. Bleakney (10, 17), the "foot" of the ionization efficiency curve is pointed out, and Bleakney suggested that the curvature is due in part to two or more close-lying ionization potentials (e.g., $^2P_{3/2}$ and $^2P_{1/2}$ of Ar^+) and in part to the velocity distribution of the electron beam. He further pointed out that the "foot" of the helium ionization efficiency curve is not so pronounced, since there is only one low-lying ionization potential. Bleakney's ion source, involving a magnetically collimated beam of electrons transverse to the ion beam with a weak electric field sufficient to remove positive ions from the electron beam, has since been almost universally used in mass spectrometers for electron impact studies. Since then, A. O. Nier has made many notable contributions to the design of modern ion sources. We shall discuss ion sources in a more detailed manner in Chapter 3 and the Čermák-Herman ion source in Chapter 6.

Some of the applications of mass spectrometry to chemical problems are readily evident to us today. These and others which may not be quite as evident will be discussed in Chapters 9 and 10. But Thomson set aside ten pages (pp. 106–116) in his *Rays of Positive Electricity* . . . for a discussion of the applications to chemical analyses. In fact, he even included this in the full title of his book: *Rays of Positive Electricity and Their Applications to Chemical Analyses.* He suggested the uses of mass spectrometry for determining atomic and molecular weights, and for obtaining both qualitative and quantitative information in analyses superior to emission spectrography, while pointing out the necessity of using only very small samples (about 0.1 cc at STP). By means of examples, Thomson even showed the possible use of mass spectrometry in the identification of the components of air. Yet, the first purely chemical application of mass spectroscopy appears to have been made by Conrad (18). Conrad published many very beautiful plates of groups of parbolas he obtained in studies of organic compounds and drew interesting conclusions from the appearances of the parabolas.

J. A. Hipple and D. P. Stevenson (19) made the first satisfactory direct determinations of the ionization potentials of free radicals, and G. C. Eltenton (20) was the first to successfully study free radicals with a mass spectrometer, although Aston had commented upon the value of such studies in 1933. In very recent years, additional workers have aided greatly the study of free radicals; some of these studies are included in Chapters 10 and 11.

One other use of the mass spectrometer or the mass spectrograph, which is of more than just historical interest, is that of isotope separation. Aston has reported (21) that he had foreseen the use of the mass spectrograph for the separation of isotopes in 1922. Morand (22) attempted to use an ion source of anode rays to separate lithium-6 and lithium-7, but with little or no success. The breakthrough in 1934 was made by W. R. Smythe, L. H. Rumbaugh, and S. S. West (23) and by M. L. Oliphant, E. S. Shire, and B. M. Crowther (24). Smythe, *et al.* separated and concentrated the anode rays of potassium, obtaining as much as 1 mg of potassium-39 in a 7-hr run. Oliphant, *et al.* separated and collected the lithium isotopes, preparing as much as 10^{-8} g of a pure lithium isotope. In 1940, the very significant technical success of the separation and isolation of uranium-235 and uranium-238 in detectable quantities was achieved by A. O. Nier, E. T. Booth, J. R. Dunning, and A. V. Grosse (25). It was then established that uranium-235 was the uranium isotope responsible for the process of fission by neutrons, a belief which Dunning had held since 1939 (26). L. W. Alvarez and R. Cornog (27) had already used the 100-in. Berkeley cyclotron as a mass spectrograph to find helium-3 present to about 10^{-7}% in natural helium. In late November of 1941, E. O. Lawrence began to convert the 37-in. Berkeley cyclotron to a large mass spectrograph. On December 2, 1941 an ion beam current of 5 μamp was received at the collector, ten times as large as that by Nier, *et al.* By the end of 1941, the first 37-in. mass spectrograph had attained a separated sample enriched to 3% uranium-235. On January 14, 1942 a 9-hr run at 50 μamp produced 18 μg of material enriched to 25% uranium-235. By February, the ion beam was up to 1400 μamp, and by the middle of February, a total of over 0.2 mg enriched to 30% uranium-235 had been obtained. With some further design changes, ion source modifications, and different collectors, a new unit was installed in the 37-in. magnet in February 1942; this was the birth of the "calutron." Further details and descriptions of calutrons and other electromagnetic separators will be found in Chapter 4.

2.2 HISTORICAL INSTRUMENTS

There are a number of mass spectrometers and mass spectrographs which could suitably be described under the heading of Historical Instruments. The early development of a mass spectrometer by A. J. Dempster, a mass spectrograph by F. W. Aston, their subsequent modified instruments, and the instruments of Bainbridge, Jordan, Mattauch, Herzog, Bartky, Lozier, and many others could be described in detail. However, we shall only discuss four early historical instruments: Thomson's parabola mass spectrograph, Aston's first mass spectrograph, Dempster's first mass spectrometer, and Lozier's tube. Not that these are singularly the most important, but rather because it is believed that the discussion of these four instruments will aid in developing the basic concepts of mass spectroscopy as well as provide the reader with a sense of the exciting surge of interest and activity in the field of mass spectroscopy during this time. Other types of mass spectrographs and mass spectrometers will be treated further in Chapters 4 and 5.

THE PARABOLA MASS SPECTROGRAPH

The very significant investigations of Thomson, some of which have been described earlier in this chapter, were carried out using a positive-ray parabola instrument. The greatest interest in this instrument is of an historical nature; but certainly it is instructive to learn the principles of operation of the parabola mass spectrograph, which was of great productivity in the hands of Thomson.

The type of analyzer used by Thomson was first employed by W. Kaufmann (28) in studies of cathode rays. The ions (largely positive ions, but also some negative ions) formed in the discharge, enter the analyzer along the x-axis through a fine-bore opening in the cathode, which also provides collimation. (See Figure 2–10.) Thomson credits F. W. Aston for the basic physical arrangement. The analyzer is composed of parallel and coterminous electric and magnetic fields which analyze the various ions according to the

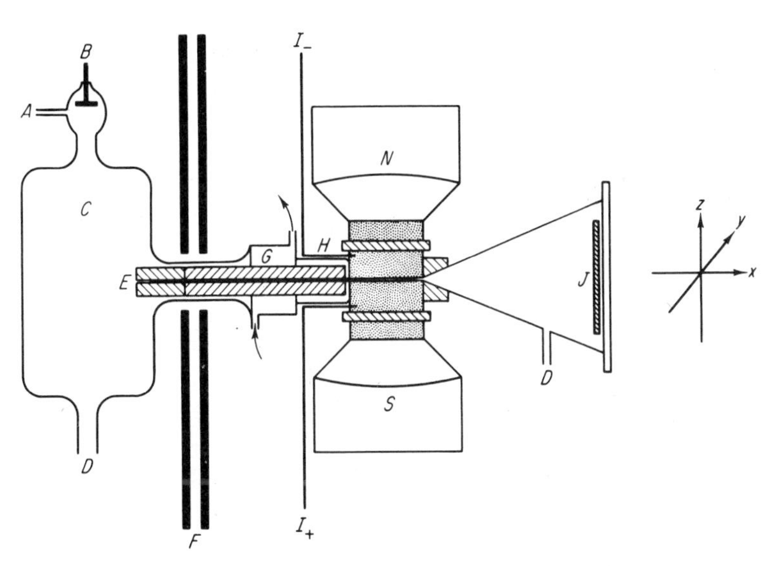

Fig. 2-10. Schematic representation of Thomson's parabola mass spectrograph. A, gas inlet; B, anode; C, discharge tube; D, to vacuum pumps; E, cathode; F, magnetic shields; G, water jacket for cooling; H, insulators; I, electrical field leads; J, photographic detector.

m/e ratio, the electric field deflecting the ions in the z-direction, and the magnetic field causing deflection in the y-direction. Figure 2–10 depicts the more refined instrument reported on by Thomson (1, 12); his other instrument had been described earlier (29).

It is instructive to turn here to a physical treatment of the motions of ions in electric and magnetic fields.

In a uniform electric field E of length x, a charged particle of mass m and charge e receives a constant acceleration a_E in the z-direction of

$$a_E = F_E/m = eE/m, \tag{2–1}$$

where F_E is the force of the electric field. If the charged particle is initially injected into this electric field at a velocity of v_0 along the x-axis, we see that (where t is time)

$$x = v_0 t \tag{2–2}$$

and that the displacement of the charged particle in the z-direction is

$$z = \int_0^t \int_0^t (eE/m)\, dt^2 = (eE/2m)t^2. \tag{2–3}$$

Eliminating t between Equations (2–2) and (2–3) yields

$$z = (eE/2m)(x/v_0)^2 \tag{2–4}$$

for the displacement of the charged particle in the z-direction when it emerges from the electric field. Note that Equation (2–4) is the equation of a parabola in x and z.

However, at the same time that this charged particle is experiencing the force of the electric field, it is also experiencing in a parallel magnetic field H an acceleration a_H in the y-direction of

$$a_H = F_H/m = (Hev_0/c)/m, \tag{2–5}$$

where c is the velocity of light, 3×10^{10} cm/sec. Again,

$$x = v_0 t \tag{2–2}$$

and

$$y = \int_0^t \int_0^t (Hev_0/mc)\, dt^2 = (Hev_0/2mc)t^2, \tag{2–6}$$

and, by eliminating t between Equations (2–2) and (2–6), we obtain

$$y = (Hev_0/2mc)(x/v_0)^2 = Hex^2/2mcv_0. \tag{2–7}$$

Now, for constant m/e, E, H, and x, we see that Equations (2–4) and (2–7) may be written as

$$z = k'/v_0^2 \tag{2–8}$$

and

$$y = k''/v_0, \tag{2–9}$$

respectively. Upon combining Equations (2–8) and (2–9), we have the equation governing the operation of the parabola mass spectrograph:

$$y^2 = kz, \tag{2–10}$$

where

$$k = (k'')^2/k', \tag{2–11}$$

$$= (Hex^2/2mc)^2/(eEx^2/2m), \tag{2–12}$$

or

$$k = (e/m)(H^2/Ec^2)(x^2/2). \tag{2–13}$$

Note from Equation (2–13) that k is proportional to e/m, or $1/k$ depends on the m/e ratio. Also, k depends on the applied electric and magnetic fields and the geometric parameters (e.g., x) of the instrument. It is readily recognized that Equation (2–10) is the equation of a parabola.

EXAMPLE 2–1. Consider a group of CH_4^+ ions. What would be the values of y and z for this ion in a parabola mass spectrograph with an electric field of 450 volts and a magnetic field of 2800 gauss, both of length 3.0 cm?

The electronic charge is 4.8×10^{-10} esu and the speed of light is 3×10^{10} cm/sec. From Equation (2–13),

$$k = \frac{(4.8 \times 10^{-10})(2800)^2(300)(3.0)^2}{(16/6 \times 10^{23})(3 \times 10^{10})^2(450)(2)} \text{ cm},$$

since 300 practical volts = 1 esu. Then,

$$k = \frac{4.8 \times 10^{-10} \times 6 \times 10^{23} \times 7.85 \times 10^6 \times 300 \times 9.0}{16 \times 9 \times 10^{20} \times 450} \text{ cm}$$

or

$$k = 0.473 \text{ cm}.$$

Using Equation (2–10), we calculate the following values:

y (cm)	z (cm)	y/z
0.0	0.00	–
0.2	0.09	2.35
0.4	0.34	1.17
0.7	1.04	0.67
1.2	3.04	0.40
1.6	5.41	0.30
2.2	10.2	0.22

Combining Equations (2–4) and (2–7), we obtain

$$y/z = (H/Ec)v_0, \tag{2–14}$$

from which we see that the ratio of y/z is a measure of the velocity of the charged particle.

All particles of the same m/e value, regardless of their velocities, impinge on the photographic detector in a parabola whose vertex lies at the undeflected position of the particles. There is a different parabola for each ion of different m/e in the positive ion beam. Figure 2–11 shows in a schematic way the kind of results obtained by Thomson. Note that the physical arrangement of the electric field in Figure 2–10 causes the deflection of the positively charged particles in a z-direction and the negatively charged particles in a $-z$-direction. The very broad lines, indicating the y- and z-axes in Figure 2–11 are not present experimentally, but have been placed in this figure to aid in noting the separation of the positively charged and the negatively charged ions. Also, it should be noted that the physical arrangement of the magnetic field in Figure 2–10 causes the positively charged ions to be deflected in the $-y$-direction and the negatively charged particles in the y-direction. To summarize these remarks, the positive-ion parabolas should be observed in the upper-left quadrant, and the negative-ion parabolas

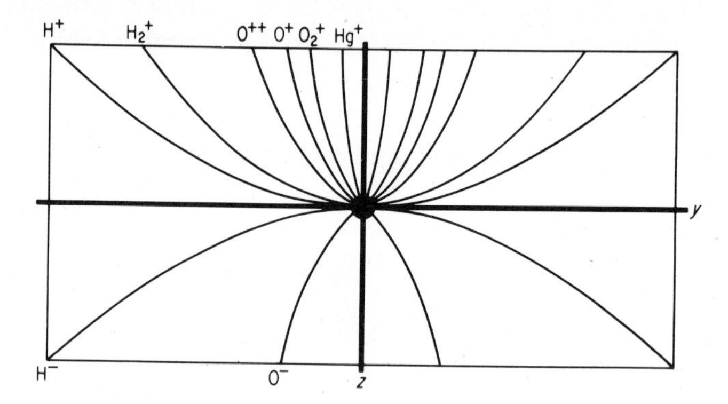

Fig. 2-11. Hypothetical photographic record of a parabola mass spectrograph.

should be observed in the lower-right quadrant. Why then the full parabolas, observed in all four quadrants? This occurs because in actual practice the magnetic field is reversed after one-half exposure of the photographic plate, so that measurements of distances on the record may be made with greater ease and accuracy.

Recall that

$$z = k'/v_0^2. \tag{2–8}$$

But the kinetic energy T_0 of the charged particle, at the moment of injection into the electric and magnetic fields, is

$$T_0 = mv_0^2/2 \tag{2-15}$$

so that

$$z = b/T_0, \tag{2-16}$$

where

$$b = (eE)(x/2)^2. \tag{2-17}$$

That is, the z-displacement is inversely proportional to the kinetic energy of the charged particle. Now, there will be some definite maximum energy that the charged particles may acquire, corresponding to the full potential drop across the discharge tube; therefore there will be some minimum z-displacement on the photographic detector. Thus, all of the parabolas will end at fairly sharp points equidistant from the y-axis. The energy that the ions of various m/e acquire is not dependent upon the m/e value; therefore, the intensities of the various parabolas will be similar, although not identical. Figure 2–12, a variation of Figure 2–11, illustrates the actual experimental data and these comments. How far out do the parabolas extend? Since an ion of any given m/e may acquire energies from $T = 0$ to $T = T_0$, the parabolas will extend outward infinitely. However, as $z \to \infty$, one would expect the intensity to decrease greatly. For intermediate values of z, one might anticipate approximately similar intensity distributions for any given parabola.

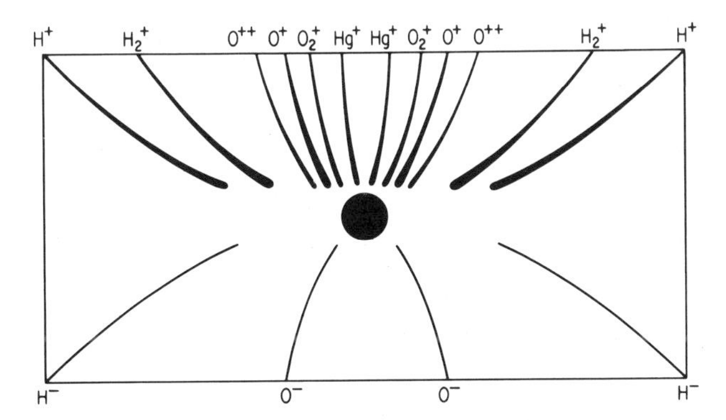

Fig. 2-12. Illustration of a typical photographic record obtained with a parabola mass spectrograph.

Example 2–2. Consider the same data given in Example 2–1. However, we shall add the restriction that the initial velocities v_0 of the ions can take values up to a maximum derived from the potential in the discharge, given as 1000 volts. What minimum value of z would be observed?

$$T_{max.} = \tfrac{1}{2}mv^2_{max.} = eV_{max.}$$
$$= (1000/300)(4.8 \times 10^{-10}) = 1.6 \times 10^{-9} \text{ ergs},$$
$$v^2_{max.} = 2 \times 1.6 \times 10^{-9} \times 6 \times 10^{23}/16 = 1.2 \times 10^{14} \text{ cm}^2/\text{sec}^2,$$
$$v_{max.} = 1.1 \times 10^7 \text{ cm/sec}.$$

Therefore, from Equation (2–14),

$$(y/z)_{max.} = (2800)(300)(1.1 \times 10^7)/(3 \times 10^{10} \times 450),$$
$$= 6.23 \times 10^{-8} \times 1.1 \times 10^7 = 0.69.$$

From the table in Example 2–1, it is seen that a value of $z = 1.0$ cm will be the minimum observed value of z.

This may also be seen from Equations (2–16) and (2–17):

$$b = 4.8 \times 10^{-10} \times (450/300) \times (9.0/4),$$
$$= 1.62 \times 10^{-9} \text{ erg-cm},$$

and thus

$$z_{min.} = b/T_{max.} = 1.62 \times 10^{-9}/1.6 \times 10^{-9} = 1.0 \text{ cm}.$$

From Equations (2–10) and (2–13),

$$y^2 = K(e/m)z, \tag{2–18}$$

where K is a constant equal to

$$K = (H^2/Ec^2)(x^2/2). \tag{2–19}$$

Rearranging Equation (2–18), we obtain

$$m/e = K(z/y^2). \tag{2–20}$$

Now, if z is held constant, Equation (2–20) becomes

$$m/e = K'/y^2, \tag{2–21}$$

and it follows that

$$\frac{(m/e)_1}{(m/e)_2} = \frac{y_2^2}{y_1^2} = \left(\frac{y_2}{y_1}\right)^2, \tag{2–22}$$

which provides a simple means of calibrating the m/e values of the different parabolas if the m/e value of one parabola is known or can be determined.

The parabola photographs are strikingly beautiful; but because of its inherently poor resolving power (resolving power is defined and illustrated in detail in Chapter 3), the parabola mass spectrograph is fundamentally suited only to critical investigations of ions of small m/e values. For example,

Thomson's parabola mass spectrograph could separate ions differing in mass by only one part in 15.

We should note before leaving our discussion of the first parabola mass spectrograph that Thomson also made use of an instrument without coterminous electric and magnetic fields, where the magnetic field extended beyond the electric field in the direction of the detector. Also, E. Gehrcke and O. Reichenheim (30) surface ionized NaCl, LiCl, KCl, etc., from a surface emission ion source, accelerated the ions by means of a potential drop, and then bent the ions using a strong magnetic field at right angles to the electric field in observing Li^+, Na^+, Sr^{++}, etc. Indeed, other types and designs of mass spectrometers and mass spectrographs were to follow very quickly Thomson's parabola instrument.

Although now largely of historical interest, the parabola spectrograph still has useful applications alongside of its numerous descendants. A specific advantage of the parabola instrument is that it records simultaneously both positive and negative ions and hence is suited for ionization and dissociation studies. A. Henglein and H. Ewald (31) have reported studies of some ion dissociations in a parabola spectrograph.

ASTON'S FIRST MASS SPECTROGRAPH

F. W. Aston's first mass spectrograph (6) employed successively an electrostatic and a magnetic field. With the arrangement shown schematically in Figure 2–13, Aston succeeded in obtaining velocity focusing of the ion beams. As we have already seen, Aston used his mass spectrograph mainly for the very early and significant isotopic mass measurements. For reasons of historical importance, we shall examine Aston's instrument in somewhat more detail.

In the arrangement shown in Figure 2–13, the positive ion beam is collimated by means of slits S_1 and S_2 and then is dispersed by means of the electric field between plates P_1 and P_2. One may consider, to a first approximation, that the positive ions, upon leaving the electric field, radiate from a virtual source z halfway through the electric field. A group of these ions, selected by slit S_3, are allowed to pass between the parallel pole faces of a magnet. For simplicity, the magnet poles in Figure 2–13 are shown as being circular. The magnetic field is uniform and of such direction as to deflect the positive ions in a direction opposite to the deflection caused by the electric field, and thus to cause the ions to fall on the photographic plate D.

Ions of velocity v and of a given m/e value are deflected through an angle θ by means of the electric field E, and for fairly small angles of θ,

$$\theta v^2 = l_e E(e/m), \tag{2–23}$$

where l_e is the length of the ion path in the electric field. Similarly, these

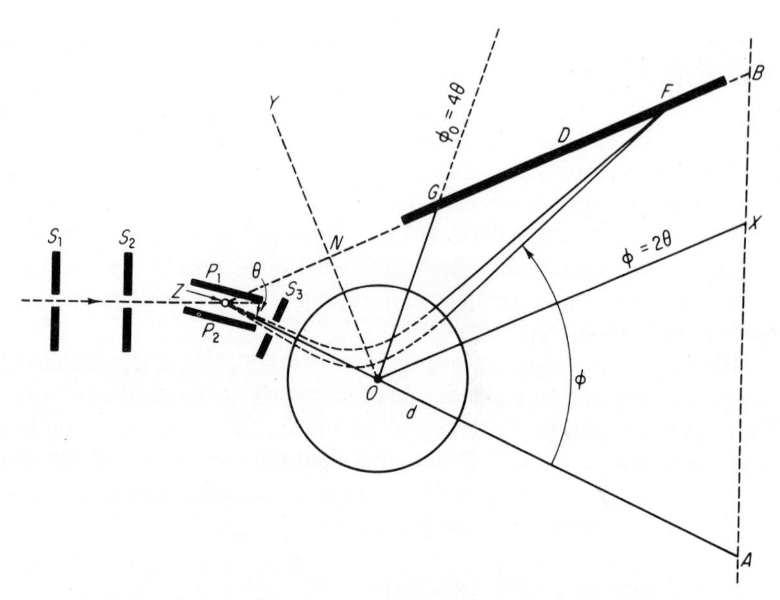

Fig. 2-13. Aston's first mass spectrograph (velocity-focusing).

ions are then deflected through an angle of ϕ in the magnetic field H, whereby

$$\phi v = l_h H(e/m), \tag{2–24}$$

where l_h is the length of the ion path in the magnetic field. For values of θ selected over only a small range by s_3, l_e and l_h are essentially constant. Maintaining constant E and H for ions of a given m/e, we see that θv^2 and ϕv are constant. Therefore, when the velocities of ions of a given m/e vary,

$$\frac{\delta\theta}{\theta}\,\frac{2\,\delta v}{v} = 0 \tag{2–25}$$

and

$$\frac{\delta\phi}{\phi}\,\frac{\delta v}{v} = 0. \tag{2–26}$$

Thus,

$$\frac{\delta\theta}{\theta} = \frac{2\,\delta\phi}{\phi}. \tag{2–27}$$

As an illustration of the utility of Equation (2–27), let us assume that the angles θ and ϕ are small, and that the magnetic field is concentrated at the center of the poles O. Now let distance ZO be equal to b. For ions of a given m/e but of varying velocities, the breadth of the ion beam at O will be

$b\,\delta\theta$, and at some distance r beyond O the breadth B will be

$$B = b\,\delta\theta + r(\delta\theta + \delta\phi) \tag{2-28}$$

or

$$B = \delta\theta\left[b + r\left(1 + \frac{\delta\phi}{\delta\theta}\right)\right]. \tag{2-29}$$

Inserting Equation (2–27), the breadth at the distance r is

$$B = \delta\theta\left[b + r\left(1 + \frac{\phi}{2\theta}\right)\right]. \tag{2-30}$$

However, the electric and magnetic deflections are in opposite directions, so that we may say (Figure 2–13) that θ is a negative angle, i.e., $\theta = -\theta'$. As long as $\phi > 2\theta'$, the breadth as given by Equation (2–30) will become zero at a value of r given by

$$b = -r[1 - (\phi/2\theta')] \tag{2-31}$$

$$= -r + (r\phi/2\theta'), \tag{2-32}$$

$$b\cdot 2\theta' = -2r\theta' + r\phi \tag{2-33}$$

$$= r(\phi - 2\theta'), \tag{2-34}$$

or

$$r = \frac{b\cdot 2\theta'}{(\phi - 2\theta')}. \tag{2-35}$$

That is, focusing is achieved at $r \cos(\phi - 2\theta')$, $r \sin(\phi - 2\theta')$, with reference to the axes OX, OY, as shown in Figure 2–13; this is indicated by point F. As long as the position of slit S_3 remains fixed, the foci will all lie on the straight line ZB drawn through Z parallel to OX. Thus, the photographic plate D placed along ZB will be be in focus for various values of m/e, whatever the fields or the ion velocities. These results are found to be correct within usual practical limits for large circular pole pieces.

In order to study the positions of the focus F on the photographic plate D corresponding to different values of m/e when E and H are constant, let us consider a single ion beam, assuming perfect focusing conditions. Furthermore, let R be the radius of curvature of the m/e ion beam in the magnetic field and d be the radius of the magnetic field. Therefore, from the geometry, as shown more clearly in Figure 2–14,

$$\tan(\phi/2) = d/R. \tag{2-36}$$

Since θ and E are constant, the kinetic energy of the ions is constant, so that the radius of curvature R in the magnetic field varies as $\sqrt{m}$. Therefore,

$$\tan(\phi/2) = \sqrt{m_0/m}, \tag{2-37}$$

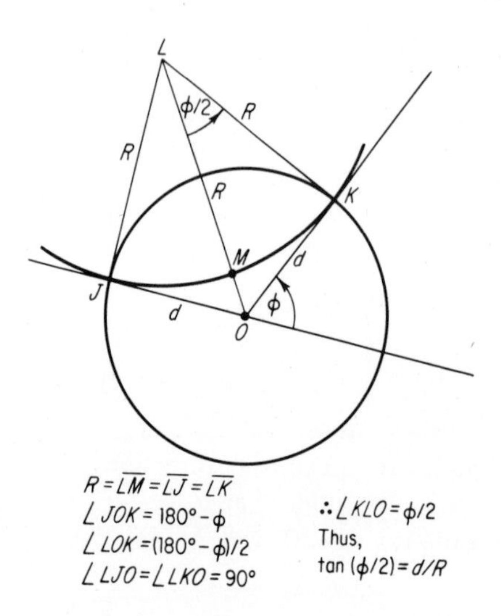

Fig. 2-14. Geometry of ion deflection in a magnetic field.

where m_0 is a constant and may be interpreted as that mass which, under the conditions of the experiment, is bent through $\phi = 90°$.

Referring now to Figure 2–13, if $\overline{NO} = p$, a constant, where $\overline{NO}$ is the length of the perpendicular dropped from O to ZF, then

$$\frac{\overline{NF}}{\overline{NO}} = \frac{r \cos(\phi - 2\theta')}{r \sin(\phi - 2\theta')} \tag{2-38}$$

or

$$\overline{NF} = p \cot(\phi - 2\theta'). \tag{2-39}$$

The combination of Equations (2–37) and (2–39) gives a rather complicated expression for $\overline{NF}/p$ in terms of m_0 and m (32). However, the differential of $\overline{NF}$ with respect to m vanishes when

$$\tan(\phi/2) = \tan 2\theta. \tag{2-40}$$

Therefore, the m/e scale on the photographic plate is very nearly linear in the vicinity of $\phi = 4\theta$ (point G in Figure 2–13). This *linear law* was observed in the very early work with Aston's mass spectrograph with $\theta = 5°42'$ and aided greatly in early precise determinations of masses from the photographic records. (See Chapter 10.)

The arrangement of electrostatic and magnetic fields in Aston's mass spectrograph gave no direction focusing; this resulted in both intensity and resolution superior to that of the parabola mass spectrograph, but yet inferior to that obtained by Dempster. The resolution of Aston's first mass spectrograph was about one in 130.

DEMPSTER'S FIRST MASS SPECTROMETER

If all of the ions formed in the ion source possess the same energy, a magnetic field alone would be sufficient to carry out the mass analysis of the ions. A. J. Dempster (14) devised and constructed a mass spectrometer based on this idea [essentially identical to that used by J. Classen (33) in the determination of e/m for electrons], obtaining ions all of the same energy, by causing the ions to be accelerated through a specific potential difference, large in comparison to the energy with which they were originally generated. The first apparatus constructed by Dempster (shown in Figure 2–15) had a resolution of one in 100. Because of the great utility of this design even today,

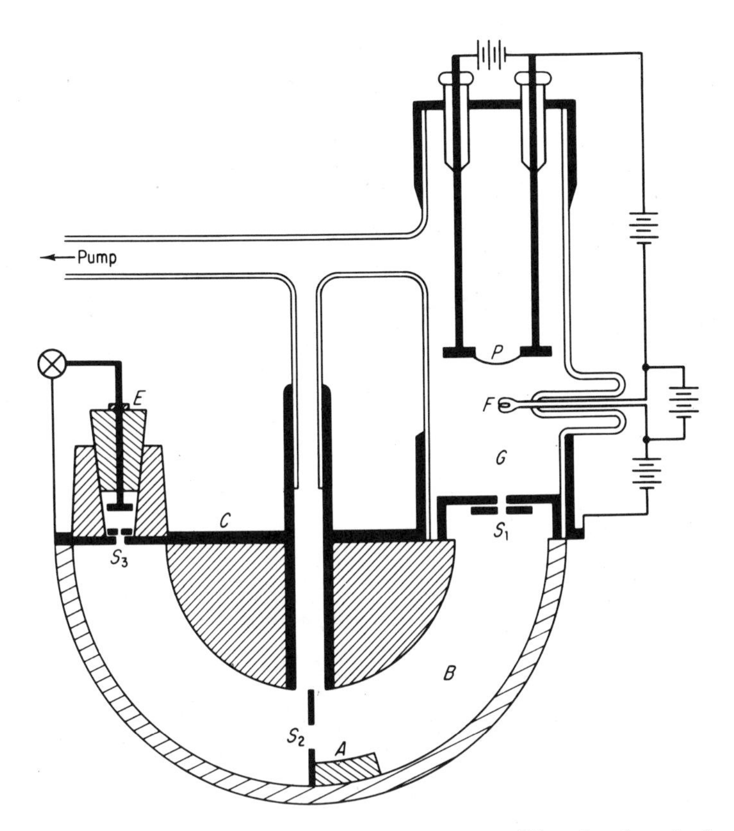

Fig. 2-15. Dempster's first mass spectrometer (direction-focusing).

as well as the historical importance of this instrument, we treat of it in more detail in the following paragraphs.

As shown in Figure 2–15, Dempster's mass spectrometer consisted of an ion source housed in a glass tube *G*, an analyzer *B*, and a quadrant electrometer detector *E*. Dempster produced ions in two different ways: (a) by emitting electrons from a hot filament *F* and causing them to bombard samples on the platinum strip *P*, and (b) heating the samples on the platinum strip directly. A potential drop between *P* and S_1 provided the accelerating potential for the ions and thereby produced ions of nearly the same energies. After passing through the adjustable slit S_1, the ion beam was bent in a semicircular path by means of a strong magnetic field.

A magnetic field of about 3000 gauss was produced between two semicircular iron plates, each slightly over 1-in. in thickness and about 5 in. in diameter, and separated by approximately 5/32 in. Slit S_2 was used in the analyzing section to prevent undesired reflected ions and/or electrons from reaching slit S_3, also an adjustable slit. The electrometer connection was made through an ebonite plug in a ground conical joint to the ion detector plate.

The equation for the Dempster instrument is

$$m/e = H^2R^2/2E, \tag{2–41}$$

where H is the magnetic field, R is the radius of curvature of the ions in the magnetic field, and E is the accelerating potential. In Chapter 3 we shall return to the derivation and discussion of Equation (2–41).

Accelerating potentials of 500–1800 volts were used. Experimentally, the magnetic field was held constant and the mass spectrum was swept by varying the accelerating potential between P and S_1. The mass spectrum was therefore a plot of ion current measured by the quadrant electrometer versus the accelerating potential.

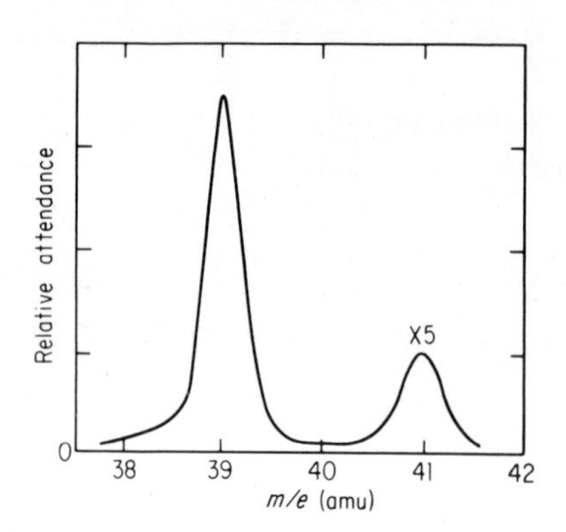

Fig. 2-16. Mass spectrum of potassium with the Dempster mass spectrometer (modified apparatus).

Figure 2–16 shows a typical result determined by Dempster with his modified apparatus (34) and a Wilson tilting electroscope. The ratio of the two peak heights (i.e., $m/e = 39$ and $m/e = 41$) was 17.5: 1 for the potassium isotopes, giving a mean atomic weight of 39.1 for potassium, in good agreement with the presently accepted value of 39.102.

There is another point (in addition to those of resolution and ion beam intensities mentioned earlier) to take note of in comparing Aston's and Dempster's instruments: whereas Aston used his deflecting field as "prisms" to disperse, Dempster used the magnetic field as a "lens" to condense or focus.

THE LOZIER TUBE

W. W. Lozier (35) constructed a tube, not using mass analysis, for the study of both positive and negative ions. Although not strictly a mass spectrometer, it borders on mass spectroscopy and is of historical interest, although, indeed, such instrumentation is still being used today. [See, for example, M. A. Fineman and A. W. Petrocelli, (36) in which a Fox gun (Chapter 8) is employed to give an electron energy spread of only 0.1 to 0.2 volts in their study of the ionization and dissociation of carbon monoxide.] A more refined and elaborate version of the Lozier tube was described by J. T. Tate and W. W. Lozier (37), and we shall discuss their apparatus here.

In the Lozier tube (see Figure 2–17), electrons emitted from the filament F are accelerated by a potential drop on the electrodes A and A' towards the electron collector E along the axis of the tube. The magnetic field H, produced by a solenoid external to the apparatus, is employed to maintain a nondivergent electron beam. By varying the energy of the electron gun, one can determine the minimum energy required to produce ions of a given kinetic energy.

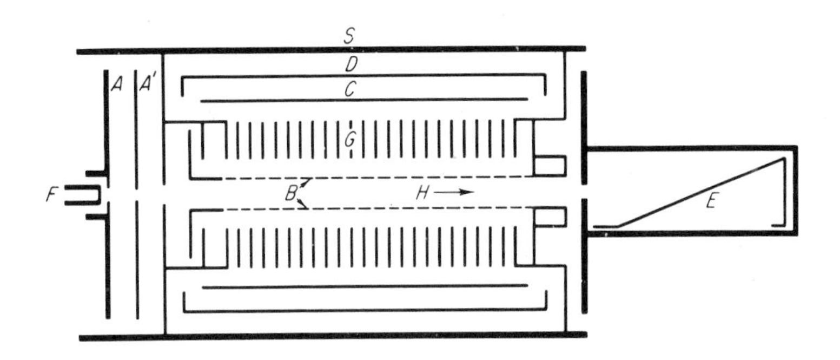

Fig. 2-17. The Lozier tube (after Tate and Lozier). A, A′, electron accelerating electrodes; B, cylindrical gauze; C, ion collecting cylinder; D, guard cylinder; E, electron collector; F, filament; G, thin cylindrical disced grids; H, magnetic field direction; and S, shield.

Ions are formed along the axis of the cylinder and pass out perpendicularly through the gauze B and the grids G. The ions are just able to reach the ion collector C in the presence of a retarding field V_R applied between C and G. It has been shown by Lozier that, for ions formed with a kinetic energy of V_F,

$$V_F = V_R + \frac{300eb^2H^2}{8mc^2}, \tag{2-42}$$

where b is the radius of the collector C in centimeters, m/e is the mass-to-charge ratio, H is the magnetic field in gauss, and c is the velocity of light in centimeters per second. For singly charged ions of mass 15, we see that

$$V_F - V_R = \frac{300eb^2H^2}{m(8)(9)} \times 10^{-20},$$

and if $b = 3$ cm and $H = 100$ gauss, we see that

$$V_F - V_R = \frac{(300)(6.02 \times 10^{23})(4.8 \times 10^{-10})(9)(10^2)(10^{-20})}{(8)(15)(9)}$$

or

$$V_F - V_R = 0.07 \text{ volt}.$$

Therefore, for the ions of larger m/e values, $V_F = V_R$. (We readily note that for H^+ ions, $V_F \neq V_R$.) The retarding potential is used to prevent collection at C of ions initially formed with less than any given amount of kinetic energy. Thus V_R is used to determine the kinetic energies of the ions.

By applying a voltage of the appropriate polarity between the gauze B and the grids G, one can collect, as desired, either the positive ions or the negative ions. Note, however, that whichever charged ions are being collected, all of those ions formed are collected, and not just some small fraction of them.

If the energy imparted to the molecule by the electron impact is V_i and the change in potential energy of the molecules upon dissociation is $(U_2 - U_1)$, then we see that kinetic energy of the dissociation products T_{dp} is

$$T_{dp} = V_i - (U_2 - U_1). \tag{2–43}$$

Consider now a diatomic molecule AB. The kinetic energy of the ion A^+ (or it could as well be that of A^-) is simply

$$T_{A^+} = \left(\frac{m_B}{m_A + m_B}\right) T_{dp}, \tag{2–44}$$

so that

$$T_{A^+} = \left(\frac{m_B}{m_A + m_B}\right) [V_i - (U_2 - U_1)], \tag{2–45}$$

and since, as we noted above, V_R is used to determine the kinetic energies of the ions,

$$V_R(A^+) = \left(\frac{m_B}{m_A + m_B}\right) [V_i - (U_2 - U_1)]. \tag{2–46}$$

A plot of $V_R(A^+)$ versus V_i should be a straight line, with a slope of $[m_B/(m_A + m_B)]$ and a V_i-axis intercept (where $V_R = 0$) of $V_i = (U_2 - U_1)$. Thus, for diatomic molecules, we can identify the ion being collected by means of the slope, and the minimum energy required for the process, $(U_2 - U_1)$, may be determined from the intercept.

EXAMPLE 2–3. Consider the study of CO in a Lozier tube. The data obtained for the various positive ions are shown in Figure 2–18, and data for the various negative ions are shown in Figures 2–19 and 2–20.

In Figure 2–18 are indicated, at the different retarding potentials, thresholds for four different processes involving positive ions, designated A, B, C, and D. In Figure 2–19 is indicated a low-energy process involving negative-ion formation, designated process E. Finally, in Figure 2–20 are given the data for processes F and G, higher energy processes involving negative ions. Using the data of Figure 2–18, plots of V_R versus V_i for the positive ions are given in Figures 2–21 and 2–22.

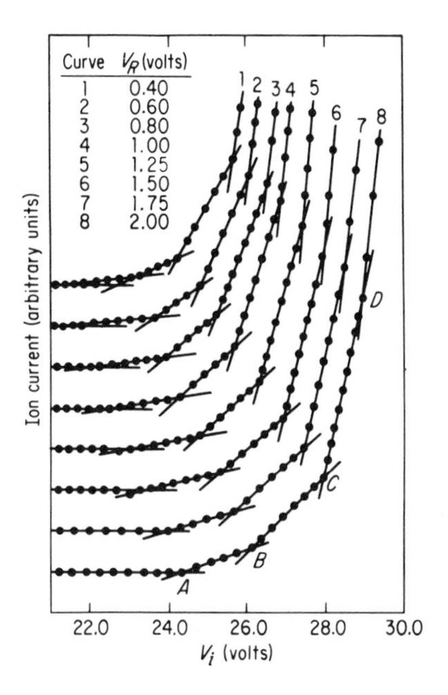

Fig. 2-18. Ionization efficiency curves of positive ions at various retarding potentials.

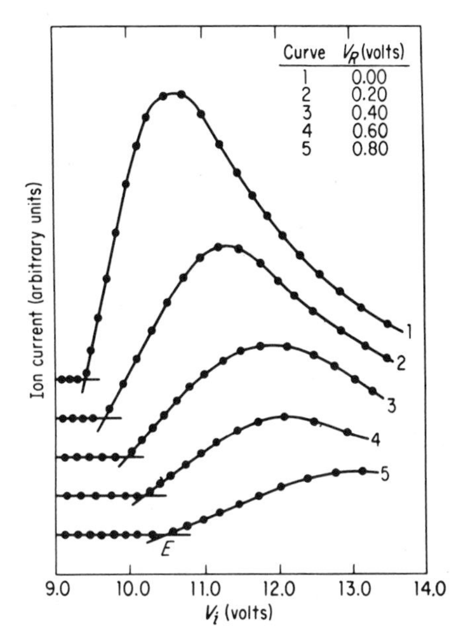

Fig. 2-19. Ionization efficiency curves of the negative ions appearing at low energy at various retarding potentials.

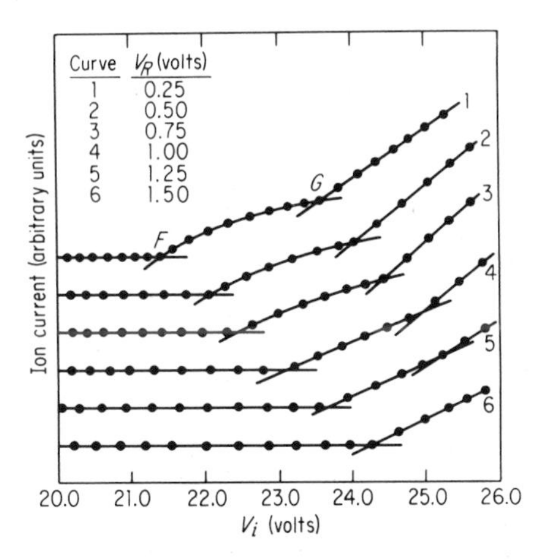

Fig. 2-20. Ionization efficiency curves of other negative ions at various retarding potentials.

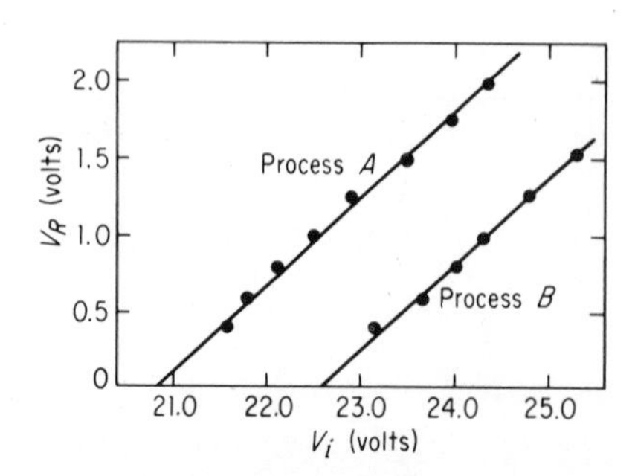

Fig. 2-21. Retarding potential *vs* electron energy for processes A and B.

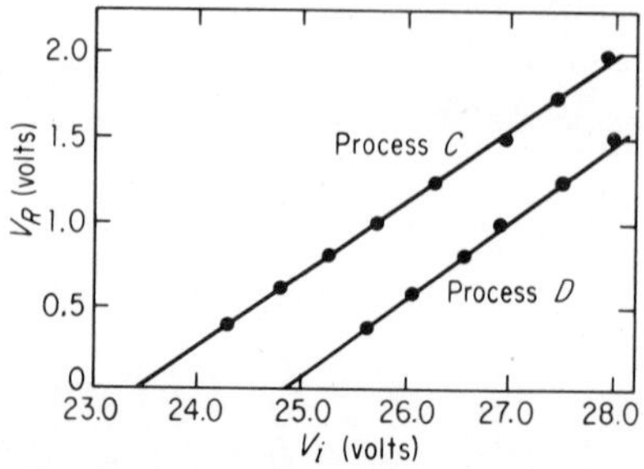

Fig. 2-22. Retarding potential *vs* electron energy for processes C and D.

TABLE 2-1. IDENTIFICATION OF THE ION DETECTED IN EACH OF THE PROCESSES

Process	Charge	V_R vs. V_i	m_B	$m_{A^\pm}$	$A^\pm$
A	+	0.56	15.7 (16)	12	C^+
B	+	0.56	15.7 (16)	12	C^+
C	+	0.43	12.00(12)	16	O^+
D	+	0.46	12.9 (12)	16	O^+
E	—	0.75	21.0 (?)	?	$(?)^-$
F	—	0.43	12.0 (12)	16	O^-
G	—	0.57	15.9 (16)	12	C^-

Similarly, using the data of Figure 2–19, V_R versus V_i is plotted for process E in Figure 2–23. And the plot of V_R versus V_i for processes F and G, given in Figure 2–24, was constructed from the data shown in Figure 2–20.

At this point we know that processes A to D involve positive ions and processes E to G involve negative ions. Now, from the slopes of the curves in Figures 2–21 to 2–24, we can determine the mass of the ions being de-

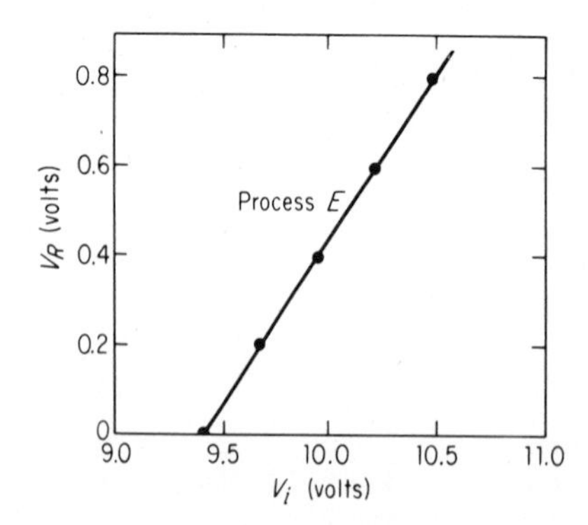

Fig. 2-23. Retarding potential *vs* electron energy for process E.

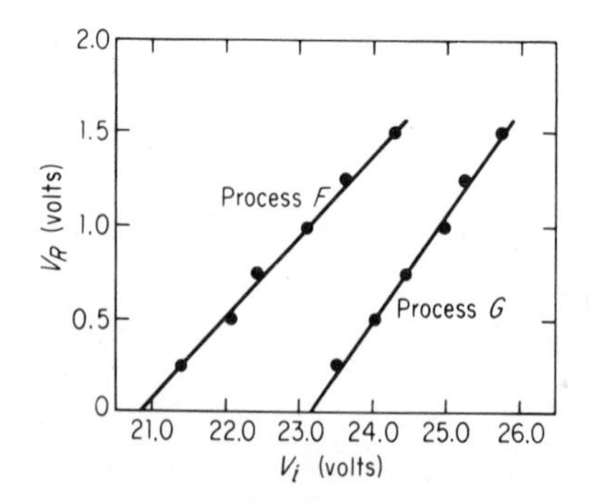

Fig. 2-24. Retarding potential *vs* electron energy for processes F and G.

tected. Table 2–1 shows the slope of the curve for each process, the m_B calculated, and finally, $m_{A^\pm}$, giving the ion being detected.

In Table 2–2 are given the ions detected in the various processes and the

TABLE 2–2. IDENTIFICATION OF THE INDIVIDUAL PROCESSES AND THEIR ENERGIES

Process	$A^\pm$	$U_2 - U_1$ (ev)	Details of Process
A	C^+	20.8	$CO + e \longrightarrow C^+ + O^- + e$
B	C^+	22.6	$\longrightarrow C^+ + O + 2e$
C	O^+	23.4	$\longrightarrow O^+ + C^- + e$
D	O^+	24.8	$\longrightarrow O^+ + C + 2e$
E	$(?)^-$	9.4	$\longrightarrow ?$
F	O^-	20.8_5	$\longrightarrow C^+ + O^- + e$
G	C^-	23.2	$\longrightarrow O^+ + C^- + e$

energies $[V_i = (U_2 - U_1)$ at $V_R = 0]$ of the processes. One readily notes that the energies of processes A and F are the same, so that C^+ and O^- are formed in the same process

$$CO + e \longrightarrow C^+ + O^- + e, \tag{2–47}$$

and that the energy of processes C and G are very nearly the same, so that O^+ and C^- are formed in the same process:

$$CO + e \longrightarrow C^- + O^+ + e. \tag{2–48}$$

Also, from observation of the energetics one finds no negative ions associated with either process B or process D. Therefore, these processes must involve neutral atoms:

$$CO + e \longrightarrow C^+ + O + 2e \tag{2–49}$$

and

$$CO + e \longrightarrow O^+ + C + 2e. \tag{2–50}$$

Only process E remains unidentified. The slope of V_R versus V_i gave $m_B = 21$, thus indicating $m_{A^-} = 7$. The meaning of such a result is unclear. However, the energetics aid us. The very low energy of this process indicates that electron capture has occurred. The shapes of the curves in Figure 2–19 also suggest this. However, the process is not simply electron capture, but rather it is dissociative electron capture, leading to a negatively charged ionic fragment and a neutral fragment. Oxygen is known to readily capture electrons, so we will propose that process E is

$$CO + e \longrightarrow O^- + C. \tag{2–51}$$

This example illustrates what can be done with a Lozier tube without mass analysis. We shall postpone further treatment of the data from this example to Chapter 8. The apparatus is generally not suited to studies of substances more complex than *AB*-type molecules [although recently Asundi and Craggs (38) used a Lozier tube in studies of SF_6 and C_7F_{14}]. Also, ionization efficiency curves and ionization cross sections can be determined, but we have seen that even the ionization efficiency curves have limited significance, since the measured ion current includes contributions from several different types of ions (see Figures 2–18 to 2–20).

REFERENCES

1. J. J. Thomson, *Rays of Positive Electricity and Their Application to Chemical Analyses*, Longmans, Green and Co., London, 1913.
2. H. G. J. Moseley, *Phil. Mag.*, **26**, 1024 (1913); **27**, 703 (1914).
3. F. W. Aston, *Phil. Mag.*, **45**, 934 (1923).
4. K. T. Bainbridge, *Phys. Rev.*, **44**, 123 (1933).
5. F. Soddy, *Ann. Repts. Progr. Chem. Soc.* (*London*), **10**, 262 (1913).
6. F. W. Aston, *Phil. Mag.* **38**, 707 and 709 (1919).
7. E. Goldstein, *Berl. Ber.*, **39**, 691 (1886).
8. W. Wien, *Wied. Ann.*, **65**, 440 (1898); *Ann. Physik*, **8**, 244 (1902).
9. J. J. Thomson, *Phil. Mag.*, **24**, 668 (1912).
10. W. Bleakney, *Phys. Rev.*, **34**, 157 (1929).
11. S. Meyerson, *J. Chem. Phys.*, **37**, 2458 (1962).
12. J. J. Thomson, *Phil. Mag.*, **24**, 209 (1912).
13. A. J. Dempster, *Phil. Mag.*, **31**, 438 (1916).
14. A. J. Dempster, *Phys. Rev.*, **11**, 316 (1918).
15. H. D. Smyth, *Proc. Roy. Soc.* (*London*), **102**, 283 (1922).
16. D. D. Taylor, *Phys. Rev.*, **47**, 666 (1935).
17. W. Bleakney, *Phys. Rev.*, **40**, 496 (1932).
18. R. Conrad, *Phys. Z.*, **31**, 888 (1930).
19. J. A. Hipple and D. P. Stevenson, *Phys. Rev.*, **63**, 121 (1943).
20. G. C. Eltenton, *J. Chem. Phys.*, **15**, 455 (1947).
21. F. W. Aston, *Mass Spectra and Isotopes*, second edition, Edward Arnold and Co., London, 1942, p. 257.
22. M. Morand, *Compt. Rend.*, **182**, 460 (1926).
23. W. R. Smythe, L. H. Rumbaugh, and S. S. West, *Phys. Rev.*, **45**, 724 (1934).
24. M. L. Oliphant, E. S. Shire, and B. M. Crowther, *Proc. Roy. Soc.* (*London*), **146**, 922 (1934).

25. A. O. Nier, E. T. Booth, J. R. Dunning, and A. V. Grosse, *Phys. Rev.*, **57**, 546 (1940).
26. R. G. Hewlett and O. E. Anderson, Jr., *The New World, 1939–1946*, Pennsylvania State University Press, University Park, Pa., 1962, pp. 14 and 668.
27. L. W. Alvarez and R. Cornog, *Phys. Rev.*, **56**, 379 and 613 (1939).
28. W. Kaufmann, *Phys. Z.*, **2**, 602 (1901); *Nachr. Kgl. Ges. Wiss. Gottigen*, 143 (1901).
29. J. J. Thomson, *Phil. Mag.*, **20**, 752 (1910); **21**, 225 (1911).
30. E. Gehrcke and O. Reichenheim, *Verh. d. Phys. Ges.*, **8**, 559 (1906); **9**, 76, 200, and 376 (1907); and **10**, 217 (1908).
31. A. Henglein and H. Ewald, in *Mass Spectroscopy in Physics Research*, National Bureau of Standards Circular 522, 1953, pp. 205–210.
32. F. W. Aston and R. H. Fowler, *Phil. Mag.*, **43**, 514 (1922).
33. J. Classen, *Jahrb. Hamburg Wiss. Anst.*, *Beiheft* (1907); *Physik Z.*, **9**, 762 (1908).
34. A. J. Dempster, *Phys. Rev.*, **20**, 631 (1922).
35. W. W. Lozier, *Phys. Rev.*, **36**, 1285 and 1417 (1930).
36. M. A. Fineman and A. W. Petrocelli, *J. Chem. Phys.*, **36**, 25 (1962).
37. J. T. Tate and W. W. Lozier, *Phys. Rev.*, **39**, 254 (1932).
38. R. K. Asundi and J. D. Craggs, *Proc. Phys. Soc.* (*London*), **83**, 611 (1964).

CHAPTER 3

BASIC INSTRUMENTATION

We recall from Chapter 1 that the mass spectrometer and the mass spectrograph consist of three major components: ion source, analyzer, and detector. Although we have examined previously four historical instruments, we have not considered in detail each of the basic components. Each of these basic components may consist of several types and yet accomplish its intended purpose in the overall scheme of the mass spectrometer or mass spectrograph. It is necessary therefore to discuss these components and their various types before we proceed to discussions of other instrumentation in Chapter 4. The particular types of each component currently used in commercially available instruments will be emphasized slightly compared to the others.

3.1 ION SOURCES

There have been and are a number of different types of ion sources employed in mass spectrometers and mass spectrographs. Table 3–1 briefly summarizes a few of these along with some of their more salient features. In the succeeding paragraphs we shall discuss the more common, currently used ion sources. We shall place much greater emphasis upon the electron bombardment ion source than any other type, because this particular source is the most widely used source in modern mass spectroscopy. Other sources, because of their fairly limited uses, shall be discussed in less detail, and a few highly specialized sources shall not be discussed at all. If the reader

TABLE 3–1. ION SOURCES

Type	Approximate Spread in Energy (ev)	Uses
Electron bombardment	0.1–5.0	General purposes
Photoionization	0.01–0.2	Molecular spectroscopy
Surface ionization (hot anode)	0.2	Isotopic abundance, chemical purity, and general analysis
Secondary ion	5–100	Solid samples and surface phenomena
Gaseous discharge	1000	Packing fractions
Gaseous discharge in magnetic field	100	Leak detection
Arc discharge	2–10	Intense beams (e.g., isotope separation)
Hot spark	1000	Packing fractions and general analysis

desires information about the latter group, he may find an abundance of information in a number of the books listed in Appendix V.

THE ELECTRON BOMBARDMENT ION SOURCE

Positive ions may be produced by passing a beam of electrons through a gas at pressures of about 10^{-4} to 10^{-6} mm (Hg). Pressures other than these may be employed, but this range is common to many applications. The energy of the electron beam is usually controlled, and, if the energy is greater than the ionization potential of the gas, the electrons may cause ionization and/or fragmentation of the gas molecules.

A diagrammatic sketch of a fairly simple electron bombardment ion source is shown in Figure 3–1. Electrons are emitted from the heated filament F, usually well removed from the ionization chamber and often constructed of tungsten; however, tantalum, rhenium, and various coated filaments have been employed by some workers. Electrons emitted from F are attracted to grid (or plate) G_1 by maintaining G_1 at a potential positive with respect to F. Plates G_1 and G_2 both have small slits, of the order of 1×3 mm, to allow only a finely collimated beam of electrons to enter the ionization chamber C. The energy of the electrons entering C is controlled by the potential drop between F and G_2. In the region C, there is, in principle, no electric field, for plates G_2 and G_3 are maintained at the same potential. The electrons pass through the slit in G_3 (somewhat larger than in either G_1 or G_2) and are collected by the anode trap T. The electron emission current i_e of the filament F is determined by the current flowing between F and G_1, whereas the trap current i_t is determined by the number of electrons reaching the anode trap T. The potential of T is usually maintained positive with respect to G_3 so that secondary electrons liberated by electron bombardment of the metal

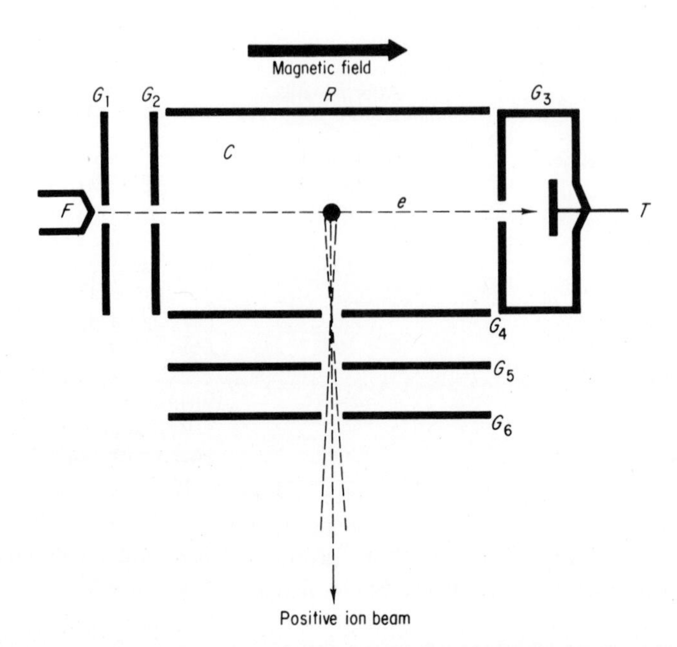

Fig. 3-1. Schematic diagram of an electron bombardment ion source.

anode cannot escape back into the region C. In addition, it is common to hold the electron beam in alignment along a spiral path with a weak magnetic field ($\sim 10^2$ gauss).

We have then, in the region of C, bounded by the slit systems of G_2 and G_3, a fairly well-defined beam of electrons of known energy. This is the ionizing electron beam, and it is this beam which intercepts gaseous molecules in the ionization chamber region. Samples are introduced to the ionization chamber region perpendicular to both the electron beam and the final ion beam, as shown by the black dot in the center of the ionization chamber in Figure 3–1. Materials having vapor pressures of the order of a few tenths of a millimeter or more are admitted to the ion source through a "gas leak," to be discussed later. In high-temperature work, crucibles are placed a few millimeters from the electron beam, and the sample is distilled into the electron beam as a well-collimated molecular beam. If the energy of the electron beam is sufficiently great, ionization of the molecules may occur. At still greater electron energies, ionization and subsequent dissociation or fragmentation may also occur. Thus, the various positive ions, with which we shall now be concerned, are produced in the ion source by means of electron bombardment of the sample molecules.

Between the repeller plate R and grid (or plate) G_4 there is a weak electric field that may be used to either repel or draw out the positive ions from C (depending upon the specific potentials upon these plates or grids). The potential difference between R and G_4 is usually quite small (of the order of only a few volts per centimeter). Actually, the moderate magnetic field in the direction of the electron beam causes the necessary separation of the ions from the electrons because the relatively heavy positive ions move in the direction of the electric field between R and G_4 and suffer only small deflections due to the magnetic field. The electrons, however, having much smaller mass, are collimated by the magnetic field.

The positive ions, drawn or repelled out of the ionization chamber, are accelerated by a large potential difference—usually from 1000 to 3000 volts—between grids (or plates) G_4 and G_6. Thus, the positive ions acquire a large kinetic energy. In addition, these ions also possess some small thermal energy (about 0.03 ev), plus any excess kinetic energy with which the ions may have been formed. Usually, the excess kinetic energy is small, but in certain cases it may be 1 ev or more. The positive ion beam emerging from grid (or plate) G_6, commonly in the current range of 10^{-10} to 10^{-15} amp, is a divergent beam of various ions of different masses (and charges), but of very nearly the same kinetic energy.

In order to achieve longer life of the filament, many of the commercial instruments employ tungsten filaments (and such other metal filaments as rhenium and tantalum). Many of the older instruments (as well as the ion sources in some of the present mass spectrometers) use coated filaments, which have at least two significant advantages: (a) a reduction of the operating temperature of the filament, thereby reducing the problems which might be encountered in pyrolysis; and (b) because of the lower temperature, a reduction in the Maxwellian spread of the energy of the electrons emitted is achieved. Other filament materials also may be employed. For example, lanthanum boride, LaB_6, coated on a tungsten filament has been used as a filament in an omegatron tube (1). McGowan and Kerwin (2) have compared mass spectra obtained with a carbon filament and with a tungsten filament and found that there is less dissociation with a carbon filament. Furthermore, it was noted that the C^+ ion intensity increases only slightly over that observed using a tungsten filament.

The electron bombardment ion source is probably the most reliable of all ion sources, for it gives a low energy spread (see Table 3–1) and a very steady ionizing beam, and it is the source most used in modern mass spectroscopy. For most mass spectrometric studies using this ion source, electron ionizing energies of 0–100 ev are commonly employed. However, it is not unusual to use electron energies of up to 300 or 400 volts, and 1000 ev electron energies are often employed when using this source to produce highly multiply charged ions for *packing fraction studies*. Electron bombardment ion sources produce ion beams whose energy is homogeneous; therefore they will work with any type of mass analyzer (see Section 3.2). Except when packing fraction studies are to be made, this source can be used without velocity focusing or velocity selection. Further detailed information about electron bombardment ion sources may be found in Barnard's *Modern Mass Spectrometry*, wherein not only the theory of various types of these ion sources is discussed, but also the techniques of operating these sources are given.

THE PHOTOIONIZATION ION SOURCE

Ionization of molecules can also be accomplished by using electromagnetic radiation of sufficiently short wavelength. Many ionization processes require about 10 ev or more; this corresponds to photons having wavelengths of about 1200 Å or less. K. Watanabe, T. Nakayama, and J. Mottl have studied the photoionization of many pure substances (3). A photoionization source was incorporated into a mass spectrometer by A. Terenin and B. Popov (4), and L. Kerwin (see Appendix V) has described more recent experiments by F. P. Lossing using a krypton discharge photoionization source. Also recently, H. Hurzeler, M. G. Inghram, and J. D. Morrison (5) have employed photoionization sources in a mass spectrometer. These latter workers were the first to employ beams of ultraviolet radiation continuously variable in energy, and with very low energy spreads (from a Seya-Namioka monochromator), together with a mass spectrometer to analyze the products from the photoionization processes. Use of a photon beam permitted Hurzeler, *et al.* to more efficiently extract the ions from the ion source region and, more importantly, to study fine structures in the ionization efficiency curves.

B. Steiner, C. F. Giese, and M. G. Inghram (6) have carried out photoionization of alkanes, and F. A. Elder, C. Giese, B. Steiner, and M. Inghram (7) have studied the photoionization of alkyl free radicals. Lossing found that a slit of 0.1 cm^2 admitted sufficient light from an ordinary discharge tube to produce ion beams of about the same intensity as those produced with an ordinary electron bombardment ion source. A disadvantage of this type of source is that at the present time it is not possible to obtain monochromatic spectral lines across the whole range of 5 to 30 or 50 ev. The use of LiF windows between the source and the monochromator causes a cut-off of the photon beam at about 9.5 ev. Hopefully, this disadvantage will be overcome in the future, possibly through use of windowless systems. The photoionization source is relatively simple in its construction, and it is stable. The use of such a source with a vacuum monochromator would provide excellent measurements of appearance potentials if lower wavelength photons could be employed. The determination of ionization potentials by photoionization may usually be made to within ± 0.02 ev, seldom poorer than ± 0.05 ev, and even to as close as ± 0.005 ev.

One of the very obvious applications to which the photoionization source could be put would be in analytical mass spectrometry. Advantage could be taken of the somewhat simpler mass spectra obtained in certain cases. Apparently only Vilesov and Akopyan (8) have applied this technique to the analysis of mixtures of complex organic compounds. They discussed the various considerations, technical requirements, and advantages of the photoionization source in their report. However, the use of "simpler" mass spectra does not solve all problems; in fact, some analytical problems might become insoluble, e.g., mixtures of isomers.

Looking to the future, it is very likely that we shall soon see the use of laser sources in certain mass spectrometers, and some very interesting studies made with such sources. Some beginnings in this direction are noted in Section 11.4.

THE SURFACE EMISSION ION SOURCE

The surface emission ion source is of use in analyzing elements which have low ionization potentials. The material to be analyzed is applied to the filament wire or ribbon and is then inserted into the ion source unit. By heating the filament in the vacuum of the mass spectrometer system, a part of the substance on the high-melting filament is vaporized, and some of it may be evaporated directly as ions. The ions so produced are then accelerated and collimated into an ion beam by means of the collimating slits in the ion source. A schematic illustration of the surface emission ion source is shown in Figure 3–2.

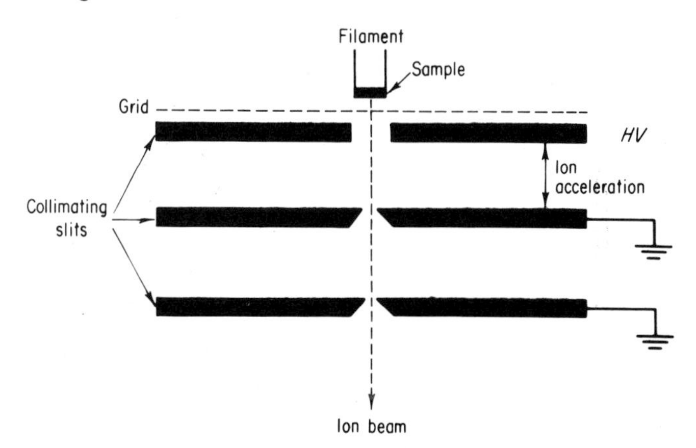

Fig. 3-2. Schematic diagram of a surface emission ion source.

The ratio of the number of positively charged particles to the number of neutral particles evaporated from the filament, according to I. Langmuir and K. H. Kingdon (9), is given by

$$n_+/n_0 = e^{-(I-\phi)/kT}, \tag{3–1}$$

where ϕ is the work function of the filament material in electron volts, I is the ionization potential in electron volts of the material evaporated from the filament, k is Boltzmann's constant (equal to 1.38×10^{-16} erg/deg), and T is the absolute temperature. Although Equation (3–1) applies specifically only for elements, it is qualitatively correct for many compounds. Eliminating the constant k from Equation (3–1), we may write this equation as

$$n_+/n_0 = Ae^{11,600(\phi - I)/T}, \qquad (3\text{–}2)$$

where A is a constant at a given temperature and both ϕ and I are now expressed in electron volts. The factor 11,600 is $1/k$, together with unit factors: (23,061 cal/1.9872 cal) = 11,600.

EXAMPLE 3–1. If, in an analysis of silver metal (first ionization potential = 7.57 ev) we may assume A to be 0.5, to what temperature must a tungsten filament (work function of 4.50 ev) be heated in order to obtain a ratio of $n_+/n_0 = 5 \times 10^{-16}$?

Using Equation (3–2),

$$n_+/n_0 = 5 \times 10^{-16} = e^{-35.23} = [e^{11,600(4.50-7.57)/T}]/2.$$

Therefore,

$$\frac{(11,600)(3.07)}{T} = 34.54,$$

or

$$T = (35,600)/(34.54) = 1030^\circ \text{ K}.$$

That is, a temperature of 757° C must be achieved.

EXAMPLE 3–2. What would be the ratio of n_+/n_0 for the surface ionization of an aluminum sample (first ionization potential = 5.98 ev) from a tungsten filament at 757° C?

$$747^\circ + 273^\circ = 1030^\circ \text{ K},$$

$$\frac{11,600(4.50 - 5.98)}{1030} = -16.67,$$

$$e^{-16.67} = 10^{-7.24} = 10^{0.76} \times 10^{-8},$$

or

$$n_+/n_0 = 3 \times 10^{-8}.$$

Thus, as the ionization potential of the material being evaporated is decreased, the ratio of n_+/n_0 increases. Similarly, as the work function of the filment material is increased, the ratio of n_+/n_0 increases. Tungsten is usually employed ($\phi = 4.5$ ev) at higher temperatures (although tantalum and rhenium may also be used), whereas either platinum or tungsten may be employed at lower temperatures. This particular source has the specific advantage that it does not ionize background gases, and therefore the spectrum obtained is usually much freer of impurities than that obtained from the more commonly employed electron bombardment source. However, the emission from the filament is difficult to regulate.

The grid in Figure 3–2 was introduced by D. C. Hess, G. Whetherill, and M. G. Inghram (10) to suppress "tertiary" ions. The ions produced from the sample on the filament cause secondary electron emission at the first collimating slit; the electrons then are accelerated back toward the filament; and this electron bombardment causes the formation of "tertiary" ions, which are seen as "extra" peaks in the mass spectrum. This suppressor grid prevents the "tertiary" ions from entering the mass spectrometer.

The surface emission ion source is very selective in its ionization, and, in this respect, is conveniently adaptable to the detection of certain impurities in very small amounts. Table 3–2 indicates some of the elements that may be analyzed using the surface emission ion source. The physical and chemical form of the sample being studied is of importance. Small samples may be evaporated onto the filament from solution, but if the sample evaporates at a low temperature, fractionation effects and lowered efficiencies may be found. J. W. Frazer, R. P. Burns, and G. W. Barton (11) have described low-background tungsten filaments for use in surface emission sources.

White, Collins, and Rourke (12) were the first to employ a canoe-shaped single-filament surface emission source. Here a strip of rhenium or tungsten is folded to form the shape of a canoe or boat to hold the sample. This type of source gives a much greater efficiency than does the usual single filament. In fact, this type of filament has nearly the same efficiency as the three-filament ion source, possibly because it is equivalent to a closed-up three-filament source.

Inghram and Chupka (13) developed the three-filament ion source. In this source, two filament strips are held in parallel planes to each other while the third filament strip is located in a plane perpendicular to and between the other two filaments. The sample is loaded onto one of the outer filaments and the rate of evaporation of the sample from this filament is controlled by regulating the current passed through the filament. The center filament is heated to a very high temperature and causes the ionization

TABLE 3–2. SOME ELEMENTS WHICH CAN BE ANALYZED WITH SURFACE EMISSION ION SOURCES

Aluminum	Gallium	Neodymium	Samarium	Tungsten
Calcium	Hafnium	Potassium	Sodium	Uranium
Dysprosium	Holmium	Promethium	Strontium	Ytterbium
Erbium	Indium	Rhodium	Terbium	Yttrium
Europium	Lithium	Rubidium	Thulium	Zirconium
Gadolinium	Lutetium	Ruthenium	Titantium	

to occur at a maximum efficiency. Other three-filament ion sources have been described by L. N. Gall', R. N. Gall', Yu. S. Rutgaizer, and A. M. Shereshevskii (14), and by M. S. Chupakhin (15) and M. S. Chupakhin and E. Gradsztain (16). E. E. Muschlitz, H. D. Randolph, and J. N. Ratti (17) have recently described an ion source providing a reasonably high-intensity beam of negative ions with a narrow ion energy spread, and Crouch (18) has described a method for the thermal ionization of elements of high ionization potential.

The parallel filament is a recent modification of the triple filament; in it all three filaments are in parallel planes. This filament was developed by Patterson and Wilson (19) to allow comparison of an unknown sample with a standard. This allows discrimination effects to be eliminated and at the same time gives a little better efficiency than the ordinary triple filament.

THE ARC DISCHARGE ION SOURCE

A schematic diagram of the arc discharge is shown in Figure 3–3. The arc is initiated and maintained by electrons passing from the filament, through the gas being studied, to the anode. The pressure of gas in the discharge region is usually about 0.01 mm (Hg). If a magnetic field is employed to collimate the electron beam in the discharge, the pressure of the gaseous sample may be reduced to about 10^{-4} mm (Hg).

The arc discharge source produces relatively monoenergetic electrons (about 2–10 ev spread) but is rather unstable. This source is used largely for the production of intense ion beams, and for the quantity separation of isotopes where intense ion beams are obviously necessary.

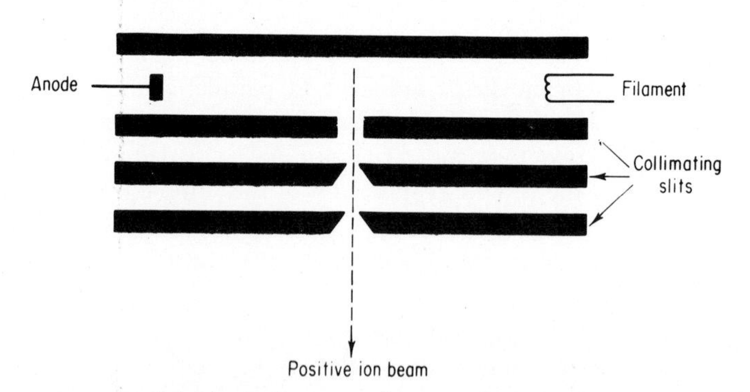

Fig. 3-3. Schematic diagram of an arc discharge ion source.

THE HOT SPARK ION SOURCE

The hot spark ion source is very similar in construction to the surface ionization ion source shown in Figure 3–2. Only one major change is made: the filament is removed and in its place is introduced a primary electrode, consisting either of the material to be analyzed or a tube packed with the material to be analyzed. The guard ring now serves as the secondary electrode, and an oscillator circuit maintains a spark discharge between the primary electrode and the edges of the hole through the secondary electrode. The discharge carries some of the primary electrode into the vapor phase, a certain amount in the form of ions. As with the surface ionization source, the positive ions are then accelerated and collimated into an ion beam.

J. G. Gorman, E. J. Jones, and J. A. Hipple (20) first constructed and demonstrated the use of a spark source with a double-focusing mass spectrograph for analyses of steel samples. A double-focusing mass analyzer is necessary with a spark source in order to obtain good resolution, for the ion beam produced with the spark source has a large energy spread (21).

The hot spark source produces an abundance of multiply charged ions and will analyze any element that can be put into a solid form as either the element or a compound of the element. This source uses a small sample and gives a very high sensitivity for almost all of the elements, if it is operated at low pressures [about 10^{-5} mm (Hg)]. The sensitivity is seldom poorer than 0.1 ppm, and over half of the elements have detection limits below 0.003 ppm (22). In order to achieve highest sensitivity, most spark source instruments must employ photographic plates for detection (see Section 3.3). This in turn introduces plate calibration problems. A very important advantage of this source is that it provides a general freedom from matrix effects. Also, its sensitivity is approximately equal for all of the elements [varying generally (23) by not more than a factor of 3]; this allows the ion beam to be representative of the sample composition and the production of ions to vary directly as the concentration of the element in the sample. Advantage has been taken of these features in a recent search for new isotopes (see Section 10.5).

In addition to being used for the analysis of elements and metals, the spark source has also been used in mass spectrographic studies of inorganic solids and organic materials (24). Organic materials, compacted into hollow aluminum electrodes, yield large abundances of fragment ions. Certainly, many additional investigations with spark ion sources will be made in the future.

THE GASEOUS DISCHARGE ION SOURCE

The gaseous discharge ion source is largely of historical interest and has been described briefly in Chapter 2. It was with such an ion source that Thomson did his early studies in mass spectrometry. It is interesting to note, however, that very recently Knewstubb and Tickner (25) have used mass spectrometry to study the ions in the positive and negative columns in the glow discharges in the rare gases.

Because the discharge ion sources include an electrical field, they differ significantly from the other types of ion sources. Different types of discharges (e.g., dc glow and ac discharges) with their differing field conditions may well produce different relative abundances of ions. The gaseous discharges also present ion beams with large energy spreads that can adversely affect the resolution of the mass analyzer (however, in many cases single-focusing instruments may still be employed). Knewstubb (26) has recently reviewed much of the work with different gaseous discharge ion sources.

FIELD EMISSION ION SOURCE

Field ionization of molecules and atoms in electric fields of about 10^8 volts/cm produce positive ions. These very large electric fields can be obtained by holding very fine metal points at high potentials. R. H. Good, Jr., and E. W. Müller (27) and more recently Müller (28) have reviewed field ionization. However, M. G. Inghram and R. Gomer (29) were the first to use field emission as a source of ions in a mass spectrometer.

Inghram and Gomer (29) showed that the mass spectra of molecules were much simpler using a field ionization source than with the electron bombardment ion source. In addition to the studies of molecules on surfaces, mass spectrometers with field emission ion sources open up some analytical possibilities because of the simplicity of the mass spectra. However, as noted in the discussion of photoionization sources, simpler spectra do not always present an analytical advantage. It is common that the field ionization mass spectra show a very large parent molecule-ion and much smaller amounts of fragment ions. Table 3–3 compares several mass spectra from field emission and electron bombardment ion sources. H. D. Beckey (30) has reported on field ionization mass spectrometry and has indicated many of the possibilities of this type of ion source.

Another way of producing very large electric fields would be to use radial electric fields, such as those obtained by fixing a very fine wire along the axis of a cylinder of much larger radius. In the vicinity of the wire, large electric fields are produced, as may be seen from the expression

$$E = \frac{V}{r \ln (b/a)}, \qquad (3\text{–}3)$$

where b is the radius of the cylinder, a is the radius of the central wire, and r is the distance away from the center of the wire at which the electric field is calculated (V is the potential drop between the wire and the cylinder). At the surface of the smooth wire $r = a$, so that

$$E = \frac{V}{a \ln (b/a)}. \qquad (3\text{–}4)$$

For a smooth wire 0.0005 in. in diameter ($a = 6.3 \times 10^{-4}$ cm), a cylinder of $\frac{1}{2}$-in. diameter ($b = 0.63$ cm), and a potential difference between the wire

TABLE 3–3. A COMPARISON OF ELECTRON BOMBARDMENT AND FIELD IONIZATION MASS SPECTRA

Molecule	m/e	Ionic Species	Relative Abundance: Conventional Mass Spectrometer	Relative Abundance: Field Ionization Mass Spectrometer*
CH_3OH	32	CH_3OH^+	67.0	100.0
	31	CH_2OH^+	100.0	43.0
	30	CH_2O^+	1.0	
	29	CHO^+	65.0	
	28	CO^+	6.5	
	18	H_2O^+	2.0	
C_2H_6	30	$C_2H_6^+$	22.3	100.0
	29	$C_2H_5^+$	20.3	
	28	$C_2H_4^+$	100.0	
	27	$C_2H_3^+$	31.1	
	26	$C_2H_2^+$	21.9	
	25	C_2H^+	3.6	
	24	C_2^+	0.7	
	15	CH_3^+	4.6	25.0
	14	CH_2^+	3.5	
CH_3COCH_3	58	$CH_3COCH_3^+$	25.0	100.0
	57	$CH_3COCH_2^+$	0.8	
	44	CH_3CHO^+	2.3	
	43	CH_3CO^+	100.0	
	42	CH_2CO^+ and $C_3H_6^+$	7.0	
	41	$C_3H_5^+$	2.2	
	39	$C_3H_3^+$	3.9	
	38	$C_3H_2^+$	2.4	
	37	C_3H^+	2.2	
	29	CHO^+ and $C_2H_5^+$	4.3	
	28	CO^+ and $C_2H_4^+$	1.8	
	27	$C_2H_3^+$	8.2	
	26	$C_2H_2^+$	6.0	
	25	C_2H^+	1.6	

*These data are from Reference (29).

and the cylinder of 10 kv, we find that

$$E = \frac{1 \times 10^4}{(6.3 \times 10^{-4}) \ln (0.63/6.3 \times 10^{-4})}$$

or

$$E = \frac{1 \times 10^4}{(6.3 \times 10^{-4})(6.9)},$$

so that

$$E = 2.3 \times 10^6 \text{ volts/cm},$$

which is not sufficient for field ionization. However, Robertson, Viney, and Warrington (31) used this approach and found that a field intensification factor of about 70, caused by the surface roughness of their wires, allowed the use of this method as a field ionization source of ions. The adaptation of this type of ion source for use in mass spectrometry is obvious.

3.2 MASS ANALYZERS

The heart of the mass spectrometer or the mass spectrograph is the mass analyzer. The Lozier tube described in Chapter 2 does not resolve the ions formed on the basis of mass, although, as we saw by example, the mass of the detected ions can be determined from diatomic molecules; for this reason the Lozier tube is not properly termed a mass spectrometer.

The mass analyzer sorts the different masses present in the ionized sample and allows one to determine the mass and the abundance or relative intensities of each of the ionic species present. Three of the several methods which are commonly used for analysis are *the magnetic analyzer*, *the electrostatic analyzer* (not a mass analyzer, but because it is used in conjunction with mass analyzers we shall discuss it briefly in this section), and *the time-of-flight analyzer*.

A very brief listing of some of the various types of analyzers used in different mass spectrometers and mass spectrographs is presented in Table 3–4. After we treat the three types of analyzers mentioned above, we shall conclude our discussion of mass analyzers with a short description and a few examples of resolving power.

THE MAGNETIC ANALYZER

The positive ions produced in the ion source are accelerated (i.e., they gain kinetic energy) by falling through a potential of V (in erg/esu); therefore the work done on the positive ions is eV, which is equal to the kinetic energy T (in ergs) acquired. Thus,

$$T = mv^2/2 = eV, \tag{3–5}$$

where e is the charge in esu, m is the mass in g, and v is the velocity of the ion in centimeters per second. Now, in the presence of a magnetic field perpendicular to the direction of motion of the positive ion beam, shown in Figure 3–4, each ion experiences a force at right angles to both its direction of motion and the direction of the magnetic field, thereby bending or deflecting the beam of the ions.

TABLE 3–4. SOME MASS SPECTROMETERS AND SPECTROGRAPHS OF VARIOUS TYPES OF ANALYZERS

Analyzer Type	Instrument Type	Workers	Year	Approximate Resolving Power
Parabola	Electromagnetic	Thomson	1913	15
Direction-focusing	180° magnetic	Dempster	1918	100
Velocity-focusing	Electromagnetic	Aston	1919	130
Direction-focusing	180° magnetic	Bleakney	1929	15
Direction-focusing	180° magnetic	Bainbridge	1930	100
Double-focusing	180° magnetic, 90° electrostatic	Dempster	1935	7000
Double-focusing	60° magnetic, 127° 17′ electrostatic	Bainbridge and Jordan	1936	7000
Double-focusing	90° magnetic, 31° 50′ electrostatic	Mattauch and Herzog	1936	3000
Direction-focusing	60° magnetic	Nier	1940	80
Direction-focusing	180° magnetic	Hoover and Washburn	1940	500
Pulse-type velocity selector	Time-of-flight	Stephens	1946	2
Rf time-of-flight	Omegatron	Hipple, Sommer, and Thomas	1949	Variable
Rf time-of-flight	Bennett	Bennett	1950	30
Rf time-of-flight	Bennett	Glenn	1952	250
Parabola	Electromagnetic	Henglein and Ewald	1953	50
Pulsed time-of-flight	Linear time-of-flight	Wolff and Stephens	1953	20
Pulsed time-of-flight	Linear time-of-flight	Katzenstein and Friedland	1955	100
Pulsed time-of-flight	Linear time-of-flight	Wiley and McLaren	1955	150
Pulsed time-of-flight	Linear time-of-flight	Harrington	1962	500

The ions experience a force of

$$F_H = Hev/c \tag{3–6}$$

(in dynes) in a magnetic field of H oersteds, where c is the velocity of light in a vacuum ($c = 2.9979 \times 10^{10}$ cm/sec). This force due to the magnetic field must equal the centrifugal force of the ion F_C; i.e.,

$$F_C = F_H, \tag{3–7}$$

where

$$F_C = mv^2/r. \tag{3–8}$$

Therefore,

$$\frac{mv^2}{r} = \frac{Hev}{c}. \tag{3–9}$$

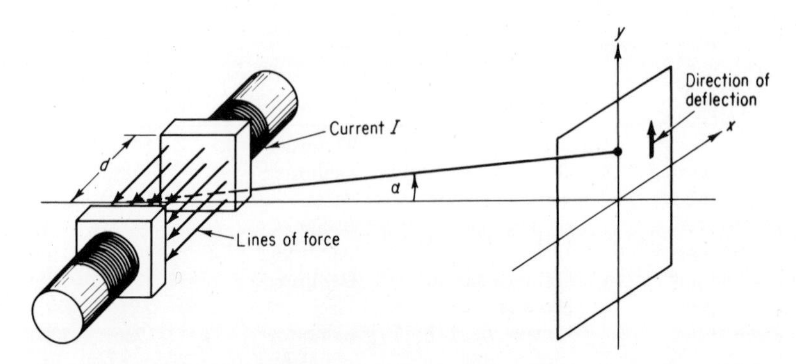

Fig. 3-4. Uniform magnetic deflection system consisting of two parallel pole pieces energized by means of an electromagnet.

Rearranging, Equation (3–9) becomes

$$v = \frac{Her}{mc}, \tag{3–10}$$

and inserting Equation (3–10) into Equation (3–5), we obtain

$$\left(\frac{m}{2}\right)\left(\frac{Her}{mc}\right)^2 = eV \tag{3–11}$$

or

$$\frac{H^2 e^2 r^2}{2mc^2} = eV \tag{3–12}$$

or

$$\left(\frac{m}{e}\right) = \frac{H^2 r^2}{2Vc^2}. \tag{3–13}$$

If the constants are evaluated, Equation (3–13) may be written as

$$(m/z) = H^2 r^2/20{,}740V, \tag{3–14}$$

where, now, m is the mass in atomic mass units (e.g., m of CO_2^{++} is 44), z is the number of electronic charges (e.g., z of CO_2^{++} is 2), H is in gauss, r is in centimeters, and V is the volts of the potential drop. For an instrument with a fixed value of the radius r, we can write Equation (3–13) as

$$\left(\frac{m}{e}\right) = k\left(\frac{H^2}{V}\right), \tag{3–15}$$

where $k = r^2/2c^2$. Equation (3–15) shows the manner of the dependence of the m/e ratio of the ions upon the magnetic field and upon the accelerating potential.

The angle of deflection (radius) is usually fixed for a given analyzer tube (60°, 90°, 180°), so that to focus ions of given m/e values on the detector system, either H or V must be varied. It is seen from Equation (3–15) that increasing the magnetic field H will focus heavier and heavier ions on the detector, and that increasing the accelerating potential V will focus successively lighter ions on the detector.

EXAMPLE 3–3. Consider an electromagnetic mass spectometer with a radius of curvature of 12.00 in. and operating at an accelerating potential of 2500 volts. What must be the magnetic field so that the $C_3H_5^+$ ion ($m/e = 41$; $m = 41.0399$ on the carbon-12 = 12.0000 scale) will be brought into focus on the detector?

To solve this problem, we shall make use of Equation (3–13). Here, r must be in centimeters and V in units of erg/esu. The relation, 300 practical volts = 1 erg/esu, is needed for the conversion to the proper units. Therefore,

$$V = 2500/300 = 8.333 \text{ erg/esu}$$

and

$$r = 12.00 \times 2.54 = 30.48 \text{ cm.}$$

Now, using Equation (3–13) in a rearranged form,

$$H^2 = 2V(m/e)c^2/r^2,$$

we have

$$H^2 = \frac{2 \times 8.333 \times (41.0399/6.024) \times 10^{-23} \times 9 \times 10^{20}}{(30.48)^2 \times 4.802 \times 10^{-10}}.$$

The factor of 9×10^{20} (i.e., c^2) is necessary to convert esu^2 to emu^2. Avogadro's number N_0 is 6.024×10^{23}. Therefore,

$$H^2 = 2.29 \times 10^6,$$

from which we see that

$$H = 1514 \text{ gauss.}$$

More simply, using Equation (3–14),

$$H^2 = \frac{20{,}740 \times 2500 \times 41.0399}{1 \times (30.48)^2} = 2.29 \times 10^6$$

or

$$H = 1514 \text{ gauss.}$$

Similarly, to focus the $C_3H_7^+$ ion ($m/e = 43$; $m = 43.0558$ on the carbon-12 = 12.0000 scale) under the same conditions as above, a magnetic field of

$H = 1550$ gauss is required. Therefore, in order to focus successively heavier ions on the detector, stronger magnetic fields are required.

EXAMPLE 3–4. For a certain electromagnetic mass spectrometer, the Xe^+ ion at $m/e = 132$ was observed at $H = 2085$ gauss. What magnetic field would be necessary to focus the CCl_3^+ ions at $m/e = 117$, 119, 121, and 123 if the accelerating potential were left unchanged?

We have seen that the mass-to-charge ratio is proportional to the square of the magnetic field. Therefore,

$$(m/e)_1 = b(H_1)^2 \tag{3–16}$$

and

$$(m/e)_2 = b(H_2)^2, \tag{3–17}$$

where b is the proportionality constant. Thus, we may write the ratio

$$\frac{(m/e)_1}{(m/e)_2} = \left(\frac{H_1}{H_2}\right)^2. \tag{3–18}$$

Therefore, for the $m/e = 117$ ion (using masses on the unified scale),

$$\left(\frac{H_1}{2085}\right)^2 = \frac{116.907}{131.906} = 0.8863$$

$$H_1/2085 = 0.94143,$$

so that

$$H_1 = 1963 \text{ gauss.}$$

That is, the CCl_3^+ ion of $m/e = 117$ would be observed at 1963 gauss. We may note in passing that if the values of 117 and 132 had been used for the calculation, the answer would be the same, an error of only about 0.2 gauss being introduced in the less accurate case.

Similarly, the CCl_3^+ ions at $m/e = 119$, 121, and 123 would be observed at magnetic fields of 1980, 1996, and 2012 gauss, respectively.

A typical magnetic analyzer was shown schematically in Figure 3–4. The ion beam exiting from the ion source enters the magnetic field and is deflected. The ions of different masses follow paths of different radii of curvature in the magnetic field and analysis is effected. Now we should consider the ion beam of a single mass-to-charge ratio. Because the exit slits from the ion source have a finite width, a divergent ion beam enters the analyzing field. That is, the ions have different directions. However, the magnetic analyzer causes the divergent beam of ions of a given energy to be refocused. This is termed *direction-focusing* and is shown in Figure 3–5.

The general problem of magnetic direction-focusing has been solved by R. Herzog (32); the equation of direction focus for the ion beam entering

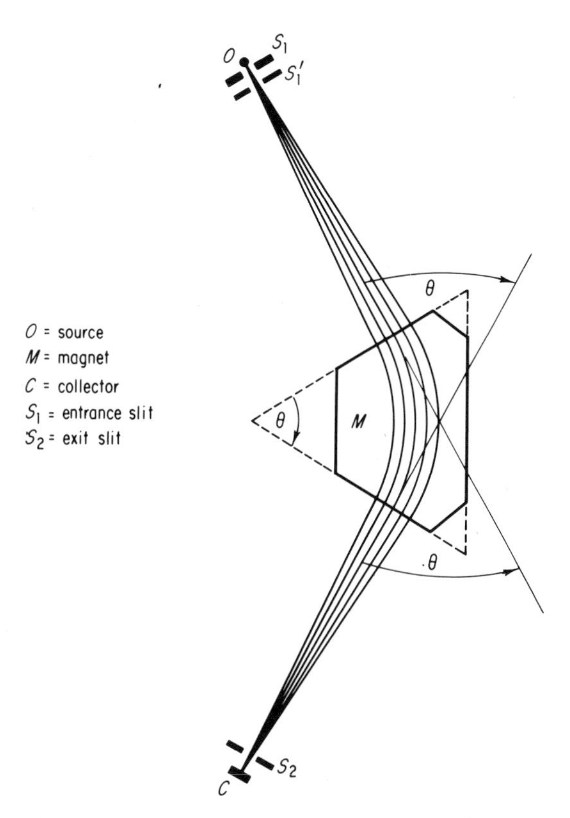

Fig. 3-5. Focusing of a divergent ion beam by a wedge-shaped ($\theta = 60°$) magnetic field.

and leaving the magnetic field at right angles (or nearly right angles) to the faces of the magnetic field is

$$(l_{oH} - g_H)(l_{iH} - g_H) = f_H^2, \tag{3–19}$$

where

$$f_H = r_H \csc \theta \tag{3–20}$$

and

$$g_H = r_H \cot \theta. \tag{3–21}$$

Here, l_{oH} is the distance from slit S_1 to the face of the magnetic field, or the *object* distance, and l_{iH} is the distance from the exit face of the magnetic field to the point of focus (at the collector C in Figure 3–5), or the *image* distance. The radius of curvature is r_H and θ is the angle through which the ion beam is deflected.

For the case of the *symmetrical* 60° analyzer, shown schematically in Figure 3–5, $l_{oH} = l_{iH}$; therefore,

$$l_{oH} - g_H = f_H = l_{iH} - g_H$$

or

$$l_{iH} = l_{oH} = f_H + g_H$$
$$l_{iH} = l_{oH} = r_H(\csc 60^\circ + \cot 60^\circ)$$
$$l_{iH} = l_{oH} = r_H(1.1547 + 0.5774)$$
$$l_{iH} = l_{oH} = 1.7321 r_H.$$

Thus, the image and object distances are $1.7321 r_H$ from the face of the magnetic field. A. O. Nier (33) first used this type of analyzer, and it has since come to be called the Nier 60° analyzer (see Chapter 4). In principle, the resolving powers of the symmetrical 60°, 90°, and 180° mass analyzers are identical. However, since the ion path length is shortest for the 180° configuration, under comparable vacuum conditions the 180° instrument may have better resolving power as a result of less gas scattering. There is no fundamental difference between any of them, and each will perform equally well the tasks required of a direction-focusing mass analyzer.

THE ELECTROSTATIC ANALYZER

Because the electrostatic analyzer is useful in a number of ways, particularly in combination with a mass analyzer, we shall describe it here. However, this analyzer is not properly a mass analyzer; rather, it is a *velocity analyzer*. Ions are deflected by an electrostatic field as shown in Figure 3–6. If, however, a radial electrostatic field is employed, such as shown in Figure 3–7, the ions will assume circular trajectories with radius

$$r_e = 2V/E, \tag{3–22}$$

where r_e is in centimeters, V is the accelerating potential drop prior to

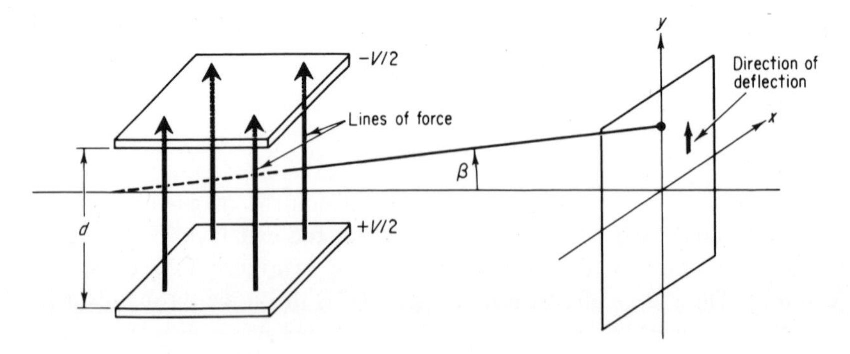

Fig. 3-6. Uniform electrostatic deflection system for positive ions consisting of two parallel planes.

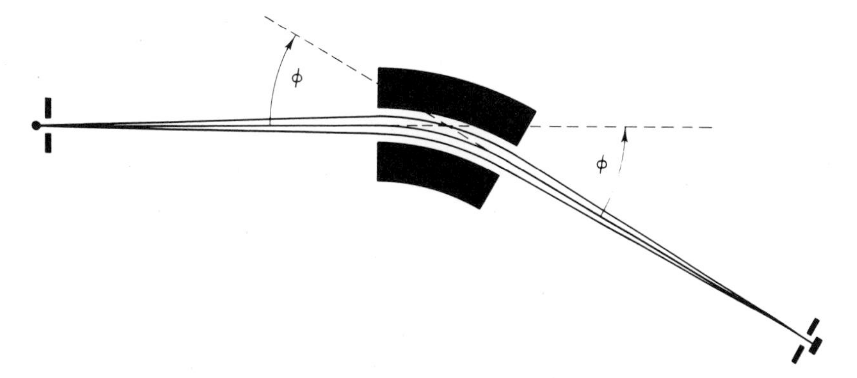

Fig. 3-7. Focusing of a divergent ion beam by means of an electrostatic field.

injection into the radial electrostatic field in esu, and E is the electrostatic field in esu-volts per centimeters.

It is immediately obvious from Equation (3–22) that the mass m is not a parameter and that the electrostatic analyzer does not analyze mass. However, V is a parameter, and therefore the instrument is an energy analyzer. This enables one to select, by means of the electrostatic analyzer, ions of a given energy.

R. Herzog (32) also solved the general problem of electrostatic direction-focusing; the equation is

$$(l_{oe} - g_e)(l_{ie} - g_e) = f_e^2, \tag{3–23}$$

where

$$g_e = (r_e/\sqrt{2}) \cot (\sqrt{2}\ \phi), \tag{3–24}$$

$$f_e = (r_e/\sqrt{2}) \sin (\sqrt{2}\ \phi), \tag{3–25}$$

and where l_{oe} is the object distance and l_{ie} is the image distance for the electrostatic field, r_e is the radius of curvature of the ion beam in the electrostatic field, and ϕ is the angle of electrostatic deflection.

For the case of the symmetrical 31° 50′ deflection analyzer, shown schematically in Figure 3–7 (see also Table 3–4), we see that

$$\begin{aligned} l_{oe} &= l_{ie} = f_e + g_e \\ &= (1/\sqrt{2}) [(r_e/\sin 45°) + r_e \cot 45°] \\ &= r_e + (r_e/\sqrt{2}) \\ &= 1.707 r_e. \end{aligned}$$

The reason for discussing the electrostatic analyzer in this section is to show its principles and how it may be combined with a magnetic mass analyzer. By proper combination of magnetic and electrostatic field one may direction focus an ion beam of a given m/e heterogeneous in energy. If one follows a direction-focusing electrostatic field with a direction-focusing magnetic analyzer, velocity focusing may also be achieved by meeting the conditions given by J. Mattauch and R. Herzog (34). These conditions are given by the equation

$$\begin{aligned}[r_e(1 - \cos\sqrt{2}\,\phi) + \sqrt{2}\,l_{ie}\sin\sqrt{2}\,\phi] \\ = \pm\{r_H(1 - \cos\theta) + l_{om}[\sin\theta + \tan\alpha\,(1 - \cos\theta)]\},\end{aligned} \tag{3–26}$$

where α is the angle between the incident ion beam and the normal to the magnetic field. The positive sign is used when the ion deviations in the two fields are in the same direction, and the negative sign is employed when the deflections are in opposite directions. To achieve simultaneous correction for direction-focusing and velocity inhomogeneities in the ion beam, i.e., to obtain *double-focusing*, Equations (3–19), (3–23), and (3–26) must be satisfied simultaneously. From Equation (3–26), double focusing can only be attained at $r_e = kr_H$ in the general case. Table 3–4 contains several examples of double-focusing and we shall discuss the Mattauch and Herzog instrument in Chapter 4.

THE TIME-OF-FLIGHT ANALYZER

In the time-of-flight analyzer, separation of ions of different masses is based on the fact that all ions are given equal energy; therefore ions of different masses will have different velocities. If there is a fixed distance of travel of the ions, the time of their travel will vary with their mass, the lighter masses traveling more rapidly and thereby reaching the ion detector in a shorter period of time.

As early as 1932, W. R. Smythe and J. Mattauch (35) experimented with the principle outlined here. W. E. Stephens (36) and M. M. Wolff and W. E. Stephens (37) successfully applied the principle (see Table 3–4). Later H. S. Katzenstein and S. S. Friedland (38) greatly improved the performance of the linear pulsed time-of-flight mass spectrometer. W. C. Wiley and I. H. McLaren (39) and W. C. Wiley (40) have described a successful instrument which is now produced commercially.

The basic design of a linear pulsed time-of-flight mass spectrometer is shown schematically in Figure 3–8. In this case, ions are formed by electron bombardment in the ion source (F is the filament, and T is the electron trap.) A voltage pulse on grid G_1 draws the ions out of the ion source and a potential drop between grids G_1 and G_2 accelerates the ions into the flight tube. The region between grids G_2 and G_3 is field free. The ions arrive at grid G_3 separated in time, and this separation is made permanent by a repelling voltage pulse on grid G_3 applied after ions of a given m/e have passed the grid and before the ions of the next m/e arrive. The positive ion currents are then measured at the collector C.

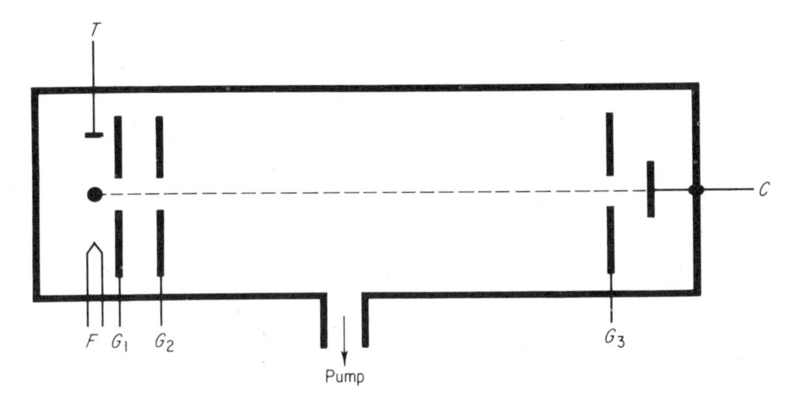

Fig. 3-8. Schematic diagram of a pulsed time-of-flight analyzer.

The kinetic energy T acquired by the ions in their drop through an accelerating potential of V (in erg/esu) is

$$T = mv^2/2 = eV \tag{3–5}$$

as before. Now, however, we do not employ a magnetic field for separation of ions of different m/e. Instead, we determine how long it takes the positive ions to reach the collector and how this flight time depends upon the m/e value. It should be pointed out that the time-of-flight analyzers are the only type of mass analyzers that do not necessarily require a magnetic field.

The time of flight t_f (in seconds) is given by

$$t_f = d/v, \tag{3–27}$$

where d is the length of the linear path of the ions and v is the velocity of the ions. Then,

$$v = \sqrt{\frac{2eV}{m}}. \tag{3–28}$$

Substituting Equation (3–28) into Equation (3–27), we obtain

$$t_f = d\sqrt{\frac{m}{2eV}} \tag{3–29}$$

or

$$t_f = d\sqrt{1/2V}\,\sqrt{m/e}, \tag{3–30}$$

or, still more simply, if d and V are maintained constant,

$$t_f = k\sqrt{m/e}. \tag{3–31}$$

Thus, the time-of-flight of the various ions is simply proportional to the square root of the mass-to-charge ratio of the ions.

EXAMPLE 3–5. A time-of-flight mass spectrometer has a flight length of 97.5 cm. The accelerating potential is 2845 volts. How long will it take a PH_3^+ ion to traverse the spectrometer from ion source to detector?

From Equation (3–30),

$$\begin{aligned} t_f &= d\sqrt{1/2V}\sqrt{m/e} \\ &= 97.5\sqrt{300/(2 \times 2845)}\sqrt{34/(4.802 \times 10^{-10} \times 6.024 \times 10^{23})} \\ &= 97.5\sqrt{300/5.69}\sqrt{34/(4.802 \times 6.024)} \times 10^{-8} \\ &= 97.5 \times 7.26 \times 1.08 \times 10^{-8} \\ &= 7.67 \times 10^{-6} \text{ sec} \\ &= 7.67\ \mu\text{sec.} \end{aligned}$$

EXAMPLE 3–6. What is the difference in the times of arrival of the PH_2^+ and the PH_3^+ ions, using the same data as given in Example 3–5?

$$\begin{aligned} t_{f_{34}} &= 7.67\ \mu\text{sec} \\ t_{f_{33}} &= 7.67(33/34)^{1/2} \\ &= 7.67 \times 0.9852 = 7.56\ \mu\text{sec} \\ \Delta t &= t_{f_{34}} - t_{f_{33}} = 7.67 - 7.56 = 0.11\ \mu\text{sec.} \end{aligned}$$

The separation in the time of arrival of mercury isotopes of adjacent mass is about 0.05 μsec; only 50 nsec! Therefore, to distinguish between the arrival of ions at the collector requires very fast electronics. It also requires that the production of ions be interrupted between the production of one group and their analysis, and the production and analysis of another group. This, therefore, requires electronic pulsing techniques as well.

From the calculations above, one can also see that if 10-kc pulsation is employed, the mass range is limited to about 5000 or 6000 amu; (practically, the usable mass range is even more limited than this). The period in which the ions are produced must be quite short, of the order of 0.25 μsec.

It is not necessary that all time-of-flight analyzers be pulsed or that the ions describe only a linear path. The Bennett radio-frequency time-of-flight mass spectrometer (41) employs a somewhat different approach and will be described in Chapter 4. The ions may also move in a magnetic field, as in the "Chronotron" (42, 43) and the "Omegatron," also treated in Chapter 4.

RESOLVING POWER

The terms *resolution* and *resolving power* have been used in the previous sections, but definitions of these terms have been withheld until now. It is now appropriate to discuss what we mean by these terms when using them to describe the performance of a given instrument.

If two peaks are "just resolved," one can just distinguish that two peaks are present. An example of this is shown in Figure 3–9.

Two adjacent peaks are *resolved* when the two ionic species are *separated.* The *resolving power* is the difficulty of separation, and is stated in terms of $M/\Delta M$, where M is the mass of a given ion. The decision as to how ΔM is to be determined for a given M is most frequently an arbitrary one.

One definition states that peaks are to be considered separated when $\Delta H/H = 0.001$ (see Figure 3–10) for two adjacent ion peaks of equal intensity. This is a rather extreme requirement; for many purposes the choice of $\Delta H/H = 0.1$ is quite satisfactory. If the curves are Gaussian, $\Delta H/H = 0.1$ and $(\Delta H/2)/H = 0.05$ lead to the same value of $M/\Delta M$. $(\Delta H/2)/H = 0.05$ is 5% of the peak height and may be selected directly from any given peak without the necessity of an adjacent peak of identical intensity. Furthermore, $2.08\Gamma_{1/2}$, where $\Gamma_{1/2}$ is the peak width at half-height of the peak, gives a value of $M/\Delta M$ equal to that determined from either the "5% peak width" or the $\Delta H/H = 0.1$ definitions, providing the curves are Gaussian. Actually, the use of $2\Gamma_{1/2}$ rather than $2.08\Gamma_{1/2}$ is usually satisfactory. It should also be noted that a 0.1% overlap of one peak onto an adjacent peak differing by 1 amu is equivalent to the "5% peak width," the $2\Gamma_{1/2}$, and the $\Delta H/H = 0.1$ definitions of resolving power.

Certainly these are not all of the definitions of resolving power, but they are usually satisfactory for most applications. The author employs the $2\Gamma_{1/2}$, the "5% peak width," or the $\Delta H/H = 0.1$ definitions in his laboratory since they generally give near-identical descriptions of the "separation" achieved. Let us examine the utility of these definitions using Figure 3–10.

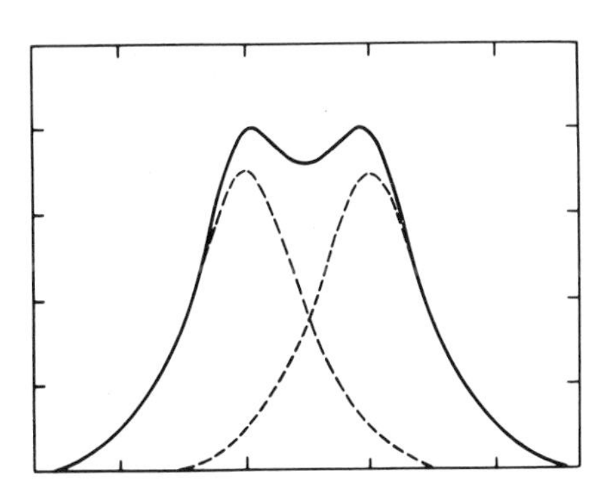

Fig. 3-9. Two adjacent peaks just resolved.

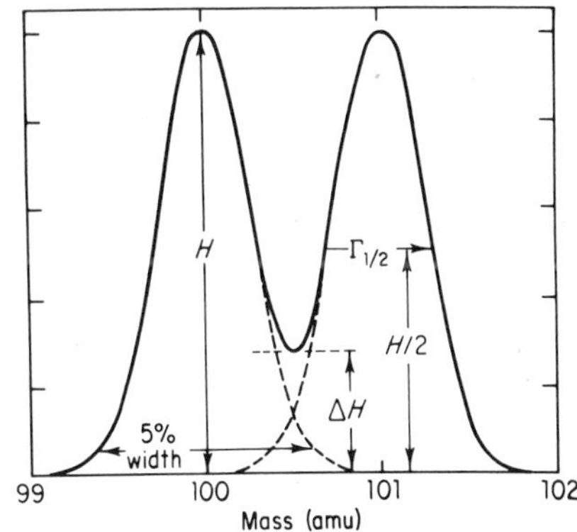

Fig. 3-10. The overlap of these two peaks leads to a calculated resolution of slightly greater than 80.

EXAMPLE 3–7. Two adjacent ion peaks, of $m/e = 100$ and $m/e = 101$, are found to be not completely separated, as shown in Figure 3–10. The utility of $\Delta H/H = 0.1$ is impaired in this case, since $\Delta H/H = 0.27$. To determine the resolution, one would have to look at other adjacent m/e values smaller than 100 until $\Delta H/H$ would equal 0.1, and then that m/e value would be equal to $M/\Delta M$.

However, we are able to use the "5% peak width" definition. Looking at the peak on the left (at $m/e = 100$) we find that 5% of the peak height occurs at 0.61 amu from the peak center, i.e., at 99.39 amu and at 100.61 amu. Thus, $\Delta M = 100.61 - 99.39 = 1.22$, and $M/\Delta M = 100/1.22 = 82$. Similarly, we see that the 5% peak values for the peak on the right (at $m/e = 101$) occur at 100.36 and 101.60, giving $\Delta M = 1.24$ and $M/\Delta M = 101/1.24 = 82$.

The width of either of the two peaks is found to be 0.585 amu at half-height by measurement. Thus, ΔM for $\Gamma_{1/2}$ is 0.585, ΔM for $2\Gamma_{1/2} = 1.17$, and ΔM for $2.08\Gamma_{1/2} = 1.22$. $M/\Delta M$ for $2\Gamma_{1/2}$ is $[(100 + 101)/2]/1.17 = 86$ and $M/\Delta M$ for $2.08\Gamma_{1/2}$ is $[(100 + 101)/2]/1.22 = 82$. Thus, one can see that $M/\Delta M$ for $2\Gamma_{1/2}$ is nearly the same as $M/\Delta M$ for $2.08\Gamma_{1/2}$.

The use of the $\Delta H/H = 0.001$ definition is more difficult here, but would give the same results ($M/\Delta M = 82$) as above. The interesting point is that this means that at $m/e = 82$ only 0.1% of the ion current due to the $m/e = 82$ ion overlaps the $m/e = 81$ and the $m/e = 83$ ion peaks. If one should state resolving power in terms of a 1% overlap of adjacent peaks, the resolving power would be about 110, rather than 82, for the above-considered example.

In Table 3–4 a number of different mass spectrometers and mass spectrographs of various types of analyzers were listed and their approximate resolving power given.

The mass spectrum of mercury vapor is shown in Figure 3–11. Note the isotope peaks corresponding to $m/e =$ 198, 199, 200, 201, 202, and 204. The abundance of the isotope of $m/e = 196$ in the spectrum is very small, but real. From the peaks in Figure 3–11, one can determine that the resolution is about 150, as determined with the $2.08\Gamma_{1/2}$ on the $m/e = 200$ and 202 peaks, and the 5% peak width of the $m/e = 204$ peak. This indicates that well less than 1% of $m/e = 202$ overlaps the $m/e = 201$ peak, and so on for the other peaks as well.

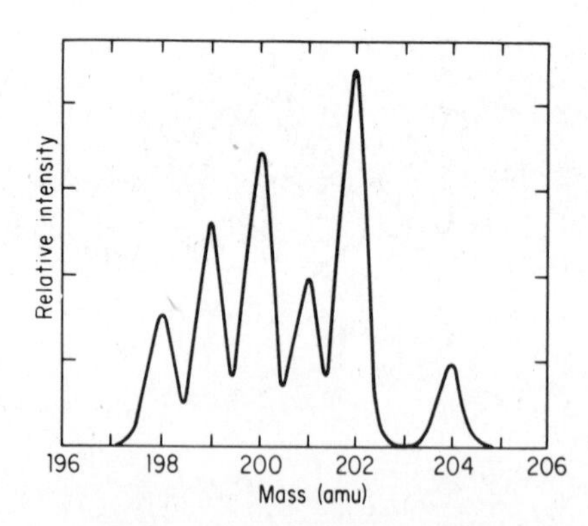

Fig. 3-11. The isotope peaks of mercury determined with a time-of-flight mass spectrometer, showing a resolution of about $M/\Delta M = 150$.

In practice, in the electromagnetic mass spectrometers, the resolving power primarily depends upon the width of the ion collector entrance slit. The width of the ion beam (determined by the mass spectrometer construction and by the ion source design) must be sufficiently small so that adjacent masses are separated at the collector entrance slit. The upper limit of the separation is determined by the ratio of the beam width to the radius of curvature of the ions. That is,

$$M = r/w, \tag{3–32}$$

where r is the radius of curvature in centimeters, w is the beam width in centimeters, and M is the mass number of separable ions. Thus, if a separation of the mercury isotopes is desired ($M = 200$) and a 15.0-cm radius of curvature is used, the beam width can not exceed 0.075 cm at the entrance slit.

The collector slit must be sufficiently narrow so that the ion beam of no more than one specific mass number may pass through the collector entrance slit and be collected. Obviously, if the slit is too wide, adjacent ion beams will be collected and good separation will not be possible. In sweeping the ion beams of various adjacent m/e values past the collector entrance slit, the *outer limits* of adjacent ion beams must be separated by a distance of at least that of the collector entrance slit width. Thus, the greatest mass number at which one can get good resolution of ion beams of adjacent mass is given by

$$M = r/(w + s), \tag{3–33}$$

where s is the entrance slit width in centimeters.

EXAMPLE 3–8. The Consolidated Electrodynamics Corporation 21–103C mass spectrometer has a radius of curvature of 12.7 cm and a beam width of approximately 0.025 cm. If their smallest entrance slit, a 7-mil slit, is used, what would be the upper limit for good separation of adjacent masses?

First, using Equation (3–32), we see that

$$M = 12.7/0.025 \cong 500;$$

that is, ions of $m/e = 500$ and $m/e = 501$ would be satisfactorily separated at the collector entrance slit. Then, with Equation (3–33),

$$M = 12.7/(0.025 + 0.018) = 300.$$

Thus, good separation is possible between $m/e = 300$ and 301; usable separation in practice is nearly 700.

3.3 ION DETECTORS

As was pointed out in Chapter 1, whether a given instrument is a mass spectrograph or a mass spectrometer is usually determined by the nature of the ion detector. A summary of three basic types of ions detectors together with two major types of amplifiers commonly used are given in Table 3–5. We shall now examine the usual combinations of these basic detectors and amplifiers.

TABLE 3–5. ION DETECTORS

Type	Range	Main Use	Advantage	Disadvantage
Photographic plate	10^{-10} coul/mm^2	Packing fractions	Sensitive, simple	Abundance measurements are imprecise
Faraday cup	Depends on amplifier	General utility	Simple	Dependent on amplifier used
Electron multiplier	Single ions to 10^{-9} amp	General utility identifications, ionization potentials	Sensitive, rapid response	Need of calibration
Electrometer tubes	10^{-15} amp	General utility	Simple	Lack of stability in dc amplifiers
Vibrating reed electrometer	Lower limit $\sim 10^{-17}$ amp	General utility	Stable	Complexity

PHOTOGRAPHIC PLATE

In earlier work, specially prepared Schuman and Ilford *Q* plates were employed. Today, the Eastman III-0 ultraviolet sensitive vacuum spectrograph plate is generally used, since it is more rugged than the special Schuman plates and is quite satisfactory for the detection of ions with energies greater than about 6000 volts. Ilford Q2 and Kodak SWR plates may also be employed (22).

Because the image density decreases sharply with an increase in the mass of the ion, the photographic emulsion detector is not suited to isotope abundance measurements or to cracking pattern determinations. In addition to this, photographic plates often have nonlinear sensitivity with the energy of the ion, the time of exposure, and the ion intensities.

On the other hand, the photographic plate is almost universally employed in packing fraction and precise mass measurements. The plates integrate the ions received, and thereby allow for the elimination of errors from intensity fluctuations and other detector instabilities. In precise mass measurements, very fine lines may be obtained with double-focusing instruments: factors limiting the precision are image widening due to scattering, the grain size of the emulsion, and the distribution of sensitive elements in the emulsion. The measurements of mass can be made with precision to the eighth significant figure, and the limitations on the precision are largely due to the precision of the comparators used to measure line displacements and the dispersion of the analyzers used.

A typical photographic plate record, obtained with a commercial Mattauch-Herzog instrument, is shown in Figure 3–12. Note that the resolving power for this instrument is of the order of 10,000. Mattauch has published plates from his instrument showing resolving powers greater by an order of magnitude.

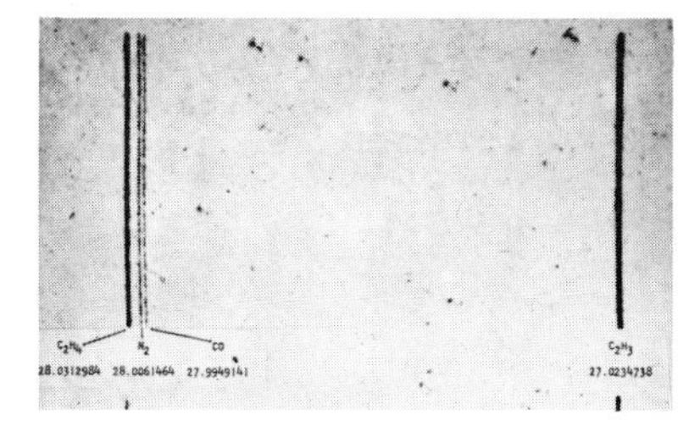

Fig. 3-12. Photographic plate record from a Mattauch-Herzog mass spectrograph. (Courtesy, Consolidated Electrodynamics Corp. Pasadena, Calif.)

FARADAY CUP

As we saw in Chapter 2, Thomson, using a Faraday cup behind the parabolic slit, was the first to detect and record electrically the intensities of positive ion beams. The current-measuring device then was a Wilson tilted electroscope. Later, W. Bleakney (44) replaced this with an electrometer tube.

Usually, the ion beam must pass through a defining slit and guard slits before reaching the ion collector. The guard slits may also be used to eliminate metastable ions (see Chapter 6) or scattered ions, allowing an improvement both in accuracy of ion beam current measurements and in resolution. Very commonly, an electron suppressor slit is incorporated just ahead of the ion detector to return to the collector any secondary electrons emitted by positive ion bombardment of the metal collector. In addition, the shape of the collector is usually designed to minimize the escape of any reflected ions and/or secondary electrons.

Multiple collector systems are also used on some mass spectrometers. A dual collector system due to A. O. Nier, E. P. Ney, M. G. Inghram (45) is shown in Figure 3–13. Here, one ion beam is collected on slit plate S, and the other ion beam is collected on the collector C. The electron suppressors surrounding these collectors are held at 22.5 volts. With the electronics shown, the ratio of the two ion currents is found by adjusting the variable resistance X to a null balance on the galvanometer G. The major advantage of such a detection system is that it operates independently of fluctuations in ion intensity.

Electrometer Tubes

Very small ion currents are found at the detector; consequently this current must be amplified before the signal can be used to drive galvanometer or recorder traces. Electrometers have long been used for this purpose.

Many different electrometer tubes and circuits have been and currently are being used to produce simple electrical amplification. The basic idea is to measure the voltage drop across a large resistance placed between the ion collector (Faraday cup) and ground. The signal developed is then

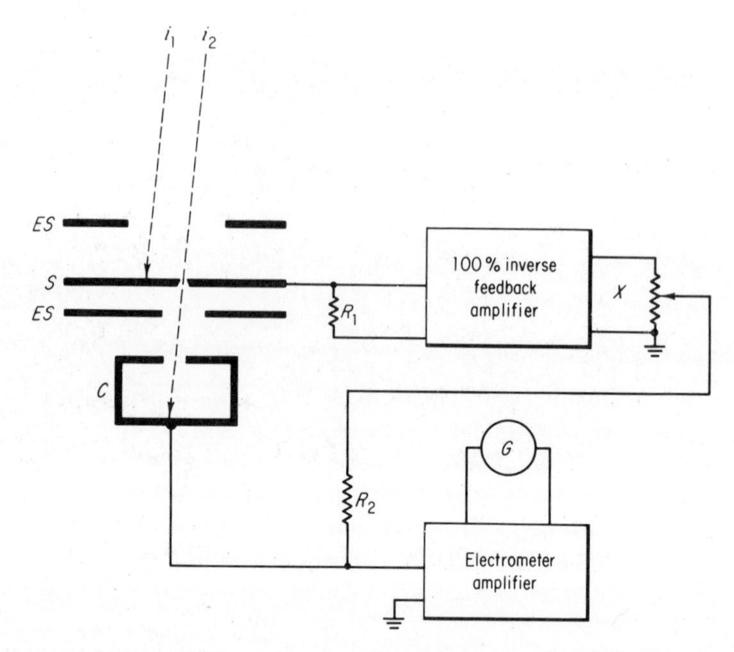

Fig. 3-13. Schematic diagram of the dual detector system of A. O. Nier, E.P. Ney, and M. G. Inghram, Rev. Sci. Instr., **18**, 294 (1947). ES, electron suppressor; S, ion collector plate slit; C, ion collector; G, galvanometer; R_1 and R_2, resistances; X, balancing adjustment.

impressed on the grid of the first electrometer tube in the dc preamplifier. Linear, wide-range, dc amplifiers of high stability are required. Some additional comments on electrometers used with electron multipliers will be made in the discussion of Electron Multipliers. More recently, the vibrating reed electrometer and also ac circuitry have been developed for some mass spectrometers.

Vibrating Reed Electrometers

The vibrating reed electrometer developed by H. Palevsky, R. K. Swank, and R. Grenchik (46) receives the dc signal from the ion collector and imposes it upon a vibrating reed condenser. The ac signal thus obtained then is conveniently amplified for driving a recorder system or may be read from a meter. This rugged and very dependable type of electrometer has a dc noise level ten times lower than that of the dc electrometer amplifiers mentioned above, and it has the advantage of an exceedingly small drift with time.

Although the use of a vibrating reed electrometer system increases the complexity of the electronics, the gain in stability and the sensitivity achieved outweigh the added complexity. Detection sensitivities of 10^{-17} to 10^{-18} amp have been reported (47).

ELECTRON MULTIPLIERS

As early as 1943, A. Cohen (48) used an electron multiplier in a mass spectrometer. The principle upon which this detector operates is a relatively simple one. Energetic ions impinge upon the metal surface of a cathode and cause the emission of a number of secondary electrons. These electrons are then accelerated and allowed to impinge upon another electrode (*dynode*), causing additional electron emission. Again and again this process is repeated, possibly using ten stages (dynodes) or more, until finally all of the electrons are collected on the anode. In this way, a large electron current can be obtained for each positive ion collected at the cathode detector. Figure 3–14 schematically shows such a multiplier.

The operation of the electrostatic electron multiplier usually involves a rather large negative potential on the cathode, with the anode held at or near ground potential. This is convenient in the mass spectrometer operation with positive ions, for it adds to the energy of the ion beam and gives somewhat greater electron emission from the cathode. This detector has high sensitivity and rapid response; but, because the amplification of the multiplier in vacuum and in the presence of various gases changes with time and sample, it is not as satisfactory as desired for ion current and abundance measurements.

The dynodes often are constructed of commercial-grade 2% beryllium-copper, magnesium-silver, and even brass. They may be sensitized by heating to near red heat in vacuum, inert atmospheres, or in hydrogen. Multiplication factors of from 10^5 to about 10^6 are usually obtained with ten or 12 dynodes. Because magnetic fields exert a rather serious influence upon the amplification, the multiplier may be immersed in an auxiliary magnetic field to improve the stability and multiplication factor, and to reduce the effects that magnetic scanning in the electromagnetic mass spectrometer could cause. Alternatively, the multiplier may be shielded from magnetic fields; this is done with several of the common electron multipliers.

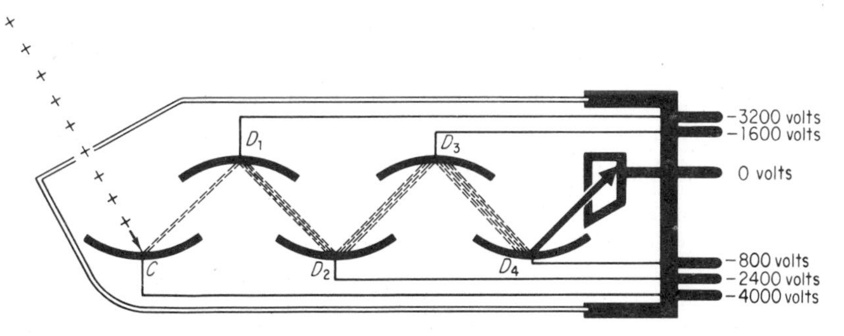

Fig. 3-14. Schematic representation of an electron multiplier. Positive ions fall on the cathode, C, and cause emission of secondary electrons; D_1 to D_4 are dynodes separated by 800 V each; A is the anode for collection of the electrons.

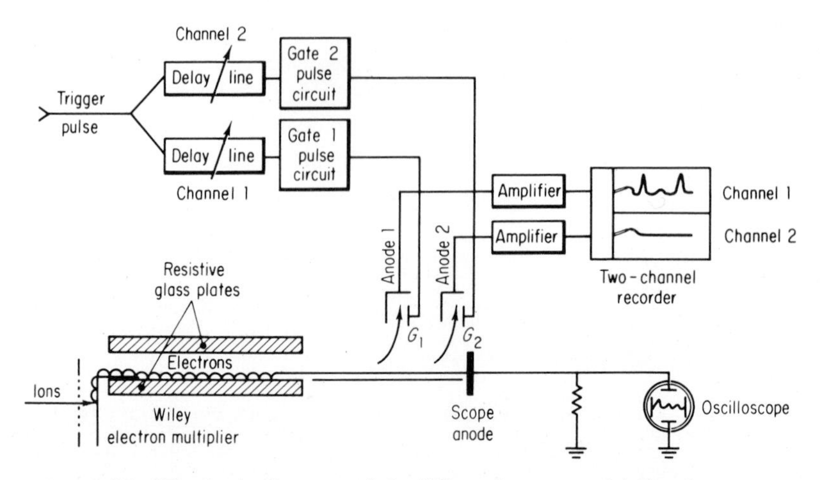

Fig. 3-15. Schematic diagram of the Wiley electron-multiplier detector.

The Wiley (40) *magnetic electron multiplier* employs crossed magnetic and electric fields to control the electron trajectories. (See Figure 3–15.) As the individual groups of ions arrive at the end of the field free-flight region (drift tube) in the time-of-flight mass spectrometer, they collide with the plane ion cathode of the magnetic electron multiplier. The plane ion cathode was chosen by Wiley and McLaren (39) because it eliminated ion transit time variations encountered with a curved ion cathode of the conventional electrostatic multiplier just discussed. Each collision produces a group of secondary electrons, and because of the crossed magnetic and electric fields present, the electrons follow cycloidal paths down the dynode strips of the multiplier. In this manner, a current gain (multiplication) of the order of 10^6 is obtained before the group of electrons reach the gating section of the multiplier.

The Wiley multiplier conveniently provides the necessary bandwidth; since each mass signal is less than 50 nsec wide at its base, a bandwidth significantly in excess of 20Mc is needed in order to not distort the shape of the pulses. This multiplier, with a bandwidth of direct current to about 500 Mc, permits many stages of multiplication to be used without loss of resolution; hence, a lower gain per stage is allowable. The large number of dynodes of the conventional multiplier have been replaced in the Wiley multiplier with field strips providing a "continuous dynode." Each of the field strips consists of a high resistance coating which has been fired onto a glass insulating support. The resistive coating is thin but very tenacious, both chemically and physically, thereby permitting chemical cleaning as well as nongritty abrasive cleaning (such as accomplished by using a pencil eraser or a fingernail, or even a cleanser such as Bon-Ami). Exposure to humid air has been found to not affect the amplifying power of this multiplier, which eliminates the need for special cathode and dynode contours, and allows a straightforward mechanical design of the *gating section* mounted at the output end of the multiplier.

The first group of electrons arriving at the gating section of the multiplier are those ions of lowest mass, and succeeding groups are successively heavier in mass. The *gate-anodes* in the Wiley multiplier operate in the following manner. An electrical pulse applied to the gate will cause the group of electrons passing the assembly at that moment to be gated onto the corresponding anode. The electrical capacity of these gate-anode assemblies is sufficiently low so that very short pulses (switching times of the order of 10 nsec are common) can be applied to the gate, thus allowing the anode to collect the electron current due to a particular mass in the sample. The gating section is commonly supplied with two gate-anode assemblies in addition to the oscilloscope display anode assembly, but it may be fitted with up to ten or more such assemblies.

Complete mass spectra can be obtained by applying the gating pulse in the magnetic electron multiplier a little later in each operating cycle of the time-of-flight instrument. This procedure causes a rapid scan of the entire mass spectrum and thereby provides a complete mass analysis while using only one gating and output channel. Continous monitoring of several mass peaks can be accomplished by applying electrical pulses to the appropriate gates at the proper times in each operating cycle of the time-of-flight mass spectrometer.

The gated electron current from the magnetic electron multiplier is measured by precision electrometers, and 100% feedback-type circuitry with high open-loop gain is used to provide low drift and to preserve the required fast response characteristics. The electrometer output is commonly 0 to 5 volts dc, which is sufficient to drive most recorders. The output from the oscilloscope anode is displayed on an oscilloscope synchronized and triggered by the master pulsing system of the mass spectrometer. Any portion of the mass spectrum can be observed in the desired detail by adjusting the sweep controls of the oscilloscope and the control of the continuously variable delay of the mass spectrometer between the ion accelerating pulse and the oscilloscope trigger.

REFERENCES

1. Y. Margoninski, S. P. Wolsky, and E. J. Zdanuk, *Vacuum*, **11**, 287 (1961).
2. W. McGowan and L. Kerwin, *J. Chim. Phys.*, **59**, 927 (1962).
3. K. Watanabe, T. Nakayama, and J. Mottl, *J. Quant. Specty. Radiative Transfer*, **2**, 369 (1962).
4. A. Terenin and B. Popov, *Z. Physik*, **75**, 338 (1932); *Physik. Z. Sowjetunion*, **2**, 299 (1932).

5. H. Hurzeler, M. G. Inghram, and J. D. Morrison, *J. Chem. Phys.*, **27**, 313 (1957); **28**, 76 (1958).
6. B. Steiner, C. F. Giese, and M. G. Inghram, *J. Chem. Phys.*, **34**, 189 (1961).
7. F. A. Elder, C. Giese, B. Steiner, and M. Inghram, *J. Chem. Phys.*, **36**, 3292 (1962).
8. F. I. Vilesov and M. E. Akopyan, *Pribory i Tekhn. Eksperim.*, **7**, (5), 145 (1962).
9. I. Langmuir and K. H. Kingdon, *Proc. Roy. Soc.*, **A107**, 61 (1925).
10. D. C. Hess, G. Whetherill, and M. G. Inghram, *Rev. Sci. Instr.*, **22**, 838 (1951).
11. J. W. Frazer, R. P. Burns, and G. W. Barton, *Rev. Sci. Instr.*, **30**, 370 (1959).
12. F. A. White, T. L. Collins, and F. M. Rourke, *Phys. Rev.*, **101**, 1786 (1956).
13. M. G. Inghram and W. A. Chupka, *Rev. Sci. Instr.*, **24**, 518 (1953).
14. L. N. Gall', R. N. Gall', Yu. S. Rutgaizer, and A. M. Shereshevskii, *Zhur. Tekhn. Fiz.*, **32**, 202 (1962).
15. M. S. Chupakhin, *Zhur. Anal. Khim.*, **17**, 665 (1962).
16. M. S. Chupakhin, and E. Gradsztain, *Doklady Akad. Nauk S.S.S.R.*, **142**, 337 (1962).
17. E. E. Muschlitz, H. D. Randolph, and J. N. Ratti, *Rev. Sci. Instr.*, **33**, 445 (1961).
18. E. A. C. Crouch, in *Advances in Mass Spectrometry*, vol. 2, R. M. Elliott (ed.), Pergamon Press, Ltd., Oxford, England, 1963, p. 157.
19. H. Patterson and H. W. Wilson, *J. Sci. Instr.*, **39**, 84 (1962).
20. J. G. Gorman, E. J. Jones, and J. A. Hipple, *Anal. Chem.*, **23**, 438 (1951).
21. J. R. Woolston and R. E. Honig, *Rev. Sci. Instr.*, **35**, 69 (1964).
22. R. Brown, R. D. Craig, and R. M. Elliott, in *Advances in Mass Spectrometry*, vol. 2, R. M. Elliott (ed.), Pergamon Press, Ltd., Oxford, England, 1963, p. 141.
23. B. Chakravarty, V. S. Venkatasubramanian and H. E. Duckworth, in *Advances in Mass Spectrometry*, vol. 2, R. M. Elliott (ed.), Pergamon Press, Ltd., Oxford, England, 1963, p. 128.
24. M. G. Inghram, *J. Phys. Chem.*, **57**, 809 (1953); F. N. Hodgson, M. Desjardins, and W. L. Baun, *J. Phys. Chem.*, **67**, 1250 (1963).
25. P. F. Knewstubb and A. W. Tickner, *J. Chem. Phys.*, **36**, 674 and 684 (1962).
26. P. F. Knewstubb, in *Mass Spectrometry of Organic Ions*, F. M. McLafferty (ed.), Academic Press, New York, 1963, p. 255.
27. R. H. Good, Jr., and E. W. Müller, *Handbuch der Physik*, vol. 21, second edition, Springer-Verlag, Berlin, 1956, p. 176.
28. E. W. Müller, in *Advances in Electronics and Electron Physics*, vol. 13, L. Marton (ed.), Academic Press, New York, 1960, p. 83.

29. M. G. Inghram and R. Gomer, *J. Chem. Phys.*, **22**, 1279 (1954); *J. Am. Chem. Soc.*, **77**, 500 (1955); *Z. Naturforsch.*, **10A**, 863 (1955).

30. H. D. Beckey, *Z. anal. Chem.*, **170**, 359 (1959); *Z. Naturforsch.*, **17A**, 1103 (1962); in *Advances in Mass Spectrometry*, vol. 2, R. M. Elliott (ed.), Pergamon Press, Ltd., Oxford, England, 1963, p. 1.

31. A. J. B. Robertson, B. W. Viney, and M. Warrington, *Brit. J. Appl. Phys.*, **14**, 278 (1963).

32. R. Herzog, *Z. Physik.*, **89**, 447 (1934).

33. A. O. Nier, *Rev. Sci. Instr.*, **11**, 212 (1940).

34. J. Mattauch and R. Herzog, *Z. Physik*, **89**, 786 (1934).

35. W. R. Smythe and J. Mattauch, *Phys. Rev.*, **40**, 429 (1932).

36. W. E. Stephens, *Phys. Rev.*, **69**, 691 (1946).

37. M. M. Wolff and W. E. Stephens, *Rev. Sci. Instr.*, **24**, 616 (1953).

38. H. S. Katzenstein and S. S. Friedland, *Rev. Sci. Instr.*, **26**, 324 (1955).

39. W. C. Wiley and I. H. McLaren, *Rev. Sci. Instr.*, **26**, 1150 (1955).

40. W. C. Wiley, *Science*, **124**, 817 (1956).

41. W. H. Bennett, *J. Appl. Phys.*, **21**, 143 (1950).

42. S. A. Goudsmit, *Phys. Rev.*, **74**, 622 (1948).

43. P. I. Richards, E. E. Hays, and S. A. Goudsmit, *Phys. Rev.*, **76**, 180 (1949); **84**, 824 (1951).

44. W. Bleakney, *Phys. Rev.*, **40**, 496 (1932).

45. A. O. Nier, E. P. Ney, and M. G. Inghram, *Rev. Sci. Instr.*, **18**, 294 (1947).

46. H. Palevsky, R. K. Swank, and R. Grenchik, *Rev. Sci. Instr.*, **18**, 298 (1947).

47. M. G. Inghram, R. J. Hayden, and D. C. Hess, *Phys. Rev.*, **72**, 349 (1947).

48. A. Cohen, *Phys. Rev.*, **63**, 219 (1943).

CHAPTER 4

INSTRUMENTS

In Chapter 2, we examined only three of the early mass spectrographs and mass spectrometers in addition to the Lozier tube in order to gain an historical perspective. Now, after having discussed in some greater detail the various types and features of the principal components of mass spectrometers and mass spectrographs, we may examine other types of mass spectrometers, including the Nier 60° instrument, the pulsed linear and the radio-frequency (rf) time-of-flight mass spectrometers, as well as the omegatron (a magnetic time-of-flight mass spectrometer), the trochoidal mass spectrometer, and the Bainbridge-Jordan and Mattauch-Herzog mass spectrographs. A few other types of mass spectrometers are briefly included following a discussion of the Calutron. In our treatment, then, we shall cover many (but not all) of the types of mass spectrometers and mass spectrographs.

4.1 THE NIER 60° MASS SPECTROMETER

The first sector-field, direction-focusing mass spectrometer was designed by A. O. Nier (1); this instrument was the forerunner of many modern mass spectrometers. The magnetic deflection angle, as pointed out in Chapter 3, was 60°. Until the development of this instrument, most mass spectrometers had 180° deflection analyzers. Later, J. A. Hipple (2) described a sector instrument of 90° deflection. All recent sector-field mass spectrometers of importance have employed either 60° or 90° deflection. The basic design of the Nier 60° instrument may be recalled by reference to Figure 3–5. The 1947 model of Nier's instrument (3) incorporated all-metal construction with a 15-cm radius of curvature, as well as twin collectors for isotope ratio measurements.

Fig. 4-1. A. O. C. Nier

The Nier 60° isotope-ratio mass spectrometer was manufactured by Consolidated Engineering Corporation (now the Consolidated Electrodynamics Corporation) as model number 21–201. A permanent Alnico magnet was used to give a stable magnetic field. The field strength for the magnetic deflection could be varied by moving iron shunts in the magnetic field with a gear drive and position indicator mechanism. Because of the difficulty in magnetic scanning, the m/e values were usually scanned electrostatically by varying the accelerating potentials. However, with the use of a suitable motor drive, it was possible to scan magnetically the mass spectrum. The twin collectors, as illustrated in Figure 3–13 and discussed in Chapter 3, were employed to obtain very precise values of isotope ratios. Recently, A. O. Nier, W. R. Eckelmann, and R. A. Lupton (4) have described the modification of a 6-in. 60° isotope-ratio mass spectrometer using a battery-operated emission regulator to permit continous use of the instrument over long periods of time with less than 5% down-time.

Several other 60° single-focusing mass spectrometers are manufactured. Nuclide Analysis Associates offer several such instruments of 6-in. and 12-in. radii of curvature for use in gas analysis, isotope-ratio determinations, high-temperature studies, etc., as well as a Reynolds (5) 4.5-in. radius of curvature mass spectrometer for gas analyses with very small samples. The Atlas-MAT CH-4 is a 20-cm, 60° instrument manufactured in Germany. Hitachi of Tokyo offers a 10-cm, 60° mass spectrometer, and Mitsubishi (Tokyo) makes a 60°, 15-cm radius of curvature instrument. These and other commercially available instruments will be discussed in more detail in Chapter 5.

4.2 THE LINEAR PULSED TIME-OF-FLIGHT MASS SPECTROMETER

In Chapter 3 we described the means of mass analysis in the time-of-flight mass spectrometer in rather general terms while noting the contributions of several workers. We shall now return to a somewhat more detailed account of the entire time-of-flight mass spectrometer and its operation. In doing this, we shall discuss basically the commercially available Bendix time-of-flight mass spectrometer.

The design of the linear pulsed time-of-flight mass spectrometer is shown schematically in Figure 4–2. The basic operation for 10-kc pulsation and 2800-volt ion accelerating potential is as follows. Electrons emitted by heating the 0.005-in. diameter tungsten filament are kept from entering the ionization region by a negative bias on the control grid. At the beginning of a cycle, a very short (250 nsec) positive pulse is applied to the control grid and the electron beam is permitted to pass through this grid. The energy of the electron beam is determined by the potential drop between the electron collimator slit (ground potential) and the filament (variable up to about −100 volts). An external magnetic field, created by simple bar magnets, collimates the electron beam. By means of the impact of electrons of this beam with gaseous molecules, ionizations and dissociations occur. During this ionization, all elements surrounding the ion chamber are at ground potential.

Immediately after the electron beam is interrupted, the ion focus grid is pulsed to about −270 volts; the duration of this pulse (about 2.5 μsec) is sufficient for all ions of interest to be drawn out of the ionization region and to pass into the accelerating region beyond the ion focus grid. A 2800-volt

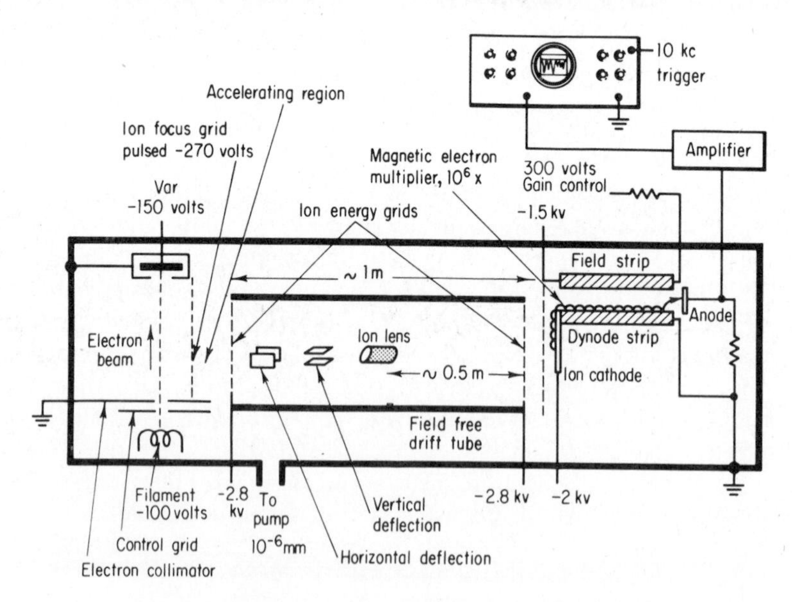

Fig. 4-2. Schematic diagram of the Bendix time-of-flight mass spectrometer and components.

potential on the first ion energy grid, about 1.6 cm distant from the electron beam, accelerates the positive ions.

As we saw in Chapter 3, mass separation results only from the mass-dependent velocities. Neither magnetic nor electric fields are employed for mass separation. From Equation (3–30) it can be seen that the time of flight, in microseconds, is given approximately by $\sqrt{2(m/z)}$, where m is the atomic mass units and z is the number of electronic charges, for an accelerating potential of about 3000 volts and a flight path length of about 100 cm.

W. C. Wiley and I. H. McLaren (6) have given a detailed treatment of the focusing action of the time-of-flight mass spectrometer. However, we can indicate the principles in brief. If the ions before pulsing were found at rest, and if they were all in a plane parallel to the draw-out (ion focus) and ion energy grids, almost any method of drawing the ions out of the source would provide infinite resolving power, regardless of the flight path length of the analyzer. Therefore, the resolving power of the time-of-flight mass spectrometer is dependent upon the source delivering the ions of a given m/e to the detector in a sharp pulse even when (as is the practical situation) the ions vary in initial position and velocity.

The effect of the variations in the initial positions of the ions is reduced since the ions farther away from the ion focus grid fall through a larger potential during the ion draw-out than do those ions nearer to the ion focus grid. Consequently, the trailing ions acquire a greater velocity and overtake the ions that were in front. By careful adjustment of the potential on the ion focus grid, one may cause all of the ions to reach the "crossover point" just as the ions pass into the electron multiplier stack. Furthermore, by making the final velocities of the ions large compared to their initial velocities, and by keeping the distance from the electron beam to the ion focus grid small compared to the flight path length, the resolution is further improved. Figure 3–11 shows the resolution obtained in the mercury Hg^+ region with a Bendix model 12–100 time-of-flight mass spectrometer.

Now, the problems of space-focusing and energy-focusing described just above are solved in practice by adjusting the pulse height of the pulse applied to the ion focus grid so that the sharpest, cleanest mass spectrum possible is observed on the oscilloscope. This adjustment represents the best compromises between space-focusing and energy-focusing.

An increase in the ion accelerating voltage will not improve the resolution of the instrument. An increase in the flight path length can give improved resolution, as can the use of time-lag energy-focusing. The use of time-lag energy-focusing has recently been described by D. B. Harrington and R. S. Gohlke (7). This method of time-lag energy-focusing overcomes the effect that initial ion energies has on the resolving power. To produce this type of focusing the beginning of the ion accelerating pulse is delayed so that a time lag occurs between the end of the electron beam pulsation and the beginning of the ion acceleration. Although this focusing method is mass dependent, an optimum time lag can be employed that will permit ions to move to new positions in the ionization region (as a function of their initial velocities) where their flight time will then be very nearly equal. With this method, Harrington and Gohlke report much greater resolving power than previously obtainable. Bendix has now made this improved resolution instrument available commercially.

Ions are decelerated slightly prior to reaching the ion cathode, as seen in Figure 4–2. Since the process of ion detection using the magnetic electron multiplier has already been described in Chapter 3, we will not repeat the discussion of the process. As noted earlier, the resolution of this instrument (without the time-lag energy-focusing) is about $M/\Delta M = 150$, with unit mass resolution to $m/e = 200$ causing only a 1% overlap on adjacent mass peaks.

The linear pulsed time-of-flight mass spectrometer is fairly sensitive [about 10^{-9} mm (Hg) lower limit]. Also, the mass spectra obtained are in good agreement between different instruments of this type, and in more than fair agreement with the magnetic analyzer mass spectrometers. In comparison to the latter instruments, the time-of-flight instruments tend to produce mass spectra slightly more abundant in the heavier ions and slightly less abundant in the lighter ions. Applications of the time-of-flight instrument will be discussed in Chapters 8 to 10.

4.3 THE BENNETT RADIO-FREQUENCY MASS SPECTROMETER

The Bennett rf mass spectrometer is a time-of-flight mass spectrometer, but different from that of the pulsed instrument discussed just above. W. H. Bennett developed this instrument in 1950 (8) and described some further developments of it in 1953 (9). A schematic diagram of this type of mass spectrometer is shown in Figure 4–3.

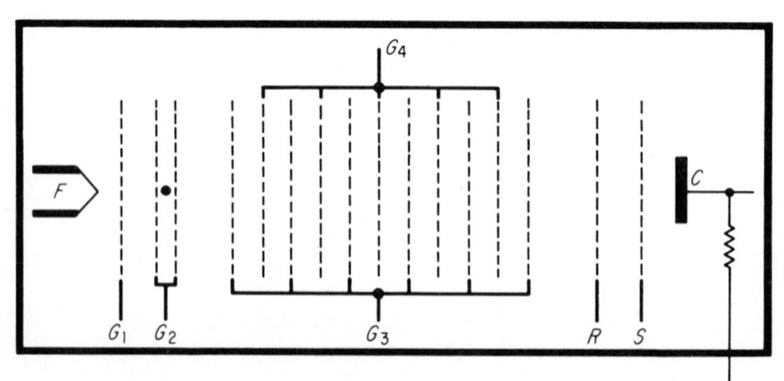

Fig. 4-3. Schematic representation of the Bennett radio-frequency mass spectrometer.

Electrons emitted from the filament F are accelerated through a potential drop of V volts between grids G_1 and G_2. In the field free region bounded by the G_2 grids, the electrons impact the gaseous molecules and the ions are formed. A dc potential between grids G_2 and G_3 draws the ions out of the region in which they were formed, and the ions are accelerated into the rf grid system. The rf signal is applied across grids G_3 and G_4, causing the ions to be further accelerated between grids. Therefore, only ions of proper velocity (i.e., m/e ratio) will be accelerated in phase by each of the grids. If the flight time between the rf grids is approximately equal to one-half of the rf period, ions will gain energy from the rf field; i.e., they will be accelerated. Actually, Bennett has pointed out that it is not correct that the transit time must be one-half the rf frequency, but, rather, that the maximum energy is gained if the ions pass the first of a series of three grid systems at a 46.5° phase angle and the second at a 180° phase angle.

In this way one can choose a retarding potential to apply to grid R, such that only those ions that have gained the maximum energy from the rf field may pass grid R, and all other ions with lesser energy may not penetrate beyond grid R. The ions passing grid R also pass through grid S and arrive at the ion collector C, and their current is measured. Grid S serves as an electron trap to repel any secondary electrons emitted due to positive ion bombardment of the ion collector.

It is apparent that ions of various m/e may be scanned by varying the frequency of the rf field. The focusing action is in time, and the ions are grouped in packets by the proper wave form of the rf voltage. Strictly speaking, the rf grids should be spaced at increasing distances in the flight tube in order to compensate for the increasingly smaller transit times of the various ions as they gain energy from the rf field. However, this latter problem is not troublesome in practice. In order to discriminate against harmonic losses, one uses multiple rf grids, possibly as many as 25 or more. Because such a large number of grids are employed, thereby tending to reduce the transmission of the positive ions, the grids are commonly made of knitted tungsten mesh of about 95% transparency.

Because the Bennett rf mass spectrometer has a continuous "duty cycle," it operates with inherently larger ion beams than the linear pulsed time-of-flight mass spectrometer. Recently, M. H. Studier (10) has shown that the time-of-flight mass spectrometer can be made to operate in a near-continous mode, with some increase in resolution, resulting in significantly larger ion beams with the time-of-flight instrument. From Table 3–4 we observe that these mass spectrometers have reasonably good resolving power; Bennett's early model has a resolving power of about 30 and an improved model due to Glenn has a resolving power of about 250.

Bennett has shown that for a three-stage mass spectrometer, each stage of which contains three grids,

$$m/z = 0.266\ V/S^2f^2, \qquad (4\text{–}1)$$

where m is in amu, S is the distance between grids in each of the three stages, f is the frequency of the rf alternating potential in megacycles, and V is the dc potential drop through which the positive ions are accelerated from the ion source to the first stage of the analyzer. These mass spectrometers, which can be made very compact, have been employed in analytical problems, and have also been used to determine appearance potentials. J. W. Townsend (11) has described a unit complete with power supplies and all electronics weighing less than 25 lb to be used in sampling the upper atmosphere in rocket flights.

4.4 THE OMEGATRON MASS SPECTROMETER

Basically, the omegatron mass spectrometer is a small cyclotron, constructed as shown schematically in Figure 4–4. Ionization occurs through the interaction of electrons and molecules along the electron beam path traversing the axis of the analyzing chamber, which has the nominal dimensions of a cube 2 cm on an edge. When the rf electric field is in resonance with the cyclotron oscillating frequency of the ions in the magnetic field H, at right angles to the rf electric field, the ions gain energy and spiral outward until they impinge upon the ion collector, where the ion current is measured by a vibrating reed electrometer.

H. Sommer, H. A. Thomas, and J. A. Hipple (12) originated this instrument and named it the omegatron. These same workers also gave the principles of operation and the resolution of the omegatron. It is instructive to

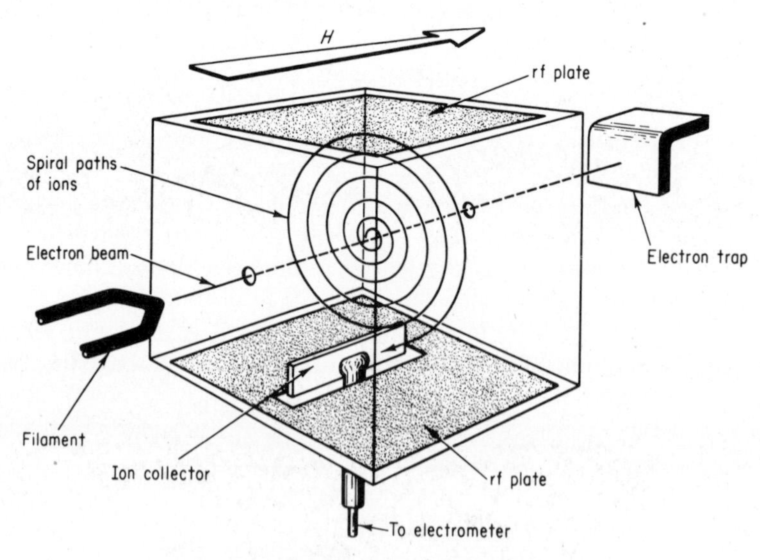

Fig. 4-4. Omegatron mass spectrometer.

examine a few of the features of the omegatron for this device is quite simple in construction and has the inherent advantage of high sensitivity since virtually all of the ions which are produced in the electron beam are collected (which is rarely the case with any other type of mass spectrometer).

The frequency of the rf field, f, when in resonance with the oscillating frequency of ions of mass m in the magnetic field H of strength B, is given by

$$f = \frac{eB}{2\pi m} = \frac{\omega_c}{2\pi} \tag{4–2}$$

where e is the electronic charge (4.803×10^{-10} esu) and ω_c is the critical angular velocity. Let us consider an example.

EXAMPLE 4–1. What rf frequency must be employed for resonance of the H^+ ion in a magnetic field of strength equal to 4697 gauss?

From Equation (4–2)

$$\begin{aligned} f &= eB/2\pi m \\ &= \frac{(4.803 \times 10^{-10})(4697/2.9979 \times 10^{10})(6.025 \times 10^{23})}{2\pi(1.0080)} \\ &= 7.16 \times 10^{6} \text{ sec}^{-1} \\ &= 7.16 \text{ Mc/sec.} \end{aligned}$$

For the same magnetic field strength and the CO_2^+ ion, we see that an rf frequency of $f = 164$ kc/sec would be required to obtain resonance.

In passing, it may be noted that a Hewlett-Packard model 650A test oscillator may be employed to supply the rf electric field.

The resolution ρ of the omegatron, in terms of $M/\Delta M$, is given by

$$\rho = \frac{M}{\Delta M} = \frac{r_0 B^2 e}{2 E_0 m}, \tag{4–3}$$

where r_0 is the distance of the collector from the point of origination of the ions (commonly about 1 cm) and E_0 is the peak rf field strength (commonly about 0.1–0.5 volts/cm).

EXAMPLE 4–2. Consider again the H^+ ion. In order to obtain a resolution of 10,000, what must be the rf electric field, providing a magnetic field of 3500 gauss is employed and $r_0 = 0.70$ cm?

From Equation (4–3),

$$\begin{aligned} E_0 &= r_0 B^2 e/2m\rho \\ &= (0.70/2)(3500/2.9979 \times 10^{10})^2 \\ &\quad (4.803 \times 10^{-10}/1.0080) \\ &\quad \times (6.025 \times 10^{23})(300)/10{,}000. \end{aligned}$$

The factor of 300 is employed to convert to practical volts. Then, $E_0 = 0.041$ volts/cm.

Conversely, if an rf electric field strength of 0.41 volts/cm were employed, $M/\Delta M$ would only be 1000 at $m = 1$ amu, and at $m = 44$ amu the resolution would only be 23. Thus, one sees immediately that the resolution drops off rapidly with increasing mass and increasing rf field strength. However, by utilizing larger magnetic field strength, the resolution may be improved, as seen from Equation (4–3). Figure 4–5 shows a typical omegatron mass spectrogram and indicates the resolution that can actually be obtained.

Note also that in Figure 4–5 the mass spectrum was scanned by varying the applied rf signal. This is a common method of mass scanning in the omegatron. However, one might also scan by varying the magnetic field strength. This latter method is advantageous, as pointed out by Sommer, Thomas, and Hipple, for use with recorders, for then the width of peaks remain constant, and if the magnetic field is varied in a linear manner with time, one will obtain a spectrum linear in mass. Recently, Brodie (13) has reported results of magnetic scanning with an omegatron.

Furthermore, at a constant magnetic field strength, the resolution varies inversely with mass. However, if E_0 is decreased as the mass is increased (rf signal is decreased), one may obtain constant resolution since the number of revolutions made by the ions in reaching the ion collector will remain

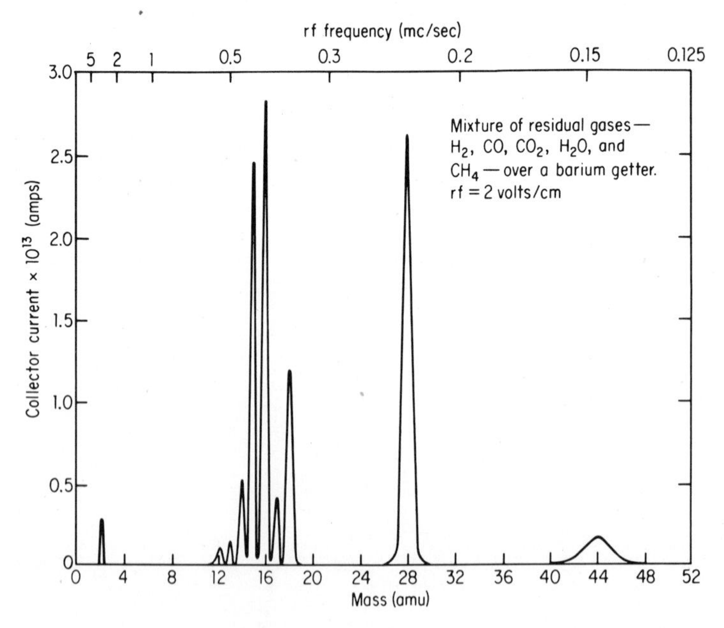

Fig. 4-5. A typical omegatron mass spectrogram. [Based on Figure 4 in the Paper by J. S. Wagener and P. T. Marth (18).]

constant. It was for these reasons that the listing for resolution was given as "variable" in Table 3–4.

The time that it takes the ions to reach the collector located r_0 from the origin of the ions is given by

$$t = 2r_0B/E_0. \tag{4–4}$$

EXAMPLE 4–3. What is the collection time of ions if a magnetic field of 4500 gauss is employed together with an rf electric field of 0.2 volts/cm and $r_0 = 1.25$ cm?

Using Equation (4–4),

$$\begin{aligned} t &= 2r_0B/E_0 \\ &= 2 \times (4500/2.9979 \times 10^{10})(1.25)(300/0.2) \\ &= 5.63 \times 10^{-4} \text{ sec} \\ &= 0.56 \text{ msec.} \end{aligned}$$

Sommer, Thomas, and Hipple have determined that the number of revolutions an ion will make in reaching the collector is

$$n = (2/\pi)(M/\Delta M) = 2\rho/\pi. \tag{4–5}$$

EXAMPLE 4–4. If the resolution ρ is 500, how many revolutions will the ion make in reaching the collector?

Using Equation (4–5),
$$\begin{aligned} n &= 2\rho/\pi \\ &= 2 \times 500/\pi \\ &= 1000/\pi = 318 \text{ rev.} \end{aligned}$$

The total length L of the path of the resonant ions is given by

$$L = n\pi r_0 \tag{4–6}$$

EXAMPLE 4–5. If the resolution of a $m = 40$ amu ion is 40, what will be the total path length of the $m = 40$ amu ion in reaching the collector? Assume $r_0 = 1$ cm.

Using Equation (4–6),

$$\begin{aligned} L &= n\pi r_0 = (2/\pi)\pi r_0\rho = 2r_0\rho \\ &= 2 \times 1 \times 40 \\ &= 80 \text{ cm.} \end{aligned}$$

Although the rf voltage applied to the omegatron is usually only a fraction of a volt, the final kinetic energy of the ions is relatively great. The final kinetic energy T is given by

$$T = E_0L/2. \tag{4–7}$$

EXAMPLE 4–6. If the H^+ ion has a resolution ρ of 10,000, what will be the final kinetic energy of the ion upon reaching the collector, if $E_0 = 0.11$ volts/cm and $r_0 = 1$ cm?

From Equation (4–7),

$$\begin{aligned} T &= E_0L/2 = 2E_0r_0\rho/2 = E_0r_0\rho \\ &= 10{,}000 \times 0.11 \times 1 \\ &= 1100 \text{ volts.} \end{aligned}$$

The maximum radius r_m attained by a nonresonant ion differing in mass by an amount ΔM from that of the resonant ions was derived by H. Sommer, H. A. Thomas, and J. A. Hipple (14) to be

$$r_m = (2r_0/m\pi)(M/\Delta M). \tag{4–8}$$

EXAMPLE 4–7. If we are collecting H^+ ions, what will be the maximum radius of ions separated in mass by only 0.01 amu, if the resolution for H^+ ion is 10,000?

From Equation (4–8),

$$\begin{aligned} r_m &= (2r_0/n\pi)(M/\Delta M) = (r_0/\rho)(M/\Delta M) \\ &= (1/\rho)(1/0.01)r_0 \\ &= (100/10{,}000)r_0 \\ &= r_0/100. \end{aligned}$$

That is, their maximum radius is only 1/100 of the distance to the collector.

D. Lichtman (15) has discussed the sensitivity of the omegatron. The maximum sensitivity S is given by

$$S = i_+/i_eP, \tag{4–9}$$

where

$$i_+ = i_e\sigma Nd, \tag{4–10}$$

i_+ is the positive ion current, i_e is the electron beam current, σ is the cross section for ionization (at a given electron energy), N is the gas density, and d is the reaction length (i.e., the length of the electron beam).

Combining Equations (4–9) and (4–10), we see that at $T = 300°$ K,

$$S = \sigma d N_0 / 1.87 \times 10^7, \tag{4–11}$$

where N_0 is Avogadro's number. If $d = 2r_0$, as is commonly the case, and taking $\sigma_{75} = 4.31 \times 10^{-16}$ cm² for CO_2 (see Appendix III), we see that

$$S = 4.31 \times 10^{-16} \times 2 \times 6.025 \times 10^{23}/1.87 \times 10^7$$
$$= 27.8 \text{ amp } i_+/\text{amp } i_e/\text{mm(Hg)}.$$

That is, $i_+ = 28 \times 10^{-12}$ amp for $i_e = 1\ \mu$amp and $P = 10^{-6}$ mm (Hg). Lichtman experimentally determined $S = 20.0 \times 10^{-12}$ for CO_2. Thus, if one can detect to 10^{-14} amp, one could detect a pressure of CO_2 as low as 5×10^{-10} mm (Hg).

Since the omegatron tube is small and also is portable, it can be attached simply to almost any vacuum system, and it can be utilized to measure pressures as low as 10^{-9} mm (Hg) with an electrometer capable of measuring 10^{-14} amp. The omegatron also has the advantage of being able to be baked and outgassed completely. Stark (16) and Zdanuk, Bierig, Rubin, and Wolsky (17) have discussed other properties of the omegatron.

The omegatron has already been found to have a large number of applications, particularly for those studies of ions with mass below approximately 40 (although WO_3^+ ions in the region of mass 250 reportedly have been observed). J. S. Wagener and P. T. Marth (18) have reported on the use of the omegatron for the analysis of gases at very low pressures. Lichtman has found that he could use the omegatron to measure pressures as low as 10^{-9} mm (Hg) with a vibrating reed capable of mesuring 10^{-14} amp. D. Alpert and R. S. Buritz (19) indicated that the sensitivity of the omegatron is comparable to that of a conventional ionization gate. A. Hebling and D. Lichtman (20) have employed ion pumps and a cryogenic forepump to obtain a vacuum of 10^{-9} Torr in their omegatron.

Berry (21) has given a theoretical treatment of the ion trajectories in the omegatron, and G. Schuchhardt (22) has given a similar treatment for an omegatron containing an electrostatic field, such as that constructed by Klopfer and Schmidt (23).

H. Sommer, H. A. Thomas, and J. A. Hipple suggested in their early papers (12, 14), in which they resolved the H_2^+-D^+ doublet and determined $\Delta M = 15.45 \times 10^{-4}$ amu, the additional possible applications of the omegatron to both analytical work and the study of appearance potentials and ionization and dissociation processes. A. Hebling and D. Lichtman (20) have presented some very interesting results of appearance potential determinations with the omegatron and their interpretations. Residual gas analysis has also been reported by a number of investigators. Certainly the features of being light, small, and relatively low cost are important features of the omegatron. The reader may also wish to read of the work of A. G. Edwards (24), Bell (25), R. J. Warnecke (26), and W. A. Morgan, G. Jernakoff, and K. P. Lanneau (27).

4.5 THE TROCHOIDAL MASS SPECTROMETER

A method of attaining perfect focus, as well as of producing a spatial mass dispersion, is to inject positive ions from the ion source into crossed homogeneous magnetic and electrostatic fields. J. A. Hipple and W. Bleakney (28) first used this principle in the construction of a trochoidal-path mass spectrometer, although it was already known that the motion of an ion moving under the influence of these crossed fields in a plane perpendicular to the magnetic field would describe a trochoidal path. If a homogeneous magnetic field is used to deflect the ions through 360°, the detector usually would have to be at the same point as the ion source. By adding a homogeneous electric field at right angles to the magnetic field, the ions can be given a linear transverse movement as well as the circular movement due to the magnetic field. This results in a trochoidal path. Thus, the detector and ion source may be separated.

A *trochoid* is the locus of a tracing point $P(x, y)$ at a distance b from the center of a rolling circle of fixed radius a, along the y-axis, that rolls without slipping on a fixed straight line, taken as the x-axis. The equation for a trochoid is

$$\left.\begin{aligned} x &= a\theta - b\sin\theta \\ y &= a - b\cos\theta \end{aligned}\right\} \tag{4-12}$$

Now, if $b < a$, we have a curtate, or oblate, cycloid; if $b > a$, we have a prolate cycloid; and if $b = a$, we have simply a cycloid. Figures 4-6 to 4-8 illustrate these three cases. In these figures, the magnetic field projects out

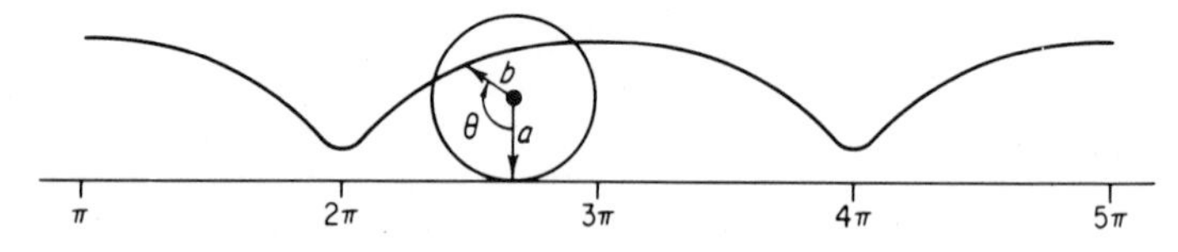

Fig. 4-6. A curtate (oblate) cycloid ($b < a$).

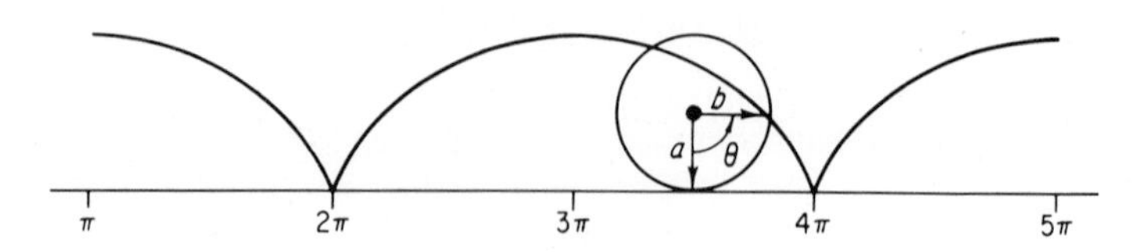

Fig. 4-7. A cycloid where $b = a$.

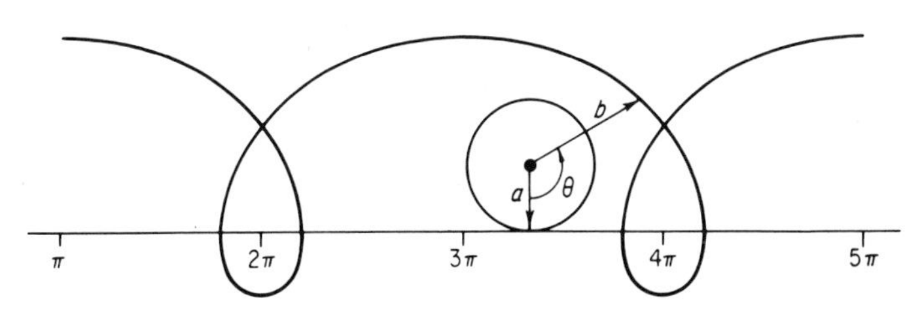

Fig. 4-8. A prolate cycloid ($b > a$).

of the plane of the paper and the electric field is perpendicular to the fixed straight line upon which the circle rolls.

From Equation (4–12) and Figure 4–8, it can be seen that at distances of $D = 2\pi a$ apart, the curves will cross in the same direction a line parallel to the x-axis, along which the circle rolls. This distance is given by

$$D = (2\pi E/H)^2 (m/e) \tag{4–13}$$

or, the radius of the rolling circle is given by

$$a = (E/H^2)(m/e) \tag{4–14}$$

and the distance b to the tracing point is given by

$$b = [(m/e)/H][v_0^2 + (E^2/H^2) - (2Ev_0/H)\cos\phi]^{1/2}, \tag{4–15}$$

where E is the strength of the electric field, H is the strength of the magnetic field, v_0 is the initial velocity with which the ions enter the crossed electric and magnetic fields (v_0 is determined by the mass m of the ion and by V, the accelerating potential for injection), and $(90 - \phi)$ is the angle between the electric field and the entering positive ion beam, as illustrated in Figure 4–9. Note that ϕ in Figures 4–8 and 4–9 is nearly 90°.

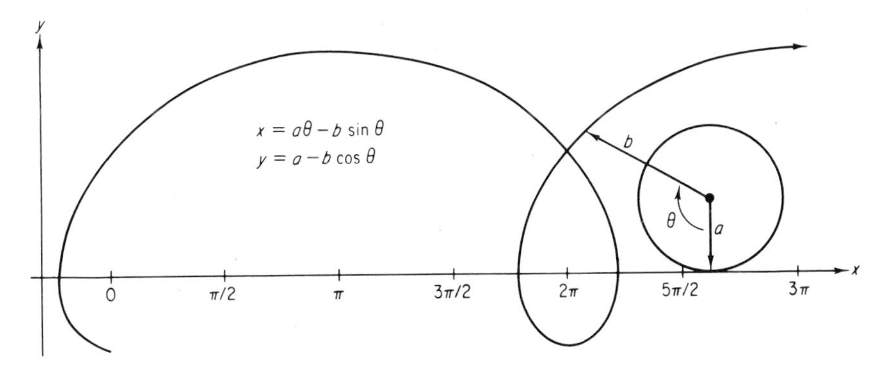

Fig. 4-9. A prolate cycloid ($b > a$). Here, $b = 2a$

Neither v_0 nor the direction of motion of the ions appears in Equation (4–13) and (4–14), so that neither D nor a depends upon these parameters. However, b does depend upon both v_0 and the direction of motion (although for practical operation the dependence of b on the direction of motion is not extremely critical).

Bleakney and Hipple constructed two instruments: one using a trochoidal path of a curtate cycloid ($b < a$; see Figure 4–6), and one using a trochoidal path of a prolate cycloid ($b = 3$ cm $> a = 1$ cm; see Figures 4–8 and 4–9). Bleakney and Hipple found the prolate cycloid path to be superior to the other in performance.

Scanning through the mass spectrum to bring the various ion beams of given m/e values past the exit slits, and causing all ions to follow the same path, requires that both E and V remain fixed while H is varied, or else that both H and the ratio of E to V remain constant while E is varied. With either of these scan modes, only two coplanar fixed slits (in an equipotential plane) must be employed. If E, H, and V are held constant, and the mode of operation is that of a mass spectrograph, we see from Equation (4–13) that D is directly proportional to m/e; therefore we have a linear mass scale.

The trochoidal mass spectrometers can focus negative ions as well as positive ions. However, this type of instrument demands uniform magnetic and electrostatic fields of large area, and this is to some extent a disadvantage.

H. W. Voorhies, C. F. Robinson, L. G. Hall, W. M. Brubaker, and C. E. Berry (29) describe a coincident field cycloid mass spectrometer which they constructed and studied. They employed a focal distance of $D = 6.00$ in. Sixty-eight picture-frame plates were employed for distributing the potential of the electric field. (3200 volts across the plate system gave an electric field of the order of 150 volts/cm.) A magnetic field of up to 10,000 gauss was employed. Optimum resolution was achieved with $V = 0.18E$, and optimum focusing was obtained using repeller voltages on the detector entrance slit of about 15% of V. Trajectory excursions between 2.2 and 2.9 in. in the vertical direction (see Figure 4–9) and 6.9 and 7.8 in. in the horizontal direction were obtained. A resolution of $M/\Delta M = 2500$ was achieved, allowing complete separation of the N_2-CO doublet (masses of 28.00615 and 27.99492 amu, respectively).

In Figure 4–10 is shown schematically a three-dimensional representation of the arrangement of the elements of the cycloidal mass spectrometer. Consolidated Electrodynamics Corporation produces two cycloidal-focusing mass spectrometers: the model 21–620A and the model 21–130.

The model 21–620A has a mass range of about 12 to 150. The model 21–130 cycloidal instrument has a 1.1-in. focal distance and uses a permanent Alnico V magnet of about 4500 gauss. It achieves unit resolution (no cross

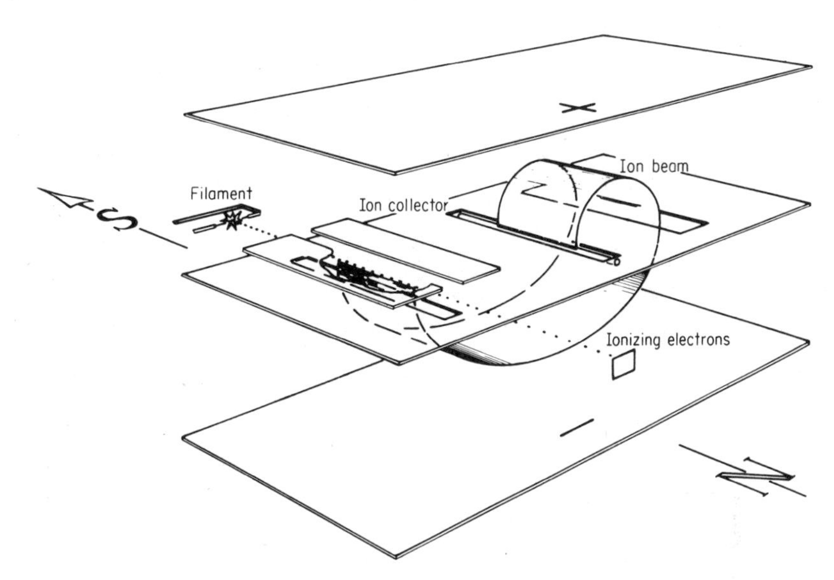

Fig. 4-10. Cycloidally-focused mass spectrometer. (Courtesy of Consolidated Electrodynamics Corporation, Pasadena, California.)

contribution between adjacent mass peaks of equal intensities) to mass 200 and usable resolution to mass 230. It is accurate in making analyses to within 1% of actual concentrations, and data are reproducible to within 0.2%. The mass range of the model 21–130 is from m/e 2 to m/e 230.

4.6 THE BAINBRIDGE-JORDAN MASS SPECTROGRAPH

Two instruments of high resolution and employing double focusing are the Bainbridge-Jordan and the Mattauch-Herzog mass spectrographs. In Chapter 3 we discussed velocity-focusing and direction-focusing instruments. An instrument which refocuses ion beams inhomogeneous both in velocity and in direction is a double-focusing instrument. This was an obvious extension after the earlier studies of the single-focusing instruments, and a number of workers constructed double-focusing instruments at about the same time.

A. J. Dempster (30) was the first to publish a description of a double-focusing instrument, one in which an electrostatic analyzer (90°) and a magnetic analyzer (180°) were used in a tandem arrangement. The third instrument of this type was reported in the literature by J. Mattauch (31). A description of this instrument will be presented in Section 4.7, below.

The report by K. T. Bainbridge and E. B. Jordan (32) was the second one of a double-focusing instrument, and it would be worthwhile to examine it here in a little more detail. A schematic diagram of the Bainbridge-Jordan mass spectrograph is given in Figure 4–11.

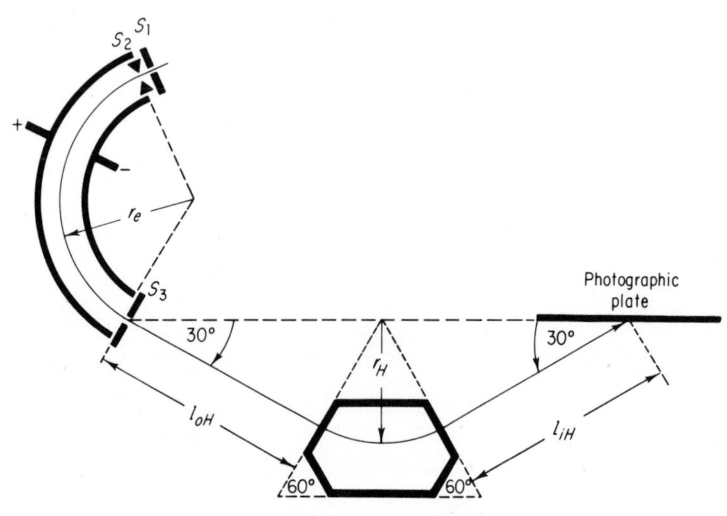

Fig. 4-11. Schematic diagram of the Bainbridge-Jordan mass spectrograph.

Bainbridge and Jordan combined a 127° 17′ direction-focusing electostatic analyzer with a 60° direction-focusing magnetic analyzer. Note that a sector magnetic field was employed here (the first use of the sector magnetic field). In many ways this type of double-focusing analyzer is one of the simplest. From Equation (3–23), one sees that the only solution for an electrostatic analyzer angle of 127° 17′ is that $l_{oe} = l_{ie} = 0$. And from the specific case considered shortly after Equation (3–21) in Chapter 3 [using Equation (3–19)] we recall that for a 60° magnetic analyzer $l_{oH} = l_{iH} = 1.732\ r_H$. If we substitute these values into Equation (3–26), we find that double-focusing is attained only if $r_e = r_H$. Bainbridge and Jordan used $r_e = r_H = 10.00$ in.

One advantage of this double-focusing instrument over the Dempster instrument is that the Bainbridge-Jordan mass spectrograph gives twice the dispersion while requiring only one-third as much field area. Another advantage is that the mass scale is very nearly linear, whereas in the Dempster instrument the mass scale varies as $\sqrt{m/e}$. As has already been seen from Table 3–4, the resolving power of the first Bainbridge-Jordan instrument was about 7000.

4.7 THE MATTAUCH-HERZOG MASS SPECTROGRAPH

The double-focusing mass spectrograph worked out by R. Herzog (33) and constructed by J. Mattauch and R. Herzog (34) employs an electrostatic analyzer of $\phi_e = \pi/4\sqrt{2} = 31°50'$ and a magnetic analyzer of $\phi_H = \pi/2 = 90°$. The geometry of this mass spectrograph is illustrated in Figure 4–13. Both the Dempster and the Bainbridge-Jordan mass spectrographs used direction-focusing analyzers in combination. The Mattauch-Herzog mass spectrograph achieves double-focusing only upon combination of the two separate fields described. From Equation (3–23) we observe that if $l_{oe} = r_e/\sqrt{2}$, then $l_{ie} = \infty$. That is, the ion beam coming from the electrostatic field is parallel, and therefore the beam behaves as if it were coming from infinity when entering the magnetic field ($l_{oH} = \infty$). Using this information in Equation (3–19) shows that for $\phi_H = 90°$, $l_{iH} = 0$. One finds by using Equation (3–26) that this geometry also gives velocity-focusing. Since no restrictions have been placed on Δ or on r_H, the double-focusing occurs simultaneously for all masses and for any value of Δ. One chooses a fairly large value for r_e so as to obtain the desired resolution; i.e., the resolution depends on r_e, the mass dispersion depends on r_H. The dispersion and the line widths vary directly as $\sqrt{m/e}$.

Fig. 4-12. J. H. E. Mattauch

The Mattauch-Herzog mass spectrograph is now being produced commercially by Consolidated Electrodynamics Corporation as their model number 21–110. A sample photographic record from this instrument has already been given in Figure 3–12. The mass spectrum covers a mass range

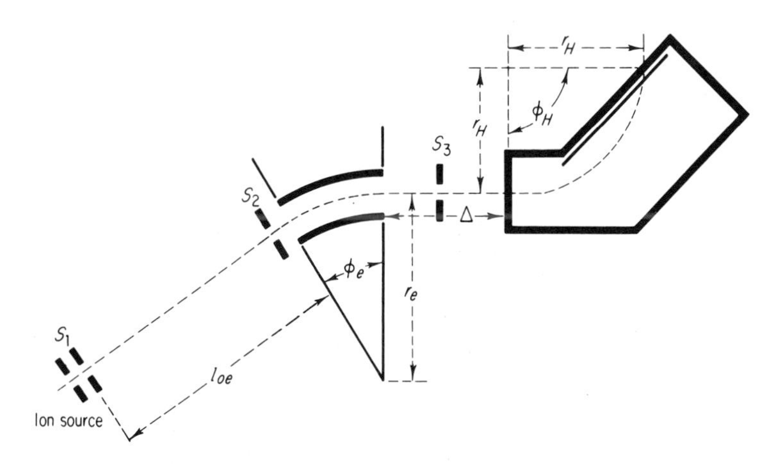

Fig. 4-13. Geometry of Mattauch-Herzog mass spectrometer. (Courtesy of Consolidated Electrodynamics Corp., Pasadena, California.)

ratio of 36:1 permitting analysis from lithium to uranium (all of the solid elements up to uranium) in a single exposure. The maximum magnetic field strength employed is 12,500 gauss and the focal plane length is about 14 in. A rf spark source, a gas ion source, and a surface emission ion source can all be used with this instrument.

Associated Electrical Industries, Ltd., of England produces a Mattauch-Herzog instrument as model number MS–7. This model provides ion accelerating voltages of from 10 to 20 kv in 2-kv steps to give a variable mass range. The 31° 50′ electrostatic analyzer of 15 in. mean radius is composed of two stainless steel plates separated by $\frac{3}{4}$-in. The electrostatic field voltage applied is 10% of the ionizing voltage. The magnetic field can be varied in 10 steps from 2000 to 16,000 gauss over a $\frac{1}{8}$-in. gap to cover a mass range of 5 to 240. An rf spark source is usually employed in the MS-7.

It is possible to utilize the Mattauch-Herzog type of instrumentation for the analysis of impurities in solid samples. Often these solid samples may be metals. Impurity levels of 1 ppm can be determined in about 15 min, and it requires only about 1 hr to analyze for impurities at the 1 ppb level.

4.8 CALUTRONS AND ISOTOPE SEPARATORS

When the positive ion beam is neutralized at the collector, the neutralized particles commonly remain on the collector electrode. As already pointed out in Chapter 3, the resistive strips of the magnetic electron multiplier may be cleaned to remove this "dirt." On the other hand, such collections may also be used to significant advantage. The mass separation achieved by the mass spectrometer and the collection of the separated isotopes of the various elements by mass spectrometric methods is an obvious source of pure samples of separated isotopes, and special instruments, termed *calutrons*, have been constructed for large-scale separations of isotopes. In Chapter 2 we briefly introduced these mass spectrometers from an historical standpoint. It is now instructive to examine their design and construction. Figure 4–14 shows a diagram of the first calutron.

Large equipment is necessary to obtain the high mass dispersion required for satisfactory separations. Large magnets of about 4-ft radius and high-voltage accelerating potentials (of the order of 30–50 kv) are typical in these large instruments. Also, special ion source design is required for producing and delivering intense ion beams which will allow large-scale (gram quantities and larger) separation. Modern mass spectrometric isotope separators use arc sources of ions and slits in lengths of the order of 1 ft. Because of the intense ion beams, special cooling and collection techniques have to be employed as well. To dwell for a moment on this last point, we can readily see that the focused ion beam dissipates a large amount of energy to the collector, causing heating and erosion effects which may allow significant losses of separated material. Special vanes and "foot-scrapers" may be

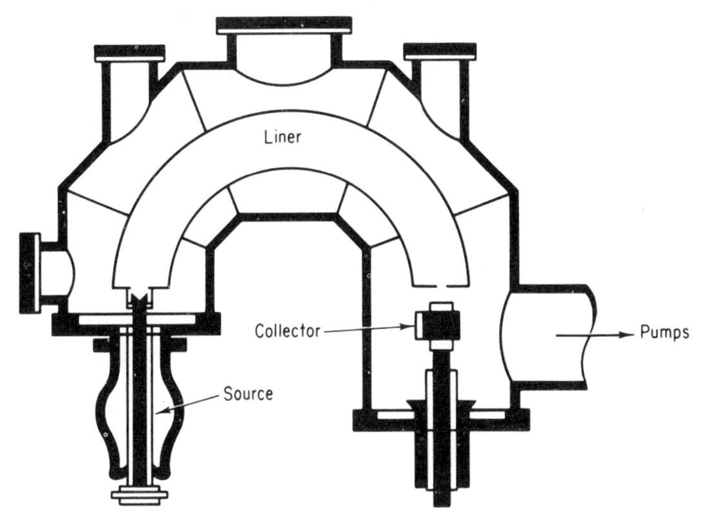

Fig. 4-14. The first calutron. A diagram of the original C-shaped tank inserted in the 87-in. Cyclotron, Berkeley, California, February, 1942.

included in the collector to aid in minimizing the loss of the separated isotopes.

In his book on *Mass Spectroscopy*, H. E. Duckworth remarks on many of the isotope separators presently in use. A. E. Cameron discusses electromagnetic separations (35), and M. L. Smith has edited a book on *Electromagnetically Enriched Isotopes and Mass Spectrometry* (36). The reader is invited to examine these writings for additional details.

By 1955 all of the elements except osmium had been successfully processed in calutrons. By 1961 all of the stable isotopes of osmium had been electromagnetically separated and were available for purchase in enrichments from 2.2 to 98.7% from Oak Ridge National Laboratory. However, for some of the other elements a factor limiting the quantity of the isotope which can be collected is the retention at the collector of the isotope. For example, the noble gases after separation must not simply be pumped out through the diffusion and roughing pumps. Actually, the noble gases can be retained in small quantities by causing the ions to penetrate a few atomic surface layers of a thin metal foil such as aluminum or silver. The neutral atoms are then retained in the metal and may later be recovered by vacuum fusion of the foils. Similarly, oxygen isotopes can be retained by making the collector of copper. Many of the isotopes separated require different methods for retention of the separated atoms.

It is obvious that, because of the intense ion beam currents obtainable in isotope separators, these rather specialized instruments may be utilized conveniently for purposes other than just isotope separation. Two such possible uses will be mentioned here. With the large beam currents, various ions may be accelerated through varying potential drops and used to bombard samples placed on the collector. An example of this would be the bombardment of different substances with $(C^{14})^+$, $(C^{14})^{++}$, etc., ions in an attempt to understand more fully the hot-atom chemistry of carbon-14. Another interesting application of the isotope separator would be the following one. If an infrared beam is placed such that it would intersect at right angles the the ion beam of the isotope separator just after the ion beam passed through the entrance slit to the collector, the infrared spectra of many different types of ions could be determined. From the analyses of the infrared spectra, the vibrational and rotational frequencies, moments of inertia, and the molecular structures of the studied ions could be determined. Certainly this last application will be an extremely important one, for it will enable much fundamental information to be obtained concerning the structures of ions. At present there is at least one isotope separator commercially available. Gamma Industrie in Paris manufactures an instrument, model EM-2 that uses a magnetic field of up to 12,000 gauss and accelerating potentials of up to 50 kv. This separator, patterned after that reported by R. Bernas, J. L. Sarrouy, and J. Camplan (37) can resolve ion beams up to $m/e = 300$ and is capable of giving ion beams of 1 ma or greater.

4.9 THE QUADRUPOLE MASS SPECTROMETER

The electric quadrupole mass spectrometer, developed by Paul, his coworkers, and others (38–46), is basically different from the other instruments described above. Using a quadrupole, rf electric field for mass analysis, magnet requirements are eliminated. A schematic diagram of the positioning of the four long, parallel (to close tolerances) electrodes is shown in Figure 4–15. Although the electrodes are shown to have a uniform hyperbolic cross section, cylindrical rods can be used if they are properly spaced. The opposite pairs of electrodes are connected together electrically.

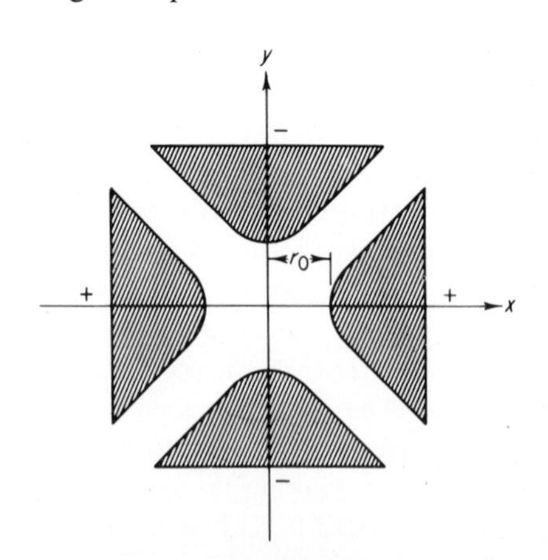

Fig. 4-15. Cross-sectional view of a quadrupole mass spectrometer.*

Both a dc voltage U and an rf voltage, $V_0 \cos \omega t$, are applied to the quadrupole array. Thus, in Figure 4–15, the voltage on the positive electrodes is $+(U + V_0 \cos \omega t)$ and that on the negative electrodes is $-(U + V_0 \cos \omega t)$. The electrodes

* The ions travel with a constant velocity in the z-direction, perpendicular to the plane of the page.

are separated by $2r_0$ and the potential $\mathscr{V}$ at any point in the field is expressed by

$$\mathscr{V} = \frac{x^2 - y^2}{r_0^2}(U + V_0 \cos \omega t). \tag{4–16}$$

Ions are injected from a conventional ion source into the rf field in the z-direction (perpendicular to the plane of the page). The lateral motions of the ions are described by the following three equations:

$$m\left(\frac{d^2x}{dt^2}\right) + \frac{2e(U + V_0 \cos \omega t)x}{r_0^2} = 0, \tag{4–17}$$

$$m\left(\frac{d^2y}{dt^2}\right) - \frac{2e(U + V_0 \cos \omega t)y}{r_0^2} = 0, \tag{4–18}$$

and

$$m\left(\frac{d^2z}{dt^2}\right) = 0. \tag{4–19}$$

Thus, the ion continues in the z-direction with the constant velocity at which it was injected into the quadrupole rf field.

In order to put Equations (4–17) and (4–18) into the form of Mathieu's equation,

$$(d^2f/d\phi^2) + (\alpha + 2q \cos 2\phi)f = 0, \tag{4–20}$$

we see that we must define three dimensionless parameters, α, q, and ϕ, as follows:

$$\phi = \omega t/2, \tag{4–21}$$

$$\alpha = 8eU/mr_0^2\omega^2, \tag{4–22}$$

and

$$q = 4eV_0/mr_0^2\omega^2. \tag{4–23}$$

Then, the Mathieu equations for the motions are

$$\frac{d^2x}{d\phi^2} + (\alpha + 2q \cos 2\phi)x = 0 \tag{4–24}$$

and

$$\frac{d^2y}{d\phi^2} - (\alpha + 2q \cos 2\phi)y = 0. \tag{4–25}$$

The solutions to these equations, giving the oscillations in the x- and the y-directions, respectively, are quite complex (47–50). As indicated by Whittaker and Watson (51), the constant α is a very complicated function of q

if the solution is to be periodic. In the range of small values of α and q, wherein our interest lies, α is a function of q in the manner shown in Figure 4–16.

As shown in Figure 4–16, there is a region of stable oscillations, where the amplitude remains finite for all values of t. This is the region enclosed in the triangular-shaped wedge. Outside of this region of stable oscillations, the amplitude increases exponentially toward infinity. Only ions of m/e values given by the appropriate α and q, U and V_0, ω and r_0 will therefore pass through the quadrupole analyzer without striking the electrodes and thereby reach the detector. The resolution increases with an increase in the α/q ratio and, in principle, becomes infinite at $\alpha = 0.23699$ and $q = 0.706$, the apex of the region of stable oscillations. Although high resolution can be attained, the resolution does not become infinite, since the resolution depends, in practice, on the positions and velocities of ions entering the quadrupole rf field. Therefore, small circular apertures are used just before the analyzer to increase the resolution.

The straight line drawn in Figure 4–16 is for $\alpha/q = 0.306$ (i.e., $U/V_0 = 0.153$). For $U = 658$ volts, $r_0 = 3.5$ cm, and a frequency of 471 kc/sec, the point m_1 is for a mass of 222 amu. Points $m_2 = 266$ amu and $m_3 = 340$ amu are for the same value of U. Note that at $U = 658$ volts (and hence $V_0 = 658/0.153 = 4300$ volts) all masses between 204 and 234 amu ($\alpha =$ 0.221 and 0.202, respectively) are stable. That is, they will pass through the quadrupole rf field to the detector, and they will not be resolved.

From this it is seen that in order to achieve high resolution, measure-

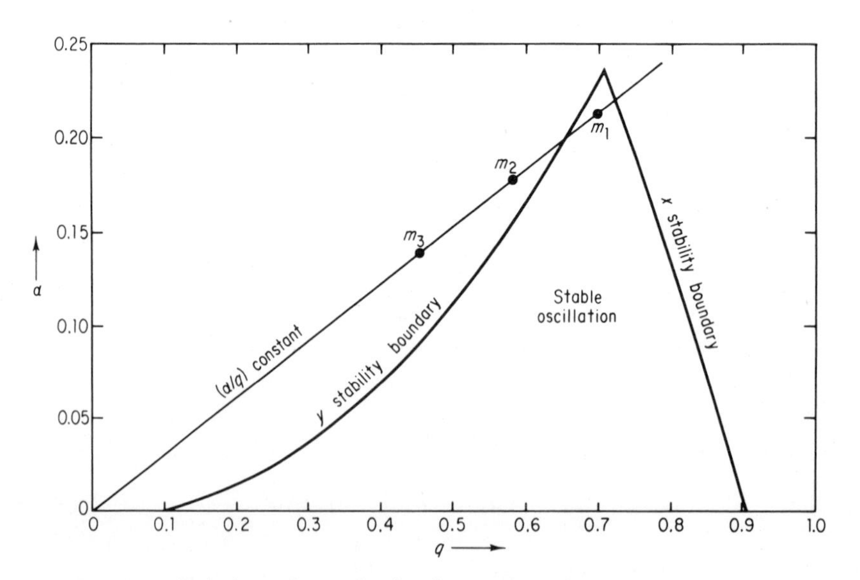

Fig. 4-16. Relation of α and q for the quadrupole mass spectrometer.

ments must be made in the apex region of the curve shown in Figure 4–16—at $\alpha = 0.237$ and $q = 0.706$—as stated earlier. This gives $\alpha/q = 0.336$. If, as in the case of the instrument described in Table 4–1, mass 200 is in focus at the apex, masses 201 and 199 would occur at $\alpha = 0.238$ and 0.236, respectively. Both of these are outside the region of stability and would, therefore, not be collected. In order to allow mass 199 to pass through the field and be collected, it is necessary that $U = 655$ volts and $V_0 = 3904$ volts.

TABLE 4–1. CHARACTERISTICS OF A QUADRUPOLE MASS SPECTROMETER FOR PRECISION MASS DETERMINATIONS (45)

Ion source	Conventional
Beam voltage	10–30 volts
Diameter of entrance aperture	1.0 mm
Quadrupole spacing (r_0)	3.5 cm
Field length (L)	582 cm
Electrode construction (each)	60 wires in bundle (stretched to 80% of breaking load)
dc voltage for $A = 200$ (U)	658 volts
rf voltage for $A = 200$ (V_0)	3924 volts
Frequency ($\omega/2\pi$)	471 kc/sec
rf periods ion experiences	> 600
rf power	290 watts
Detector	17-stage electron multiplier
Mass scanning method	Fixed ω, simultaneous change of V_0 and U
Maximum resolution achieved	16,000

Mass scanning may be accomplished either by varying U and V_0 while keeping the U/V_0 ratio constant, or by varying ω. The former method is more commonly employed. In the region of high resolution the peaks are triangular in shape, whereas at low resolution (smaller α/q) the peaks become trapezoidal.

No defining aperture for the detector is necessary. The high transmission of the quadrupole analyzer at low resolution has caused this instrument to receive serious consideration for use as an isotope separator (40, 41). The transmitted ion beam current can be increased to several milliamperes by lowering the resolution to allow several masses to be transmitted and then applying a voltage at the fundamental frequencies of the undesired ions to the x-electrodes. The resonant ions are thereby caused to strike an x-electrode, and only the desired ions finally reach the collector.

Several other applications also have been made: von Zahn, Gebauer, and Paul (45) have shown the application of this instrument, using a resolution of the order of 10,000, to the reasonably precise measurements of nuclidic masses. Also, Brubaker (44) has shown the quadrupole mass spectrometer to be suitable for satellite-based studies of atmospheric compostion. One further potential use is indicated in Chapter 11. Commercially available quadrupole instruments are noted in Chapter 5.

4.10 THE MONOPOLE MASS SPECTROMETER

The monopole mass spectrometer was designed and first constructed by von Zahn (52). The basic principles of its operation are essentially the same as those of the quadrupole mass spectrometer (Section 4.9). A diagram of the monopole spectrometer is given in Figure 4–17. The potential at any point in the space between the two electrodes (one the circular rod and the other the right angle) is given by Equation (4–16), with $y \geq |x|$.

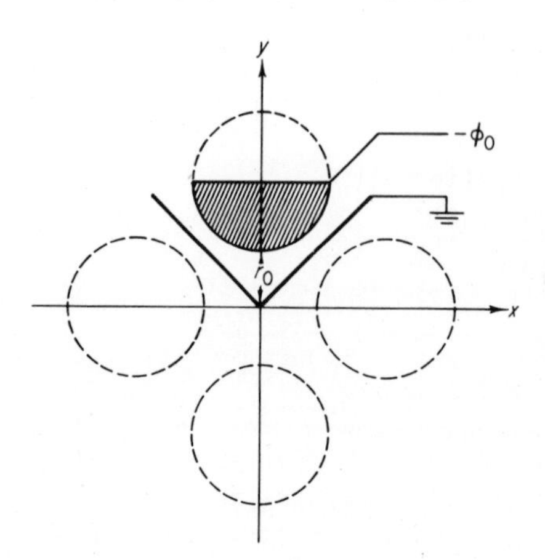

Fig. 4-17. Cross-sectional view of a monopole mass analyzer.*

The solutions to the Mathieu differential equations are as with the quadrupole instrument, except that now the motion of the ion in the y-direction represents a beat (the length and phase of which is not dependent upon the initial conditions of the ion), and the high-frequency oscillations within the beat are not oscillations about the z-axis (as is the case in the x-direction).

Ions can reach the detector only if their α, q value lies within a narrow band just on the right-hand side of the y-stability boundary shown in Figure 4–16. Furthermore, an ion can pass through the monopole field if $y > |x|$ and if the field length is less than half the length of the total beat. About 50% of the time the injected ions will strike the right-angle electrode in a very short period of time (in about one or two rf periods); the other 50% of the time the ions reach the detector.

In Figure 4–17 (and in Figure 4–15 if circular rods are used rather than hyperbolic rods), the radius of the circular electrode r_e is 1.16 times the field radius r_0:

$$r_e = 1.16\, r_0. \tag{4–26}$$

Therefore, the closest aproach, x, of the circular electrode to the right-angle electrode is given by

$$2(x + r_e)^2 = (r_e + r_0)^2$$

or

$$x = 0.707\, r_0 - 0.293\, r_e,$$

* The ions travel with a constant velocity in the z-direction, perpendicular to the plane of the page.

which leads to

$$x = 0.707\, r_0 - 0.340\, r_0 = 0.367\, r_0.$$

Thus, for $r_0 = 1.524$ cm, this closest approach is $(0.367)(1.524) = 0.560$ cm. Also, the diameter of the circular electrode is $(1.16)(2)(1.524) = 3.54$ cm.

The monopole mass spectrometer achieves a good resolving power over a wide range of α and q values. It is not necessary that the U/V_0 ratio be maintained constant as in the quadrupole instrument. Furthermore, it is not necessary to operate the monopole unit in the apex region of the stability diagram. These are important features, as is the feature that mass scanning is accomplished in the monopole unit by varying the rf frequency while maintaining U, V_0, and V, the ion injection voltage, constant. These features amount to substantial simplifications in the electronics and field configuration in the monopole spectrometer as compared to the quadrupole mass spectrometer.

EXAMPLE 4–8. Let $r_0 = 0.600$ in. (1.524 cm); $V_0 = 1000$ volts; $q = 0.520$; and $L = 27.0$ cm (the length of the quadrupole field). At what frequency would the N_2^+ ion be observed under these conditions?

To solve this problem, we shall make use of Equation (4–23),

$$\omega^2 = 4eV_0/mr_0^2q. \qquad (4\text{–}23)$$

For the specified conditions

$$\omega^2 = \frac{(4 \times 4.803 \times 10^{-10} \times 1000 \times 6.023 \times 10^{23})}{0.570 \times (1.524)^2 \times 300 \times (M/z)}$$

or

$$\omega^2 = 3.195 \times 10^{15}/(M/z),$$

where M is mass in amu and z is the number of electronic charges on the ion. Now,

$$f^2 = (\omega/2\pi)^2 = 8.100 \times 10^{13}/(M/z)$$

so that

$$f = 9.00/(M/z)^{1/2}\ \text{Mc}.$$

This means that, for an rf oscillator continuously variable over the range of 1 to 3 Mc, masses of $m/e = 10$ to 90 may be scanned under these conditions. Furthermore, $m/e = 28$ would be observed at a frequency of $9.00/(28)^{1/2} = 9.00/5.29 = 1.70$ Mc. (see Figure 4–18).

The peak height is nearly independent of the U/V_0 ratio. However, all of the observed peaks showed some tailing on the high-mass side of a peak

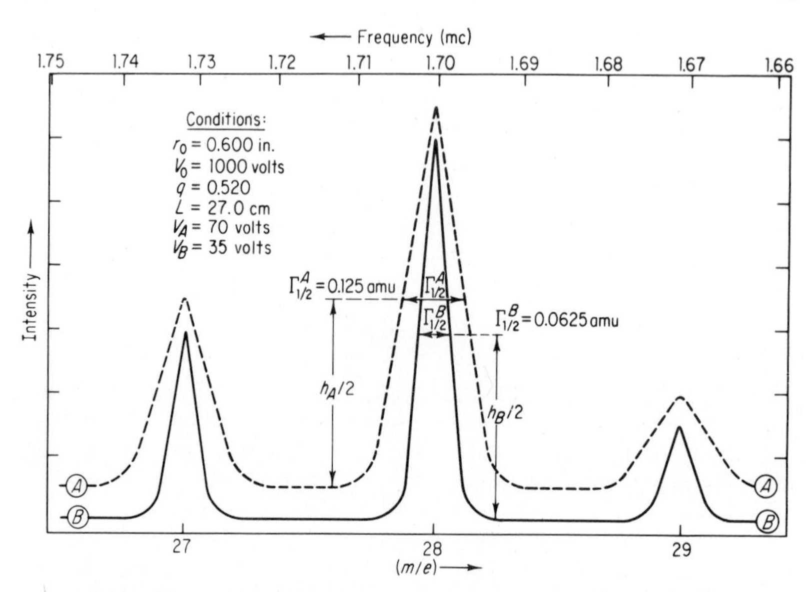

Fig. 4-18. Effect of kinetic energy of ions injected into magnetic field upon resolution.

(52). This tailing was about 0.1 % of the intensity of the peak and has been attributed (52) to insufficient mechanical precision in the alignment of the analyzing field.

The number of rf periods n necessary for a given resolving power, $M/\Delta M$, as determined by $\Gamma_{1/2}$ (see Section 3.2), is given by

$$n(\Delta M/M)^{1/2} = k, \tag{4-27}$$

where k is experimentally found to be nearly constant at the value of 1.4. [Theoretically (52), this value is 1.5 in the apex of the stability region shown in Figure 4–16.] We can see more clearly the meaning of this by examining the following example.

EXAMPLE 4–9. Consider the hypothetical partial mass spectrum given in Figure 4–18, using $r_0 = 1.52$ cm, $V_0 = 1000$ volts, $q = 0.520$, and $L = 27.0$ cm. At an ion injection energy V of 70 volts, the ion velocity is

$$v = (2eV/m)^{1/2} = [(2 \times 4.803 \times 10^{-10} \times 70 \times 6.023 \times 10^{23})/(28 \times 300)]^{1/2}$$

or

$$v = 2.20 \times 10^6 \text{ cm/sec}$$

which means that the ion will be in the monopole field for a time

$$t = 27.0/2.20 \times 10^6 = 1.23 \times 10^{-5} \text{ sec.}$$

But from data presented above, we recall that for these given conditions the frequency necessary to bring the $m/e = 28$ ions to the detector is 1.70 Mc. Therefore, the number of rf periods that the ion experiences is

$$n = 1.23 \times 10^{-5} \times 1.70 \times 10^{6} = 20.9.$$

From Figure 4–18, we see that $\Gamma^{A}_{1/2} = 0.125$ amu, so that

$$(\Delta M/M)_A = (0.125/28) = 4.47 \times 10^{-3}.$$

(This corresponds to a resolving power of 225.) From Equation (4–27) we then calculate

$$k = (20.9)(4.47 \times 10^{-3})^{1/2}$$

or

$$k = 1.4.$$

We also see that, since the velocity is directly related to the square root of the ion injection energy, the number of rf periods the ion experiences will be inversely related to the square root of the ion injection energy. Thus,

$$(\Delta M/M)^{1/2} = k/(a/V^{1/2})$$

or

$$(\Delta M/M)^{1/2} = bV^{1/2},$$

which may also be written as

$$(\Delta M/M) = dV, \tag{4–28}$$

where a, b, and d are all constants. Thus, the resolution, $(M/\Delta M)$, is inversely dependent upon the ion injection energy. If the ion injection energy is reduced from 70 to 35 volts, the resolution doubles, as shown in Figure 4–18.

It is interesting that the number of rf periods the ions need to experience for a given resolution in the monopole is nearly a factor of three less than the number of periods necessary in the quadrupole mass spectrometer. It should be noted here that because U, V_0, and V are held constant and the frequency is varied to scan the mass spectrum, all ions that are focused to the detector will experience the same number of rf periods in the analyzing field. Therefore, a constant resolving power over the entire mass range is obtained.

von Zahn (52) used an electron bombardment ion source (emission current of about 1 ma) to produce the positive ions, which were repelled from the ion source, accelerated through a potential drop of about 40 to 100 volts and then injected into the monopole field through a 2 mm² V-shaped diaphragm very near the "trough" of the right-angle electrode. A 36-mm^2 triangular exit diaphragm at the end of the 27-cm-long monopole field permitted the focused ions to fall on a 3×3 cm^2 foil detector a few millimeters beyond the exit diaphragm. Current measurements were made using a vibrating reed electrometer. Sensitivities of 7 to 430 μamp per mm (Hg) were reported under various conditions (52).

At the present time there is apparently only one commercial source of the monopole mass spectrometer (see Section 5.2). It appears very likely that this mass spectrometer design will receive a greater amount of attention in the near future and that this, together with the many possible uses for this instrument, may prompt other manufacturers to make this type of mass spectrometer available commercially.

4.11 MISCELLANEOUS

Many other types of instruments have not been treated in the preceding discussions, largely because of space limitations. However, one should note that E. G. Johnson and A. O. Nier (53) have designed a double-focusing mass spectrometer in which both the electrostatic and the magnetic sectors are of 90° design, with $r_e = 15.00$ in. and $r_H = 12.00$ in. Theoretical resolution is about 20,000. Associated Electrical Industries, Ltd., produces commercially a Nier-Johnson instrument as model number MS-9, primarily intended for high-resolution studies of organic compounds. Its ion accelerating voltage can be 3 to 8 kv, giving a mass range of $m/e = 2$ to 2000, with a magnetic field of up to 12,000 gauss.

W. Tretner (54) has designed and constructed a modification of an omegatron in order to eliminate the magnet requirement. The new mass spectrometer (or mass spectroscope) has been termed a *Farvitron*, and features a linear oscillation of the ions caused by a high-frequency electric field. This rf electric field replaces the magnetic field present in the omegatron. Reich and Flecken (55) have also studied the Farvitron for use in residual gas analysis. The resolution of the Farvitron is low (between 10 and 20), and "ghosts" due to higher and lower harmonics of the rf field appear at masses of $\frac{1}{4}$ and 4 times that of a given ion. The instrument discriminates in favor of higher masses (lower frequencies) so that the height of the peaks in the mass spectrum obtained gives only a rough indication of partial pressures. The resonant oscillatory frequency of an ion of mass m and charge e is given by

$$\nu = (k/L)\sqrt{\Phi/(m/e)}, \tag{4–29}$$

where k is a constant, L is the distance between the electric field plates, and Φ is the potential of the electric field. For $L = 38$ mm, $\Phi = 1000$ volts, ν is

1.6 Mc/sec for the hydrogen molecule-ion (54). The instrument presents fast response, easy amplification of ion currents, and rapid recording possibilities.

A coincidence mass spectrometer, developed by W. H. Johnston Laboratories, Inc., Baltimore, Maryland, for the U.S. Atomic Energy Commission, has been partially described (56). The electron lost upon ionization of a molecule in the ion source under an electron beam intensity of about 10^{-12} amp or less, is directed to an electron detector while the positive ion is drawn off in the opposite direction to an ion detector. The flight time of the electron to its detector is about 10 nsec, a time negligibly short in comparison to the flight time of the positive ion. The flight time of the positive ion, as in the linear pulsed time-of-flight mass spectrometer (see Chapters 3 and 4), is proportional to $(m/e)^{1/2}$. It is stated that since the number of molecules ionized per unit time is very small, the electron lost and the resultant positive ion can be studied by coincidence techniques. This allows the use of this mass spectrometer for studies of metastable transitions (see Section 6.4) too fast to be conveniently studied by other mass spectrometers. Also, the energy distribution of the electrons lost upon ionization and multiple ionization processes may be investigated. More recently, Vestal, Wahrhaftig, and Johnston (57, 58) have described the operation of the coincidence mass spectrometer.

In the usual mass spectrometer, it is necessary to reverse the polarities of both the magnetic field and the ion accelerating potential in order to study negative ions with the same instrument used for positive ion analysis. Inouye (59) has recently described a helicoid-type mass spectrometer in which both positive and negative ions describe helical paths in the same axial direction in the magnetic field of the instrument, but with opposite rotatory directions. He has extended the use of the instrument to the study of both positive and negative ions by continuously scanning from a negative to a positive value (without any change in the magnetic field direction) of the accelerating potential (60).

Some other commercially available mass spectrometers and mass spectrographs will be described and discussed briefly in Chapter 5.

REFERENCES

1. A. O. Nier, *Rev. Sci. Instr.*, **11**, 212 (1940).
2. J. A. Hipple, *J. Appl. Phys.*, **13**, 551 (1942).
3. A. O. Nier, *Rev. Sci. Instr.*, **18**, 398 (1947).
4. A. O. Nier, W. R. Eckelmann, and R. A. Lupton, *Anal. Chem.*, **34**, 1358 (1962).
5. J. H. Reynolds, *Rev. Sci. Instr.*, **27**, 928 (1956).
6. W. C. Wiley and I. H. McLaren, *Rev. Sci. Instr.*, **26**, 1150 (1955).

7. D. B. Harrington and R. S. Gohlke, "High Resolution Time-of-Flight Mass Spectrometer," 10th annual meeting of the ASTM Committee E-14 on Mass Spectrometry, New Orleans, La., June 3–8, 1962.

8. W. H. Bennett, *J. Appl. Phys.*, **21**, 143 (1950).

9. W. H. Bennett, "The Non-Magnetic Radio-Frequency Mass Spectrometer," in *Mass Spectroscopy in Physics Research*, National Bureau of Standards Circular No. 522, 1953, pp. 111–114.

10. M. H. Studier, "Continuous Ion Source for the Bendix Time of Flight Mass Spectrometer," 11th annual meeting of the ASTM Committee E-14 on Mass Spectrometry, San Francisco, Calif., May 19–24, 1963.

11. J. W. Townsend, Jr., *Rev. Sci. Instr.*, **23**, 538 (1952).

12. H. Sommer, H. A. Thomas, and J. A. Hipple, *Phys. Rev.*, **76**, 1877 (1949); **82**, 697 (1951).

13. I. Brodie, *Rev. Sci. Instr.*, **34**, 1271 (1963).

14. H. Sommer, H. A. Thomas, and J. A. Hipple, *Phys. Rev.*, **78**, 332 (1950).

15. D. Lichtman, *J. Appl. Phys.*, **31**, 1213 (1960).

16. D. S. Stark, *Vacuum*, **9**, 288 (1959).

17. E. J. Zdanuk, R. Bierig, L. G. Rubin, and S. I. Wolsky, *Vacuum*, **10**, 382 (1960).

18. J. S. Wagener and P. T. Marth, *J. Appl. Phys.*, **28**, 1027 (1957).

19. D. Alpert and R. S. Buritz, *J. Appl. Phys.*, **25**, 202 (1954).

20. A. Hebling and D. Lichtman, "Fragment Patterns and Appearance Potentials Using the Omegatron Mass Spectrometer," 9th annual meeting of the ASTM Committee E-14 on Mass Spectrometry, Chicago, Ill., June 4–9, 1961.

21. C. E. Berry, *J. Appl. Phys.*, **25**, 28 (1954).

22. G. Schuchhardt, *Vacuum*, **10**, 373 (1960).

23. A. Klopfer and W. Schmidt, *Vacuum*, **10**, 363 (1960).

24. A. G. Edwards, *Brit. J. Appl. Phys.*, **6**, 44 (1955).

25. R. L. Bell, *J. Sci. Instr.*, **33**, 269 (1956).

26. R. J. Warnecke, Jr., *Ann. radioelec.*, **12**, 258 (1957); *Vacuum*, **10**, 49 (1960).

27. W. A. Morgan, G. Jernakoff, and K. P. Lanneau, *Ind. Eng. Chem.*, **46**, 1404 (1954).

28. J. A. Hipple, Jr., and W. Bleakney, *Phys. Rev.*, **49**, 884 (1936); **53**, 521 (1938).

29. H. W. Voorhies, C. F. Robinson, L. G. Hall, W. M. Brubaker, and C. E. Berry, "Theoretical and Experimental Study of High-Mass High-Resolution Mass Spectrometers," in *Advances in Mass Spectrometry*, Vol. 1, J. D. Waldron (ed.), Pergamon Press, London, 1959, pp. 44–65.

30. A. J. Dempster, *Proc. Am. Phil. Soc.*, **75**, 755 (1935).

31. J. Mattauch, *Phys. Rev.*, **50**, 617 and 1089 (1936).

32. K. T. Bainbridge and E. B. Jordan, *Phys. Rev.*, **50**, 282 (1936).
33. R. Herzog, *Z. Physik*, **89**, 447 (1934).
34. J. Mattauch and R. Herzog, *Z. Physik*, **89**, 786 (1934).
35. A. E. Cameron, in *Physical Methods in Chemical Analysis*, Vol. 4, W. G. Berl (ed.), Academic Press, New York, 1961, pp. 119–32.
36. M. L. Smith, *Electromagnetically Enriched Isotopes and Mass Spectrometry*, Proceedings of the Harwell Conference, Sept. 13–16, Academic Press, New York, 1956.
37. R. Bernas, J. L. Sarrouy, and J. Camplan, in *Electromagnetic Separation of Radioactive Isotopes*, M. J. Higatsberger and F. P. Viehböck (eds.), Springer-Verlag, Vienna, 1961, pp. 121–40.
38. W. Paul and H. Steinwedel, *Z. Naturforsch.*, **8A**, 448 (1953).
39. W. Paul and M. Raether, *Z. Physik*, **140**, 262 (1955).
40. W. Paul and H. P. Reinhard, "Electric Mass Spectrometer for Isotope Separation," in *Proc. Intern. Symposium Isotope Separation*, Amsterdam, 1957 (published 1958), pp. 640–52.
41. W. Paul, H. P. Reinhard, and U. von Zahn, *Z. Physik*, **152**, 143 (1958).
42. R. Köhler, W. Paul, K. Schmidt and U. von Zahn, in *Proc. Intern. Conf. Nuclidic Masses*, H. E. Duckworth (ed.), University of Toronto Press, Toronto, Canada, 1960, p. 507.
43. F. von Busch and W. Paul, *Z. Physik*, **164**, 581 and 588 (1961).
44. W. M. Brubaker, "The Quadrupole Mass Filter," *Neuvieme Colloq. Spectroscopicum Intern.*, Lyon, France, June 5–10, 1961; W. M. Brubaker and J. Tuul, "The Influence of Ion Entrance Aperture Size and Excitation Frequency on the Performance of a Satellite Quadrupole Mass Filter," 11th annual meeting of the ASTM Committee E-14 on Mass Spectrometry, San Francisco, Calif., May 19–24, 1963; *Rev. Sci. Instr.*, **35**, 1007 (1964).
45. U. von Zahn, S. Gebauer, and W. Paul, "A Quadrupole Spectrometer for Precision Mass Measurements," 10th annual meeting of the ASTM Committee E-14 on Mass Spectrometry, New Orleans, La., June 3–8, 1962.
46. H. G. Bennewitz and R. Wedemeyer, *Z. Physik*, **172**, 1 (1963).
47. E. Jahnke, F. Emde, and F. Lösch, *Tables of Higher Functions*, sixth edition, McGraw-Hill Book Company, New York, 1960, p. 263; G. Blanch, "Mathieu Functions," in *Handbook of Mathematical Functions*, National Bureau of Standards, Applied Mathematics Series, No. 55, M. Abramowitz and I. A. Stegun (eds.), U. S. Government Printing Office, Washington, D. C., June, 1964, pp. 721–50.
48. N. W. McLachlan, *Theory and Applications of Mathieu Functions*, Oxford at the Clarendon Press, London, 1947, 401 pp.; Dover Publications, Inc., New York, 1964.
49. E. Fischer, *Z. Physik*, **156**, 1 (1959).
50. J. Vail, *Can. J. Phys.*, **42**, 329 (1964).

51. E. T. Whittaker and G. N. Watson, *A Course in Modern Analysis*, fourth edition, Cambridge University Press, London, 1940, pp. 404–28.

52. U. von Zahn, *Rev. Sci. Instr.*, **34**, 1 (1963).

53. E. G. Johnson and A. O. Nier, *Phys. Rev.*, **91**, 10 (1953).

54. W. Tretner, *Z. angew. Physik*, **11**, 395 (1959); *Vacuum*, **10**, 31 (1960); *Z. angew. Physik*, **14**, 23 (1962).

55. G. Reich and F. Flecken, *Vacuum*, **10**, 35 (1960).

56. *Chem. and Eng. News*, p. 84, June 18, 1962; U. S. Patent No. *2,999,157*; G. B. Bailey, *Report No. FC-4328*, Garrett Corporation, May 14, 1963.

57. M. L. Vestal, M. Krauss, A. L. Wahrhaftig, and W. H. Johnston, "The Coincidence Mass Spectrometer," 11th annual meeting of the ASTM Committee E-14 on Mass Spectrometry, San Francisco, Calif. May 19–24, 1963.

58. M. L. Vestal, A. L. Wahrhaftig, and W. H. Johnston, "Fast Metastable Decompositions in the Mass Spectrometer," presented at the "Symposium on Unimolecular Reactions in the Mass Spectrometer and Related Topics in Chemical Kinetics," Division of Physical Chemistry, American Chemical Society, Salt Lake City, Utah, July 7–10, 1963.

59. H. Inouye, *Jap. J. Appl. Phys.*, **3**, 215 (1964).

60. H. Inouye, *Jap. J. Appl. Phys.*, **3**, 306 (1964).

CHAPTER 5

COMMERCIAL INSTRUMENTS

Presently, there are available more than 50 different commercial models of various types of mass spectrometers which are manufactured by more than 12 industrial organizations and marketed by at least 20 different companies. The commercially available mass spectrometers and mass spectrographs are used for many different purposes, including chemical studies; metallurgical and chemical analyses; solids analyses and impurity measurements; isotopic ratio determinations; high-temperature work; partial pressure, residual gas and respiratory measurements; and leak detection.

In this chapter we shall discuss briefly most of the commercial mass spectrometers and mass spectrographs produced in England, Germany, Japan, and the United States. Although mass spectrometers are manufactured in the Soviet Union (1), the author is not familiar with the details of the commercially available Russian instruments.

There are several ways to group and discuss these instruments. But since the type of instrument often influences greatly the uses of the instrument, in this discussion the instruments have been separated into two broad divisions based essentially on resolution (which is related to versatility). Within the discussions of the instrument types, the manufacturers of the instruments will be taken up in alphabetical order.

Much of the data given in tabular form in this chapter has been gleaned from the various brochures and advertisements of the manufacturers. In some instances, certain models may have since been modified, causing changes in the data for their units. Therefore the characteristics listed in Tables 5–1 to 5–5 should be taken as generalizations; specific information would best be obtained directly from the manufacturer or his representative.

One important piece of information has been omitted from all of the tables: the cost of the instrumentation. In several cases, quotations are good only for a short period of time, and before this chapter could be written, the price would be obsolete. In other cases, costs depend significantly upon various modifications of a given model and upon accessories purchased with the basic instrumentation. Therefore, no specific costs have been given. However, the price range of mass spectrometers (including leak detectors and partial pressure analyzers) runs from less than \$5000 to more than \$100,000.

Because the specific information about detailed characteristics, accessories, and costs should be obtained directly from the manufacturer or his representative, a list of manufacturers and representatives has been included in Section 5.3. The symbols used to identify the various companies in Tables 5–1 to 5–5 are included in the list in Section 5–3.

In Tables 5–1 to 5–5, several abbreviations are employed. These are the following:

p = permanent magnet,
r = radius of curvature (in the magnetic field),
em = electromagnetic analysis,
PP = photographic plates,
DCA = direct current amplifier (with Faraday cup),
SEM = secondary electron multiplier,
VRE = vibrating reed electrometer (with Faraday cup).

It is difficult to define precisely the mass range of an instrument. It is still more difficult to give an exact resolving power for each instrument, since it depends on slit widths and the definitions of resolving power chosen. However, approximate ranges and resolving powers have been given for comparative purposes.

It is interesting to note that commercial mass spectrometers are not small business. The total U. S. market is of the order of \$5,000,000 annually. To date, Consolidated Electrodynamics Corporation (CEC) has sold the bulk of these (about 700 CEC mass spectrometers). As pointed out above, there are many new companies now manufacturing mass spectrometers. Most of these will be discussed in the following sections.

5.1 INSTRUMENTS WITH RESOLUTION > 100

Although somewhat arbitrarily, we shall consider those instruments with resolution >100 separate from those with resolution <50. Fortunately,

TABLE 5–1. SOME CHARACTERISTICS OF COMMERCIAL SINGLE-FOCUSING INSTRUMENTS

Company	Model Number	Instrument Type	Magnetic Field Deflection		Approx. Mass Range (amu)	Approx. Resolving Power	Detector
			r (cm)	H (gauss)			
AEI	MS-2	em, 90° sector	15.0		2–450	225	DCA or SEM
AEI	MS-3	em, 90° sector	10.0		2–130	100	DCA
AEI	MS-5	em	30.5		6–380	300–1000	DCA or SEM
Atlas	CH-4	em, 60° sector			1–1400	1500	DCA or SEM
Atlas	M-86	em, 180°	6.5	4200p.	2–100	100	DCA
Atlas	UF	em, 60° sector				400	DCA
CEC	21–103C	em, 180°	12.7	800–6000	2–700	500	DCA
CEC	21–130	cycloidal	(focal = 1.1 in.)	4500p.	2–230	200	DCA
CEC	21–620A	cycloidal		p.	2–150	100	DCA
GE	AMS	em, 60° sector			1–650	700	DCA
Hitachi	RMC-1	em, 90° sector	13.5			150	DCA
Hitachi	RMD-3	em, 60° sector	5.0	1400p.	1–4		DCA
Hitachi	RMS-3	em, 60° sector	10.0		1–150		DCA
Hitachi	RMU-6A	em, 90° sector	20.0	400–7000	1–500	>300	VRE or SEM
Mitsubishi	MS-415	em, 60° sector	15.0	to 10,000	1–200	150	DCA or VRE
Nuclide	G-1	em, 60° sector	15.2			500	
Nuclide	RMS-2	em, 60° sector	15.2	200–6000		130	VRE or SEM
Nuclide	RSS	em, 60° sector	11.4	to 7000		130	VRE or SEM
Nuclide	SU/HT-12-60	em, 60° sector	30.5	to 10,000	>400	2000	VRE or SEM
Nuclide	12-90-G	em, 90° sector	30.5	to 9000	1–3000	2000	SEM
Nuclide	TZD/TDD	em, 90°, tandem	30.5			1000	VRE
Nuclide	WD	em, 60° sector	15.2				
P & I	M-60-SA	em, 60° sector	15.2		1–100		DCA
SpectroMag		em, 180°	65.0				PP

there are no instruments considered in this chapter with $50 < R < 100$. Most of the instruments with $R > 100$ are rather versatile and have been used in many different applications. We wish now to consider these instruments. We shall first note the single-focusing units, then the double-focusing and time-of-flight mass spectrometers, and then a few other commercial instruments.

SINGLE-FOCUSING INSTRUMENTS

Nearly half of the commercially available instruments are single-focusing instruments. In general, these instruments are quite versatile, with applications including isotopic and chemical analyses, gas analyses, process monitoring, high-vacuum studies, and high-temperature applications. Specific uses for each instrument are not listed in Table 5–1, for it would make the table unduly long and repetitious if all the applications were counted and set down on paper. Instead, we shall consider a few of the characteristics of each of the instruments listed in Table 5–1.

The Associated Electrical Industries (AEI) MS-3 is a general-use instrument, whereas the greater resolving power of the MS-2 makes it somewhat more versatile, with a long list of uses. AEI manufactures the MS-2 series in several different modifications to optimize its use in certain applications. The AEI MS-5, with its very high resolution was developed to allow surface ionization of solids and to isotopically analyze various solids.

The Atlas CH-4, with its high resolution, allows it to be used in studying a large number of different types of problems. The M-86 model produced by Atlas is designed for chemical analyses of lower molecular weight compounds and for isotopic ratio measurements. The Atlas UF mass spectrometer is designed to determine the U^{235}/U^{238} isotopic ratios with UF_6 samples (2). Other corrosive gases can also be studied in the UF mass spectrometer.

The CEC model 21–103C has become one of the standard items of equipment in many industrial and academic laboratories, particularly in the United States. With its high resolution and mass range, and using heated inlet systems to extend the working vapor pressure range with different compounds, this mass spectrometer has become the best known of these instruments in the United States. A photograph of the CEC 21–103C is shown in Figure 5–1.

The CEC 21–620A cycloidal mass spectrometer was developed for simpler analytical applications and for process or stream monitoring. It has now grown into the new CEC model 21–130 with extended mass range and higher resolving power, giving it more versatility in chemical applications. The CEC 21–130 is shown in Figure 5–2.

The General Electric analytical mass spectrometer, with large mass range and high resolution, is no longer produced commercially.

Hitachi, of Japan, has been building mass spectrometers since about

Fig. 5-1. The CEC 21-103C mass spectrometer. (Courtesy of Consolidated Electrodynamics Corporation, Pasadena, California.)

Fig. 5-2. The cycloidal focused CEC 21-130 mass spectrometer. (Courtesy of Consolidated Electrodynamics Corporation, Pasadena, California).

1952, and now markets several instruments. The model RMD-3 is restricted in its mass range to 1–4 amu, since it was built specifically to do hydrogen-deuterium analyses. The RMC-1 is a lower resolving power instrument, whereas the RMU-6A has a much increased resolving power and versatility. The RMU-6A is marketed in the United States by the Perkin-Elmer Corporation. A photograph of the RMU-6A is given in Figure 5–3. The Hitachi RMU-6D, similar to the RMU-6A, but with greater resolution, will accomodate an accessory unit to convert the single-focusing instrument to a double-focusing mass spectrometer with a resolution greater than 12,000 and a mass range extending to 1500 amu.

Mitsubishi Electric manufactures two mass spectrometers, one of which is the MS-415, listed in Table 5–1. This is a medium mass range and resolution mass spectrometer suited to the analysis of gaseous and liquid samples of lower molecular weights.

Nuclide Analysis Associates produce a large variety of mass spectrometers, many of them custom-built. The Nuclide model G-1, with high resolution, is also suited to high-vacuum analysis. The RMS-2 is employed in isotope-ratio determinations and gas analysis, as is the RSS model. The

Fig. 5-3. Photograph of the Hitachi model RMU-6A mass spectrometer. (Courtesy of the Perkin-Elmer Corporation, Norwalk Connecticut.)

RSS is a commercial version of the Reynolds mass spectrometer and may be used for the analysis of very small quantities of a gaseous sample by a static technique. The RSS also may find application as a residual gas analyzer.

The high-resolution Nuclide model 12–60 is shown in Figure 5–4. This type of mass spectrometer can be used for the precise determination of isotopic ratios with either a multiple-filament source or an electron bombardment ion source. Neutron cross-section measurements have also been made with this instrument. The HT design is adapted with a high-temperature unit to study vaporization of solids. The SU model with a multiple-filament surface ionization ion source can be used for isotopic analysis of solids and radioactivity age determinations, and the model 12-90-G is designed for organic analysis.

Coupling two 90° deflection sector mass spectrometers in tandem produces the Nuclide TZD/TDD models. The TZD model has a "C" configuration (with zero dispersion) and the TDD model has an "S" configuration (with double dispersion). With good magnet current and ion accelerating

Fig. 5-4. The Nuclide Analysis Associates' model 12–60 mass spectrometer. (Courtesy of Nuclide Corporation, State College, Pennsylvania.)

voltage stabilization, together with high resolution, this instrument has an abundance sensitivity of a million or more for the uranium isotopes, and hence is used to measure precisely the presence in very minor amounts of other isotopes in uranium samples. A photograph of the TZD tandem mass spectrometer is shown in Figure 5–5.

The Nuclide model WD mass spectrometer has been used in isotope ratio determinations, and specifically for hydrogen-deuterium ratio analyses.

Process and Instruments produce, in addition to mass spectrometer analyzer tubes and other components, a model M-60-SA for gas analysis. Spectromagnetic Industries manufactures a large 180° broad-range mass spectrograph.

In the single-focusing mass spectrometer, the resolving power is usually less than 1000, whereas the double-focusing instruments have resolution ranging up to about 20,000. Let us turn our attention next to these double-focusing mass spectrometers and spectrographs.

Fig. 5-5. Photograph of Nuclide Analysis Associates' model TZD tandem mass spectrometer. (Courtesy of Nuclide Corporation, State College, Pennsylvania.)

DOUBLE-FOCUSING INSTRUMENTS

The double-focusing instruments of the Mattauch-Herzog type have only recently been produced commercially. In Section 4.7 we mentioned the Mattauch-type instrument and that AEI and CEC manufactured these instruments. In addition, Atlas and Mitsubishi also produce these commercially. Table 5–2 lists some of the characteristics of these instruments. A schematic diagram of the AEI MS-7 is shown in Figure 5–6, and photographs of the Atlas SM-1 and the CEC 21–110 Mattauch mass spectrometers are shown in Figures 5–7 and 5–8, respectively.

With gaseous electron bombardment and photoionization ion sources, electronic detection, and their very wide mass range and tremendous resolving power, these instruments will undoubtedly aid in the studies of mass spectra as well as continue to make significant contributions in the analysis of solids, the search for new isotopes, high-temperature studies, and impurity analyses.

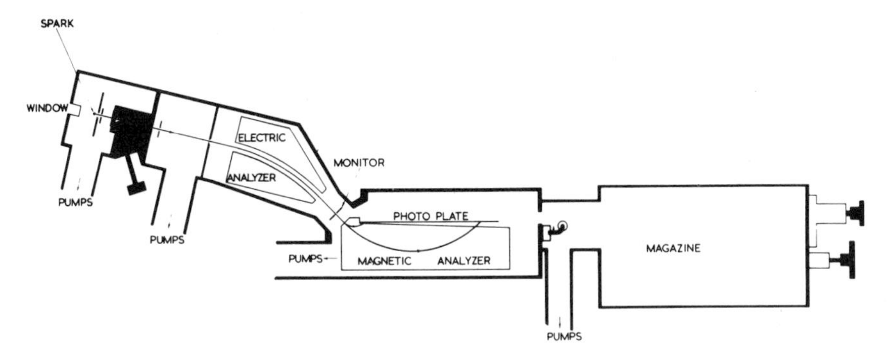

Fig. 5-6. Schematic diagram of the AEI MS-7 mass spectrometer. (Courtesy of the Picker X-ray Corporation, White Plains, New York.)

Fig. 5-7. The Atlas SM-1 mass spectrometer and spectrograph. (Courtesy of Applied Physics Corporation, Monrovia, California.)

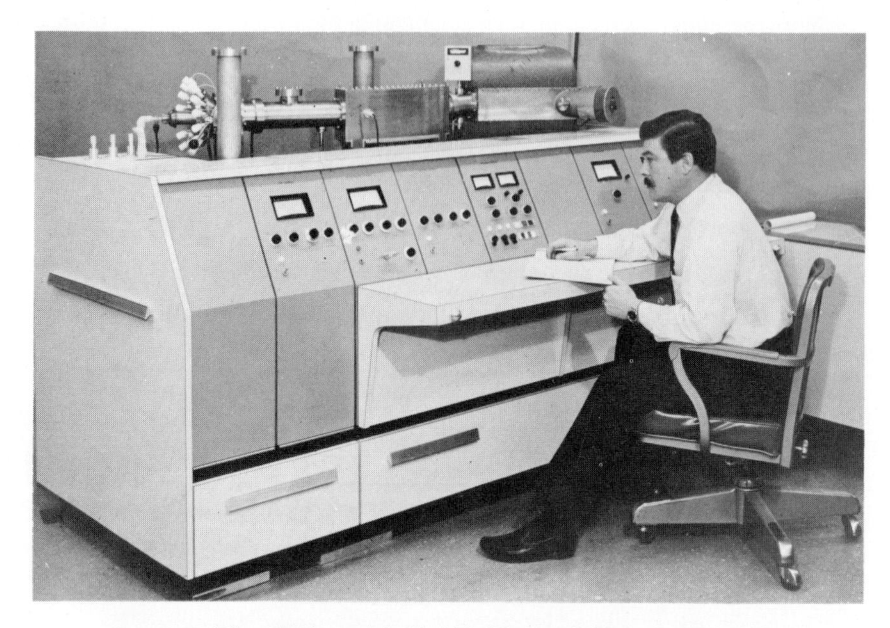

Fig. 5-8. The CEC model 21–110 Mattauch-Herzog type mass spectrometer and spectrograph. (Courtesy of Consolidated Electrodynamics Corporation, Pasadena, California).

TIME-OF-FLIGHT INSTRUMENTS

The principles of the time-of-flight mass spectrometer were discussed in Chapter 4. Table 5–3 summarizes the general characteristics of the Bendix time-of-flight and notes that Hokushin in Tokyo also markets a time-of-flight instrument.

A photograph of a Bendix model 12–101 mass spectrometer is shown in Figure 5–9. The Bendix mass spectrometers are rather versatile although not of very large resolving power. The lengthening of the drift tube and the use of near-continuous operation, as reported by Studier and discussed in Section 4.3, makes the linear pulsed time-of-flight instrument even more attractive. Time-of-flight mass spectrometers are used in a wide variety of ways, including in stream gas chromatography sample analyses, high-temperature studies, appearance potential determinations, fast reaction kinetic investigations, and others.

OTHER INSTRUMENTS

It was mentioned above that none of the instruments considered in this chapter have $50 < R < 100$. Actually, the omegatron-type mass spectrometer, formerly marketed by General Electric as their ion resonance mass spectrometer, has a variable resolution, as was shown in Section 4.4. Thus,

TABLE 5–2. SOME CHARACTERISTICS OF COMMERCIAL DOUBLE-FOCUSING INSTRUMENTS

Company	Model Number	Instrument Type	Field Deflection		Approx. Mass Range (amu)	Approx. Resolving Power	Detector
			r (cm)	H (gauss)			
AEI	MS-7	em, Mattauch, 90°	38.1	2–16,000	1–240	1000–2500	PP
AEI	MS-9	em, Nier	30.5	to 12,000	2–3000	10,000 max.	DCA or SEM
Atlas	SM-1	em, Mattauch, 76°			1–5000	5000–20,000	PP or DCA
CEC	21–110	em, Mattauch, 90°	30.5	to 12,500	2–5000	to 20,000	PP or SEM
Jeolco	JMS-01S	em, Mattauch, 90°	20.0	to 12,000	1–2000	20,000	PP or DCA
Mitsubishi	MS-115	em, Mattauch, 90°	15.0	to 20,000	1–600	500–3000	PP or DCA
Nuclide	Graf-2	em, 90°	30.0	to 15,000		3000	PP, DCA, or SEM

TABLE 5–3. SOME CHARACTERISTICS OF COMMERCIAL TIME-OF-FLIGHT INSTRUMENTS

Company	Model Number	Instrument Type	Mass Analysis	Approx. Mass Range (amu)	Approx. Resolving Power	Detector
Bendix	12–100	Time-of-flight	100–170 cm drift tube	1–700	150–250	SEM
Bendix	12–101	Time-of-flight	100–170 cm drift tube	1–700	150–250	SEM
Bendix	14–100	Time-of-flight	100–170 cm drift tube	1–700	150–250	SEM
Bendix	14–101	Time-of-flight	100–170 cm drift tube	1–700	150–250	SEM
Bendix	17–210	Time-of-flight	Drift tube	0–250	130	SEM
Bendix	17–210V	Time-of-flight	Drift tube	0–250	130	SEM
Hokushin	S–010	Time-of-flight	A Bendix time-of-flight mass spectrometer			

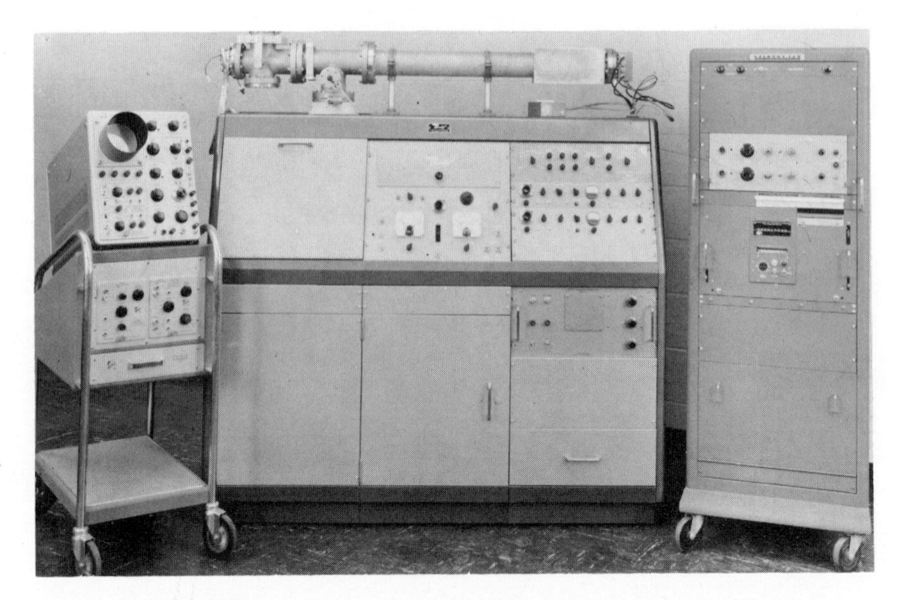

Fig. 5-9. The Bendix model 12 time-of-flight mass spectrometer. (Courtesy of the Bendix Corporation, Cincinatti Division, Cincinatti, Ohio.)

at some mass values, the resolution would lie between 50 and 100. However, for the higher mass range, the resolution is rather poor; hence, this instrument is treated more properly in Section 5.2. Although it has a high resolution at low mass values, the limitation of mass range then causes a serious decrease in versatility.

Another mass spectrometer which has only recently become available commercially is the quadrupole instrument, devised by W. Paul, *et al.* (3–8) We have examined the principles of operation of the electric quadrupole mass spectrometer earlier (see Section 4.9). Recall, however, that there are no magnets in this instrument. Also, it has a rather nice feature in that its operation is not dependent on the input energy of the ions. There are three commercially available quadrupole mass spectrometers. One is manufactured by Alloyd Electronics Corporation and another by Atlas. The Alloyd quadrupole unit is stated to have mass range of 1–800 amu and uses either a dc amplifier or a secondary electron multiplier. The Atlas unit, the AMP-3, has a mass range of 2–100 amu and an approximate resolving power, $\Delta M/M$, of 100. The Atlas unit also uses either a dc amplifier or a secondary electron multiplier (9). A few more words will be said about the Atlas quadrupole mass spectrometer in Section 5.2. A third quadrupole instrument is manufactured by Electronic Associates, Inc.

5.2 INSTRUMENTS WITH RESOLUTION < 50

Mass spectrometers with resolution <50 are not as versatile as those with resolution >100. Nonetheless, there are a number of applications for such instruments, and there are many basic studies which can be done with them. We shall see that some of these units are single-focusing sector field electromagnetic instruments in which permanent magnets are employed, and the mass range is scanned electrostatically.

Foremost among the applications of these lower resolving power instruments are their use as partial pressure analyzers, residual gas analyzers, light gas stream analyzers and process monitors, respiratory gas analyzers, and leak detectors. First, let us look briefly at the general category of instruments for partial pressure and residual gas analysis, and then at the instruments available for leak detection.

PARTIAL PRESSURE AND RESIDUAL GAS ANALYZERS

All but two of the commercial partial pressure analyzers and residual gas analyzers currently available are of the single-focusing electromagnetic

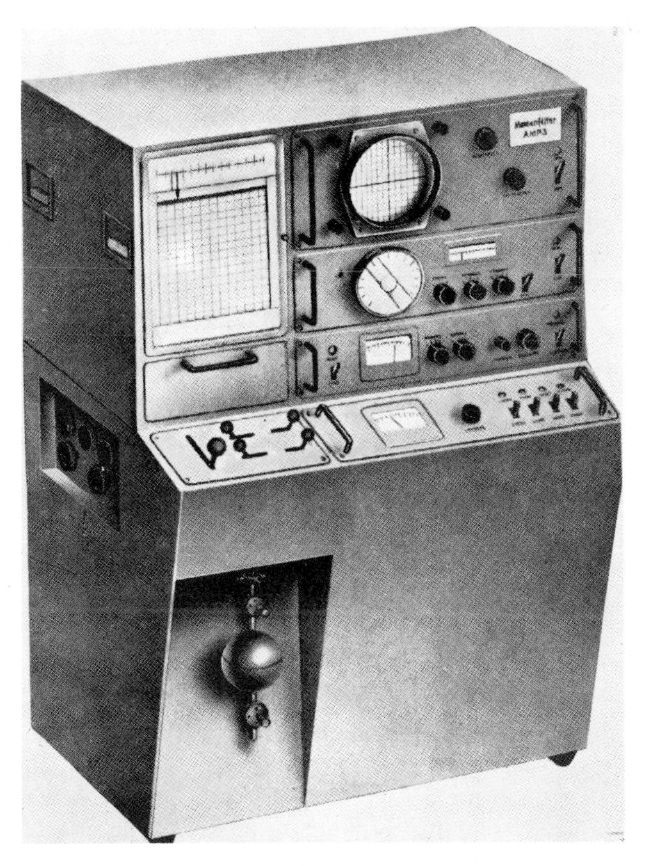

Fig. 5-10. The Atlas model AMP-3 quadrupole mass spectrometer. (Courtesy of Applied Physics Corporation, Monrovia, California.)

type. The two exceptions are the quadrupole and the omegatron mass spectrometers, which were discussed in Section 5.1.

A photograph of the Atlas AMP-3 electric quadrupole is shown in Figure 5–10. The quadrupole offers an advantage here in requiring no magnet. Note that the other partial pressure and residual gas analyzers listed in Table 5–4 all use permanent magnets, and that they all use dc amplifiers rather than the more sophisticated (and expensive) vibrating reed electrometers or secondary electron multipliers. Recently, Electronic Associates, Inc. (EAI) have produced a quadrupole instrument, as noted above.

Table 5–4 lists the various mass spectrometers used for partial pressure and residual gas analyses, and respiratory gas analyses. Also indicated in this table are some of the characteristics of these instruments. AEI offers two instruments in this category. One, the MS-10, is shown in Figure 5–11.

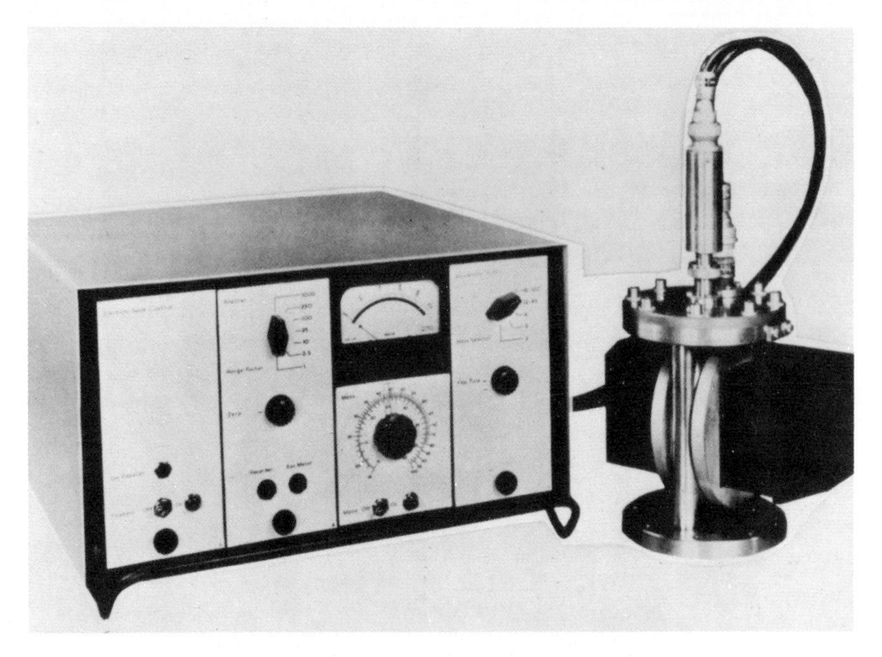

Fig. 5-11. Photograph of the Associated Electrical Industries' model MS-10 mass spectrometer. (Courtesy of Picker X-ray Corporation.)

The other, the model MS-4, is commonly found in hospitals and clinics for respiratory gas analyses, although it can be used as a simple monitor. The Atlas model AN mass spectrometer may be used for leak detection as well as for process monitoring. By modifying the model AN (to give a new model, M) to obtain greater mass range and increased resolution, the instrument may be used for respiratory gas analyses.

Also listed in Table 5–4 is a monopole unit (see Section 4.10) which just has been marketed by the General Electric Company. The monopole should have great promise as a partial pressure and residual gas analyzer.

LEAK DETECTORS

Five different leak detectors are listed in Table 5–5. Quite obviously any mass spectrometer might be used as a leak detector, but those listed in Table 5–5 are specifically intended for such applications, with two exceptions: those which do not have a fixed mass analysis at $m/e = 4$. The Atlas model AN has a variable mass range, although it possesses poor resolving power, and may be used also in residual gas analysis and other applications of analysis of simple gaseous materials, as discussed above. By modifying the Atlas AN, the Atlas model M can be obtained, with a larger mass range and improved resolution, as mentioned above.

The other exception, the Hitachi RMD–3, has a very limited mass range, but is intended specifically for hydrogen-deuterium analyses. However, it might also be considered in the leak detector category. The other three leak detectors listed in Table 5–5 employ permanent magnets and accelerating voltages that are variable over a short range in order to optimize the focus of the He^+ ions at $m/e = 4$ on the detectors. Figure 5–12 illustrates the helium leak detector.

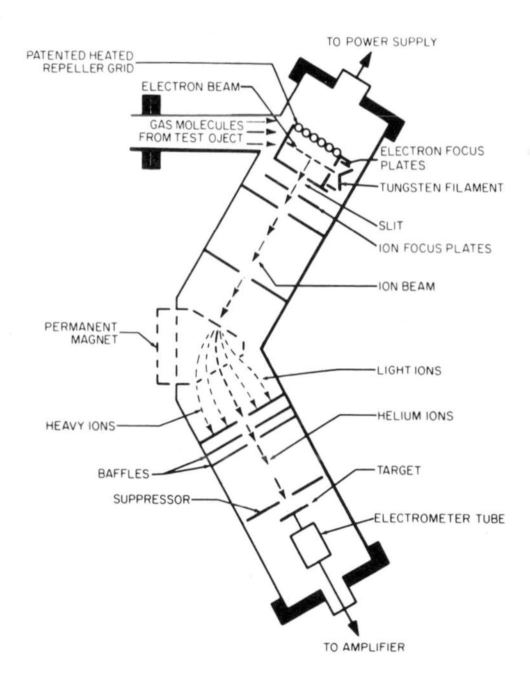

Fig. 5-12. Schematic diagram of the "vee tube" in the Vacuum-Electronics Corporation mass spectrometer leak detector, MS-9.

TABLE 5–4. SOME CHARACTERISTICS OF COMMERCIAL PARTIAL PRESSURE AND RESIDUAL GAS ANALYZERS

Company	Model Number	Instrument Type	Magnetic Field Deflection		Approx. Mass Range (amu)	Approx. Resolving Power	Detector
			r (cm)	H (gauss)			
AEI	MS-4	em, 180°	5.0	p.	17–50	50	DCA
AEI	MS-10	em, 180°	5.0	1800p.	2–100	40	DCA
Atlas	AMP-3	quadrupole	None		2–100	100	DCA or SEM
Atlas	AN				4–46	18	DCA
CEC	21–611	em, 180°		3900p.	2–80	32	DCA
CEC	21–612	em, 180°		3900p.	2–80	20	DCA
EAI	—	quadrupole	None		1–500	>100	SEM
GE	514	em, 90° sector	5.0	3000p.	2–50	40	DCA
GE	IRMS	omegatron		5000p.	1–90	>50	DCA
GE	22PC150	monopole	None		1–300	200	SEM
Sylvania	SY-1301	omegatron		5000	2–80	>50	VRE
Veeco	GA-3	em, 60° sector		p.	2–90	45	DCA

TABLE 5–5. SOME CHARACTERISTICS OF COMMERCIAL LEAK DETECTORS

Company	Model Number	Instrument Type	Magnetic Field Deflection		Approx. Mass Range (amu)	Approx. Resolving Power	Detector
			r (cm)	H (gauss)			
Atlas	AN				4–46	18	DCA
CEC	24–120A	em, 180°		p.	4		DCA
GE	M-60	em, 90° sector		p.	4		DCA
Hitachi	RMD-3	em, 90° sector	5.0	1400p.	1–4		DCA
Veeco	MS-9	em, 60° sector	5.0	p.	4		DCA

It would be possible to list some other units in this category, but they have already been listed in Section 5.2, since they have a wider mass range and higher resolution.

5.3 LIST OF MANUFACTURERS AND REPRESENTATIVES

Several of the foreign manufacturers have representatives in the United States. Picker X-Ray Corporation handles the AEI mass spectrometers, Applied Physics Corporation sells the Atlas instruments, and the Perkin-Elmer Corporation markets the Hitachi mass spectrometers. In a similar manner, Atlas in Germany and Hokushin in Japan handle the Bendix time-of-flight mass spectrometers. Many of the other companies have their own overseas outlets.

One other point might be mentioned here, and that is about trade-in policies. In late 1962, CEC inaugurated a trade-in program for older instruments when purchasing newer CEC models. This resulted from their success with a similar program for their leak detector models. Although Bendix does not have a formal trade-in program, occasionally they have taken a trade-in on one of their instruments.

The following list of manufacturers and representatives is included for the convenience of those readers who may wish to inquire of specific organizations concerning their instruments. By way of acknowledgment, it should be noted also that these organizations have been of great help in supplying the author with brochures and information about their products.

1. Associated Electrical
   Industries, Ltd.—AEI
   Instrumentation Division
   Barton Dock Road, Urmston
   Manchester, England
2. Alloyd Electronics
   Corporation—Alloyd
   35 Cambridge Parkway
   Cambridge 42, Mass.
3. Applied Physics Corporation
   2724 South Peck Road
   Monrovia, Calif.
4. Atlas Mess- und Analysen
   Technik, Gmbh—Atlas
   Woltmershauser Strasse
   442–448a
   28 Bremen 10
   Postfach 4046
   Germany
5. Beckman Instruments, Inc.
   —Beckman
   Scientific and Process
   Instruments Division
   Fullerton, Calif.
6. The Bendix Corporation
   —Bendix
   Cincinnati Division
   3130 Wasson Road
   Cincinnati 8, Ohio

7. Consolidated Electrodynamics Corporation—CEC
Analytical and Control Division
360 Sierra Madre Villa
Pasadena, Calif.

8. Electronic Associates, Inc.—EAI 4151 Middlefield Road
Palo Alto, California

9. General Electric—GE
Vacuum Products Operation
Building 4
Schenectady 5, N. Y.

10. Hitachi, Ltd.—Hitachi
Tokyo, Japan

11. Hokushin—Hokushin
Tokyo, Japan

12. Japan Electron Optics Laboratory Co. (USA), Inc.—Jeolco
828 Mahler Road
Burlingame, California

13. Mitsubishi Electric Manufacturing Co.—Mitsubishi
3, 2-Chome
Marunouchi, Chiyodaku
Tokyo, Japan

14. Nuclide Analysis Associates —Nuclide
Nuclide Corporation
642 East College Avenue
State College, Pa.

15. The Perkin-Elmer Corporation
Main Avenue
Norwalk, Conn.

16. Process and Instruments—P&I
15 Stone Avenue
Brooklyn 33, N. Y.

17. Picker X-Ray Corporation
1275 Mamaroneck Avenue
White Plains, N. Y.

18. Spectromagnetic Industries —SpectroMag
25377 Huntwood Avenue
Hayward, Calif.

19. Sylvania Electric Products, Inc. —Sylvania
Seneca Falls, New York 13148

20. Vacuum-Electronics Corporation—Veeco
Terminal Drive
Plainview, Long Island, N. Y.

REFERENCES

1. V. A. Pavlenko, A. E. Rafal'son, and A. M. Shereshevskii, *Pribory i Tekh. Eksperimenta*, **3**, 3 (1958).

2. C. Brunee, "A New Mass Spectrometer for Precision Measurement of the U^{235}/U^{238} Isotopic Ratio of UF_6," in *Advances in Mass Spectrometry*, Vol. 2, R. M. Elliott (ed.), Pergamon Press, Oxford, 1963, pp. 230–43.

3. W. Paul and H. Steinwedel, *Z. Naturforsch.*, **8A**, 448 (1953).

4. W. Paul and M. Raether, *Z. Physik*, **140**, 262 (1955).

5. W. Paul and H. P. Reinhard, "Electric Mass Spectrometer for Isotope Separation," *Proc. Intnl. Symposium Isotope Separation*, Amsterdam, 1957 (published 1958), pp. 640–52.

6. W. Paul, H. P. Reinhard, and U. von Zahn, *Z. Physik*, **152**, 143 (1958).

7. U. von Zahn, S. Gebauer, and W. Paul, "A Quadrupole Spectrometer for Precision Mass Measurements," 10th annual meeting of the ASTM Committee E-14 on Mass Spectrometry, New Orleans, La., June 3–8, 1962.

8. H. G. Bennewitz and R. Wedemeyer, *Z. Physik*, **172**, 1 (1963).

9. C. Brunee, L. Delgmann, and K. Kronenberger, "The Atlas Quadrupole Mass Spectrometer," 11th annual meeting of the ASTM Committee E-14 on Mass Spectrometry, San Francisco, Calif. May 19–24, 1963.

CHAPTER 6

TYPES OF IONS IN MASS SPECTRA

The bombardment of a molecule with energetic electrons causes ionization and dissociation if the energy of the electrons is much greater than the ionization potential of the molecule. Many analytical mass spectrometers commonly employ fixed 50- or 70-volt electron beams. The energies of these electrons are more than sufficient to cause significant ionization and fragmentation in nearly all molecules, for the first ionization potential is seldom greater than 15 ev, and never is it greater than 25 ev. For electrons with energies just above the ionization potential of a molecule, ions other than the parent-molecule ion will seldom be observed. (It should be noted, however, that there are molecules, e.g., tetrachloromethane, which do not yield parent-molecule ions, even at electron energies just scarcely greater than the ionization potentials of the molecules.) As the electron energy is increased, the parent-molecule ions may be formed with excess energy in their vibrational and electronic degrees of freedom. When the parent-molecule ion is formed with sufficient excess energy to allow further dissociation of the ion, fragment ions will be observed in the mass spectrum. With quite energetic electrons, multiply charged ions also may be formed. Increasing the energy of the electrons to 50–70 volts (or even 100 volts) causes the production of a number of different types of ions in differing quantities. A plot of the relative quantities of these ions as a function of the m/e ratio produces a mass spectrum, as we have seen in earlier chapters. However, in the region of 50 or 70 volts to 100 or 120 volts, the qualitative nature of the mass spectrum almost always remains unchanged, and the quantitative nature of mass spectrum is only slightly dependent upon the electron energies in this region. In order to understand better some of these features and to prepare ourselves for the theoretical treatments of mass spectra of molecules, we shall discuss at somewhat greater length in this chapter the various types of ions formed in the ion source of a mass spectrometer.

6.1 PARENT IONS

Parent ions (or, more correctly, *parent-molecule ions*) are formed by the removal of a single electron from the molecules admitted to the ion source, as shown by Equation (6–1):

$$M + e \longrightarrow M^{+} + 2e. \tag{6–1}$$

Assume that an electron with 10 volts of energy can just cause the reaction given by Equation (6–1) to occur. The velocity of the electron is about [Equation (3–28)]

$$v = \sqrt{0.0333 \times 4.80 \times 10^{-10} \times 1837 \times 6.02 \times 10^{23} \times 2},$$

or

$$v = 1.88 \times 10^{8} \text{ cm/sec}.$$

Now if the electron passes a molecule of about 8 Å in diameter, we see that the electron traverses this distance in about

$$t = \frac{8 \times 10^{-8}}{1.88 \times 10^{8}} \text{ sec}$$

or

$$t = 4 \times 10^{-16} \text{ sec}.$$

Now the frequencies of vibrations of bonds in molecules are of the order of 10^{14} sec^{-1} or smaller. That is, the most rapid vibrations occur in about 10^{-14} sec. We see from this rather naïve approach that the bombarding electron passes the molecule in a fraction of the vibrational period. Thus, little change occurs in the position of the nuclei during the electronic transition.

In an electronic transistion, then, the nuclear separation and velocity of relative motion are changed only to a negligible extent. This is the *Franck-Condon principle* (1, 2). Stated in other words, the electronic transition occurs so rapidly that the nuclei do not have time to move any significant distance. In Figure 6–1 is shown a potential energy diagram illustrating that the favored transition is the "vertical" one.

It is obvious that the vertical transition does not necessarily correspond to a $v'' = 0 \longrightarrow v' = 0$ transition. Such a 0–0 transition is termed an adiabatic

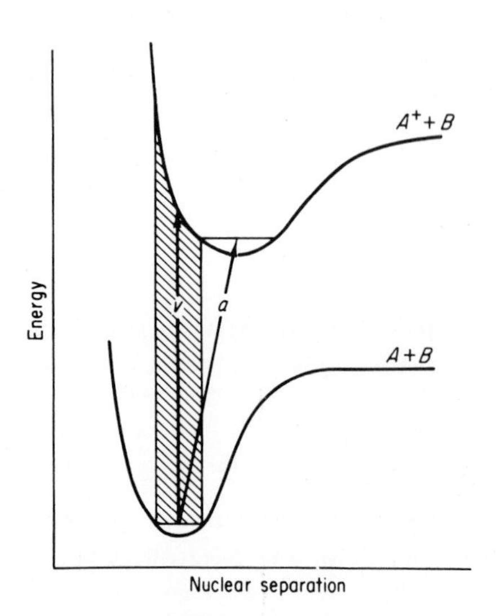

Fig. 6-1. Franck-Condon diagram illustrating vertical (v) and adiabatic (a) transitions.

transition, and corresponds to the true ionization potential of the molecule. From Figure 6–1 it can be seen that some fraction of the electronic transitions may result in dissociation, giving $A^+ + B$. (This feature will be discussed in more detail in Section 6.3.)

From Equation (6–1) it is obvious that the mass of the parent-ion M^+ is only very slightly less than the mass of the neutral molecule M. From the determination of the parent-ion m/e value with the mass spectrometer, molecular weights of samples can be determined. Because electron energies of 50 or 75 ev are commonly used in mass spectrometers, thus allowing greater fragmentation of the parent ions, it is possible that the fragmentation may be so severe that no parent ion remains. Indeed, there are compounds that do not yield parent ions upon electron impact, even at electron energies just above the ionization potential of the compound (e.g., many fluorocarbons, CCl_4, etc.). This could cause an erroneous determination of the molecular weight of a compound. For this reason, very low electron energies (of the order of 10–15 volts) are usually used in determining the molecular weight of a compound (see Section 9.4 for a discussion of low-voltage mass spectrometry), and even here care must be taken to assure that one is determining the molecular weight with the parent-molecule ion.

As the size and complexity of molecules in a given series increase, the fragmentation usually increases, reducing the abundance of the parent-molecule ions. Pahl (3) defined a parent-ion stability as

$$W_p = 1 - W_z, \tag{6–2}$$

where

$$W_z = \sum I_f/(I_p + \sum I_f), \tag{6–3}$$

W_z is the parent-ion decomposition probability, I_p is the intensity of the undecomposed parent ions (including isotopic ions), and $\sum I_f$ is the total intensity of all of the other (singly charged) ions in the mass spectrum. Combining Equations (6–2) and (6–3), we obtain

$$W_p = I_p/(I_p + \sum I_f). \tag{6–4}$$

For low molecular weight hydrocarbons, W_p is largest for acetylenic compounds, smaller for the olefins, and smallest for the paraffinic compounds. Thus, for example,

$$W_p(C_2H_6) = 0.12, \quad W_p(C_2H_4) = 0.39, \quad \text{and} \quad W_p(C_2H_2) = 0.75.$$

As the number of carbon atoms in a homologous series is increased, W_p decreases, and the relative W_p for acetylenic, olefinic, and paraffinic compounds is reversed from that stated just above.

In the discussion of the theory of mass spectra in Chapter 7, we shall further inquire into the decompositions of parent-molecule ions.

6.2 MOLECULE IONS

Molecule ions are groups of atoms that would compose a molecule in the usual sense of the word, except that they have one (or more) electrons less than needed to be a neutral molecule. To illustrate, $H_2S_2^+$ observed in the mass spectrum of $C_2H_5SSC_2H_5$ is a *molecule ion*. Similarly, H_2S^+ in the mass spectrum of C_2H_5SH, and CH_3OH^+ in the mass spectrum of CH_3OH are molecule ions. It can be seen that the examples of $H_2S_2^+$ and H_2S^+ cited are rearrangement ions, as well as molecules ions. On the other hand, the CH_3OH^+ example is not a *rearrangement ion*, but rather is a parent ion, as well as a molecule ion. Because molecule ions may be either parent ions, rearrangement ions, or fragment ions, they are discussed in more detail in subsequent section under the headings of Fragment Ions and Rearrangement Ions.

It has been the practice by some to term only parent ions as molecule ions, and all other ions as fragment ions. Such terminology is somewhat confusing, and we shall adopt in our discussions the more basic definitions and distinctions noted above.

6.3 FRAGMENT IONS

Fragment ions are those ions produced from the parent-molecule ion by various bond cleavage processes. If the ions simultaneously exhibit rearrangements of the atoms, the ion formed is termed a *rearrangement ion;* these will be discussed in Section 6.5.

An example of a process leading to a *rearrangement ion* is

$$CH_3CH_2SSCH_2CH_3 \longrightarrow HSSH^+ + 2H_2C = CH_2,$$

where $HSSH^+$ is the rearrangement ion (note that it is also a molecule ion). During the cleavage of the two C–S bonds, two H–S bonds were being formed.

Two examples of processes leading to *fragment ions* are

$$CH_3CH_2SSCH_2CH_3 \longrightarrow CH_3CH_2SS^+ + CH_3CH_2$$

and

$$CH_3CH_2SSCH_2CH_3 \longrightarrow CH_3CH_2S^+ + CH_3CH_2S.$$

Many other examples could be given, obviously. But what of the physical origins of fragment ions? To discuss this, let us consider a simple molecule, *AB*.

In Figure 6–2 are shown three possible consequences of an electronic transition, depending on the shapes of the potential energy curves for the final electronic state. The nuclear separation of the ground vibrational level of the *AB* molecule lies between *a* and *b* (see Figures 6-2A, B, C). According

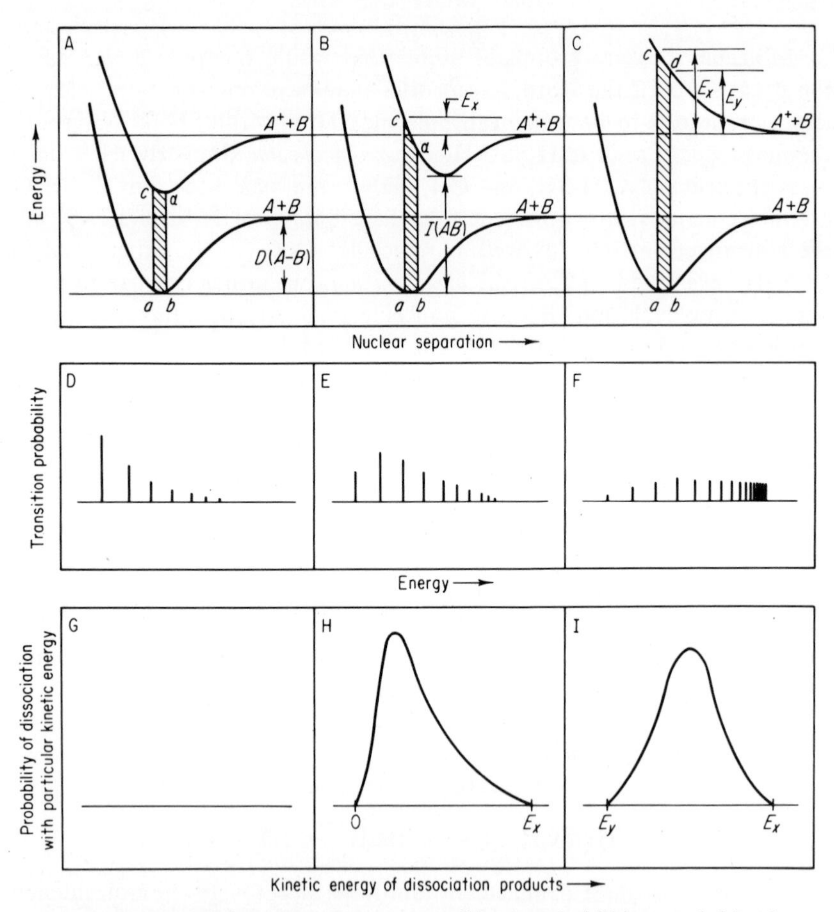

Fig. 6-2. Potential energy curves, transition probabilities, and kinetic energy distributions, showing the consequences of the Franck-Condon principle.

to the *Franck-Condon principle* (discussed in Section 6.1), the nuclear separation must also be between these same limits, indicated by c and d, after the electronic transition. The dissociation energy of AB, $D(A-B)$, is shown in Figure 6-2A.

From Figure 6-2A, we see that the final state may lie within the region of discrete vibrational levels of the potential energy curve for AB^+. The ionization potential of AB, $I(AB)$, is shown in Figure 6-2B. Such a transition produces a stable ion in the ground electronic state with some vibrational excitation. The transition probabilities of the 0–0, 0–1, 0–2, etc., transitions are given in Figure 6-2D. Notice that here the 0–0 transition is favored. At larger internuclear separations for AB^+ (a situation midway between Figures 6-2A and 6-2B), transitions to excited vibrational levels become more important, as shown in Figure 6-2E. Since there is no dissociation of AB^+ into A^+ and B resulting from this transition, there are no probabilities to be associated with particular kinetic energies (Figure 6-2G).

The final state may also lie such that it includes part of the continuum, as well as part of the discrete vibrational levels of the AB state (see Figure 6-2B). Hence, some of the transitions will lead to stable, vibrationally excited AB^+ ions, and other transitions will lead to dissociation of the AB^+ ion to give $A^+ + B$ (or $A^+ + B^-$, or $A + B^+$, etc., depending on the limit of the potential energy curve of the upper electronic state at very large internuclear separations). Thus, fragment ions may be produced. Here, the transition probabilities are generally rather similar, as shown in Figure 6-2F, and lead to the continuous region of the vibrational term spectrum at the higher energies. When dissociation occurs, the fragments are formed with relative kinetic energies ranging from 0 up to E_x, as shown in Figure 6-2H. It has been found that in many cases the kinetic energies of fragments resulting from electron impact are rather small, but in some instances these energies may be 1 ev or more. Olmsted, Street, and Newton (4) reported recently that perhaps fragment ions formed with high kinetic energies are more abundant than usually believed.

It is also possible that the final state of the transition may lie in the continuum of nuclear levels, as shown in Figure 6-2C. Then, the dissociation of the molecule accompanies all transitions from the ground state of AB to the upper electronic state. In such a case, the relative kinetic energies of the fragments (A^+ and B in this example) will be some distribution lying between E_y and E_x, as shown in Figure 6–2I.

The *electronic transition probability* is proportional to the square of the vibrational overlap integral (the integral over the product of the vibrational eigenfunctions of the two states involved), when the variation of electronic perturbation integrals with internuclear separation is small (5, 6, 7). Recent work by Nicholls (7, 8) and others has been concerned with the calculation of these Franck-Condon factors for polyatomic as well as diatomic molecules.

A number of other factors play important roles in determining the paths of fragmentation. Specifically, bond dissociation energies (i.e., the relative strengths of the various bonds) and the stabilities of the neutral fragments often influence the fragmentation processes. We shall also see in Chápter 7 that vibration frequencies and the degree of freedom influence the formation of fragment ions.

6.4 METASTABLE IONS

In the ion source of the mass spectrometer some molecules of certain gases will receive sufficient energy from the impacting electrons to fragment. But because the rate of decomposition is sufficiently slow, some of the metastable ions will live long enough to be withdrawn or repelled from the ionization chamber and begin their trip toward the accelerating region. At some point in their flight, these ions may disintegrate into smaller neutral molecules and new positively charged ions. These decompositions may occur all along the path of the ion, from the ionization region through the accelerating region and into the analyzer tube. The ion fragments thus formed are called *metastable ions*. To be correct, one should really state that these ions are the products of *metastable transitions*. The majority of the metastable transitions observed occur between the ion source and the magnetic analyzer.

The products of these metastable transitions will reach the collector along with other ions of different masses, but they are observed at neither their original mass nor their new mass. We shall shortly come to a derivation due essentially to Hipple, Fox, and Condon for the determination of the actual values of the masses at which the metastable ions will be observed. It is important to note here, however, that these metastable ions are often observed at nonintegral masses; that is, rather than at mass 39 or 40 they will be observed, for example, at 39.2; rather than at 31 or 32 they will be observed, for example, at 31.9. Again, the ion currents due to metastable ions (correctly, the ions from the metastable transitions) occur most frequently at nonintegral masses.

A second feature that these ions from the metastable transitions display is that they are very weak in intensity as compared to the parent ions and fragment ions in the mass spectra. For example, metastable ions often range from about 0.01% to about 1% of the base peak in the spectrum of a molecule. This has been put another way by Bloom, Mohler, Lengel, and Wise (9), who estimate that the intensity of the metastable ion divided by the product of the intensities of the original ion and the neutral fragment from the metastable transition is of the order of 0.01, assuming the base peak to be unit intensity.

A third feature of these ions from metastable transitions is that they present very diffuse, broad peaks, extending several mass units. Figure 6–3

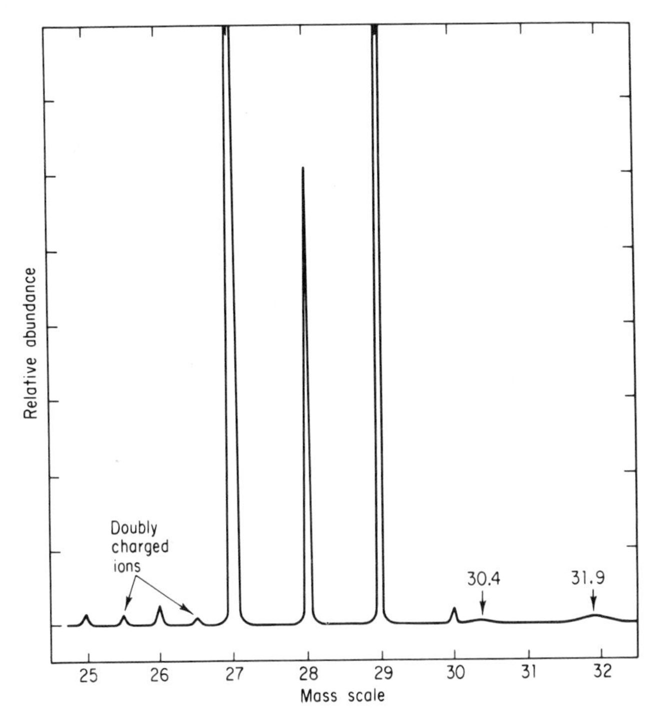

Fig. 6-3. Partial mass spectrum of *n*-butane, showing diffuse peaks due to metastable transitions.

shows a typical mass spectrum (of *n*-butane) exhibiting metastable peaks among the normal ion peaks. Another method of detecting metastable ions, that of measuring the kinetic energy of the ions, will not be discussed here. A point worth noting here is that an ion resulting from a metastable transition seems to have the same appearance potential as the same ion formed by the normal ionization and dissociation process.

An additional feature of metastable ions—which can be used for their recognition—is that, if the exit slit width is varied, their intensity varies relative to the intensities of the normal ions in the mass spectrum. Also, the metastable ion intensities relative to the other ion intensities may be varied by varying the voltage on the repeller electrode in the ionization chamber. An example of this latter variation is shown in Figure 6–4 for three of the metastables observed in the *n*-butane spectrum.

Let us now determine the mass at which one will observe metastable ions. To do this we shall follow the treatment essentially as given originally by Hipple, Fox, and Condon (10). Let the potential be 0 at the point where an ion of mass m_0 is formed and let it retain this mass until it has moved to a point with potential V_1, as shown in Figure 6–5. At V_1 the ion dissociates

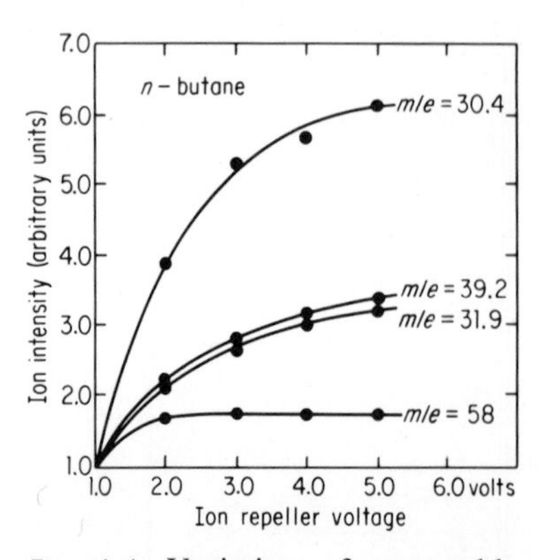

Fig. 6-4. Variation of metastable ion intensity with ion repeller voltage. [After Hipple, Fox, and Condon (10).]

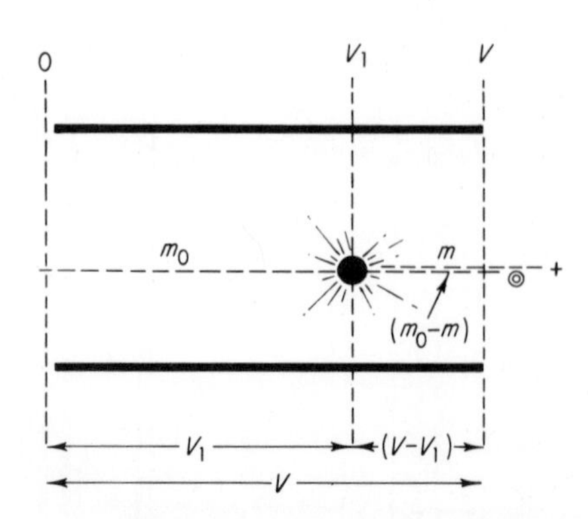

Fig. 6-5. Schematic diagram of the occurrence of a metastable transition in the ion-accelerating region.

into an ion of mass m and a neutral fragment of mass $(m_0 - m)$. The new ion is then accelerated to the region of full potential V, subsequent to which it enters the magnetic analyzer. At the point of dissociation, the kinetic energy of the ion of mass m_0 is eV_1, since the neutral fragment carries off some kinetic energy. After traveling through the remainder of the accelerating field, the kinetic energy T of the product ion is

$$T = (m/m_0)eV + e(V - V_1). \tag{6–5}$$

The radius of curvature of an ion in the magnetic field is

$$R = (c/eH)(2mT)^{1/2}. \tag{6–6}$$

Substituting, we have

$$R = \frac{\sqrt{2}\, cV^{1/2}}{e^{1/2}H}\left[\frac{m^2}{m_0}\frac{V_1}{V} + m\left(1 - \frac{V_1}{V}\right)\right]^{1/2}. \tag{6–7}$$

Now consider an ordinary ion of mass m^*. This ion has a radius of curvature in the magnetic field of

$$R = \frac{\sqrt{2}\, cV^{1/2}}{e^{1/2}H}(m^*)^{1/2}. \tag{6–8}$$

Since R is the same in Equations (6–7) and (6–8), we may equate these. Upon collecting and reducing this expression, we find that the product ion of the metastable transition appears at the detector for the same value of V and H as does the normal ion of mass m^*, where

$$m^* = \frac{m^2}{m_0}\left(\frac{V_1}{V}\right) + m\left(1 - \frac{V_1}{V}\right). \tag{6–9}$$

If the metastable transition occurs before the ion undergoes any acceleration, $V_1 = 0$ and $m^* = m$; that is, a normal ion is formed. If dissociation occurs after essentially full acceleration of the ion, but prior to the entrance of the ion into the magnetic analyzer, which is the commonly encountered case, then $V = V_1$ and

$$m^* = m^2/m_0. \tag{6–10}$$

This last equation is the equation for metastable ions.

EXAMPLE 6–1. As an example, consider the $m/e = 58$ ions of *n*-butane. If these ions pass through the accelerating region and then fragment near the exit slit to produce $m/e = 43$ ions and neutral methyl fragments, metastable ions will be observed at a mass of neither 43 nor 58, but at some other mass value. Equation (6–10) permits us to calculate this: $m^* = 43^2/58$; that is $m^* = 31.87$ or 31.9 amu. In fact, in the mass spectrum of *n*-butane, the ion product of the metastable transition just discussed is observed at $m/e = 31.9$. A somewhat more convenient form of Equation (6–10) is given in Appendix II in the form of a nomogram. The instructions for use of the nomogram are given in the accompanying description in Appendix II.

In the discussions above it was stated that the most commonly encountered metastable transitions were due to ion dissociations near the exit of the accelerating region. This is because these transitions are the most easily observed. Metastable transitions caused by fragmentation earlier in the accelerating region would be "smeared" over a wider range of the mass spectrum and therefore would be more difficult to observe and to study. Recently, N. D. Coggeshall (11) has reported a study of metastable ion transitions in a 180° mass spectrometer, including studies of metastable lifetimes. Coggeshall presents evidence for some metastables (such as that observed at $m/e = 31.9$ in *n*-butane) that may be created in different classes. He also discusses metastable peak shapes.

A similar study of metastable transitions is not conveniently made in the ordinary linear time-of-flight mass spectrometer, because the ions and neutrals resulting from a metastable transition still arrive at the same time as any undissociated ion from which the metastable would arise. Furthermore, the dissociation of an ion after it has been accelerated out of the ion source of the time-of-flight mass spectrometer does not affect the qualitative form of the mass spectrum. However, Ferguson, McCulloh, and Rosenstock (12) have shown that by applying a dc retarding potential a few centimeters ahead of the ion cathode (just prior to the magnetic electron multiplier—see Figure 4–2), ions may be retarded, but the neutral species are unaffected and appear at the original mass position. This appears to be a new, simple, yet powerful, method for studies of metastable transitions. Recently, Hunt, *et al.*, (13) have used similar techniques in studies of ion dissociation processes. These methods will be treated further in Section 11.1, along with a discussion of neutral fragment studies.

6.5 REARRANGEMENT IONS

Mass spectrometric studies show that a number of compounds yield ions with less mass than the parent ion that cannot be formed on the assumption of simple cleavage of bonds in the parent ion. As already pointed out in Sections 6.2 and 6.3, these ions are formed by rearrangements of atoms (or possibly groups of atoms) at the moment of the unimolecular decomposition of the parent ion. In addition to the examples of $H_2S_2^+$ and H_2S^+ already cited, we may cite the formation of the rearrangement ion CF_2H^+ in the electron impact study of CF_3CH_2OH:

$$CF_3CH_2OH \rightarrow CF_2H^+ + CH_2O + F.$$

It has been observed that a number of fluorine-containing compounds show rearrangement ions under electron impact, some of which are rather random rearrangements. Rearrangements involving hydrogen atoms are very common, particularly in unsaturated hydrocarbons and saturated, branched-chain hydrocarbons. It should be noted that such rearrangements are not restricted to adjacent atoms along the carbon chain.

For some molecules the rearrangement ion intensity may be so large that the rearrangement ion may form the *base peak*. (The base peak is the largest or most intense ion in the mass spectrum and is usually assigned a relative intensity of 100.00.) It is not uncommon that the production of rearrangement ions requires considerably more energy than for most of the fragmentation processes, a fact which can be brought out in an observation of the ionization efficiency curve (see Chapter 8) of the ion. Rearrangements of carbon skeletons may also occur in certain cases. Some very interesting work by S. Meyerson and P. N. Rylander (14) describes a number of intriguing carbon skeleton rearrangements.

6.6 MULTIPLY CHARGED IONS

Multiply charged monatomic ions (e.g., Hg^+, Hg^{++}, etc.) were observed by Thomson in his early studies (see Chapter 2). Later, W. Bleakney (15) measured the ionization potentials of the various multiply charged mercury ions. Many of the recent studies of multiply charged ions have been made by F. H. Dorman and J. D. Morrison (16) and by R. E. Fox (17), and have included multiply charged polyatomic ions as well as monatomic ions. From the ionization efficiency curves, it is possible to determine also the higher ionization potentials. Several such ionization efficiency curves are shown in Figures 6–6 to 6–9.

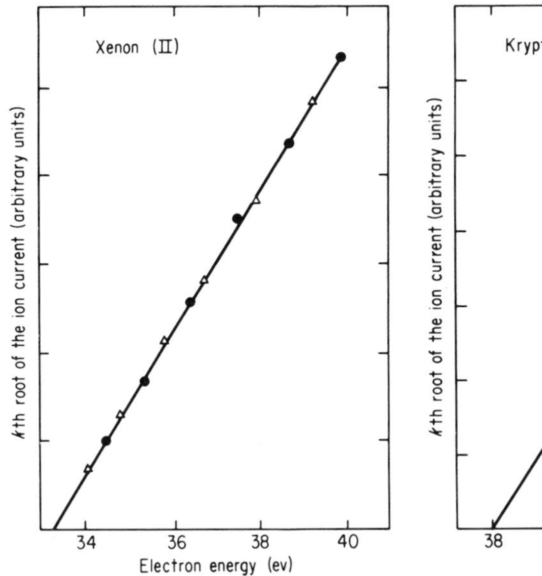

Fig. 6-6. Square root of the Xe^{2+} ion current as a function of the electron energy. [After Kiser (19).]

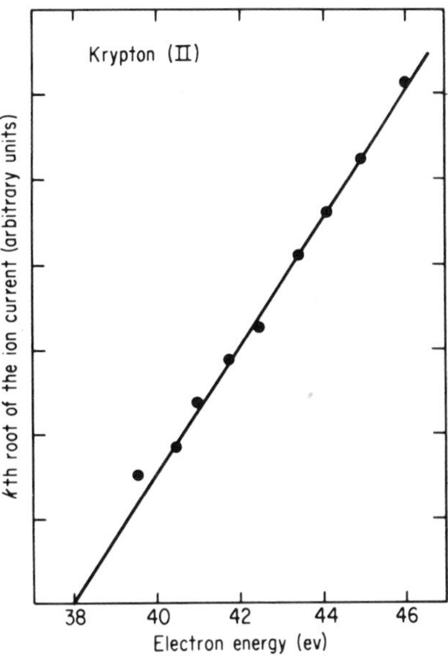

Fig. 6-7. Square root of the Kr^{2+} ion current as a function of the electron energy. [After Kiser (19).]

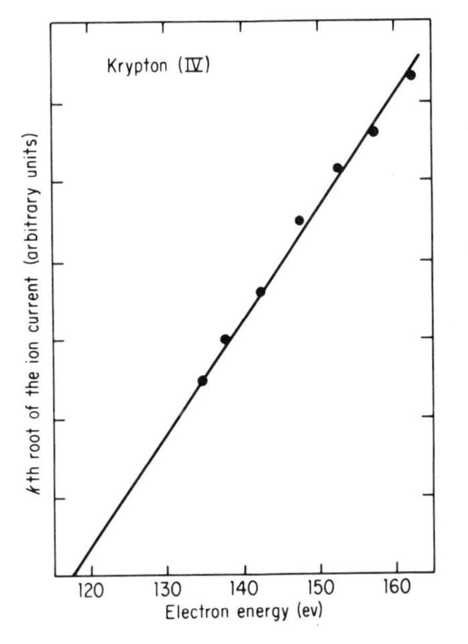

Fig. 6-8. Fourth root of the Kr^{4+} ion current as a function of the electron energy. [After Kiser (19).]

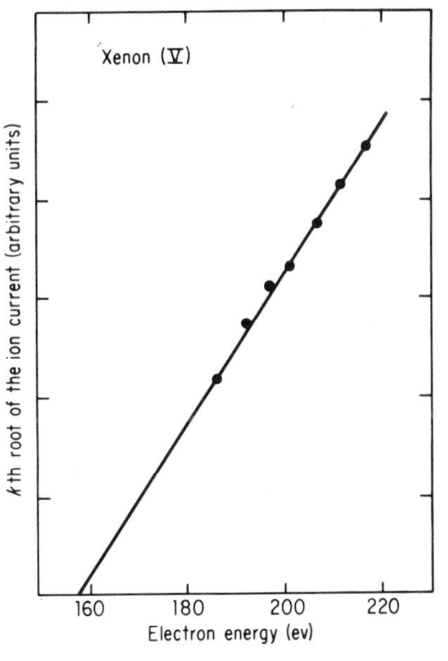

Fig. 6-9. Fifth root of the Xe^{5+} ion current as a function of the electron energy. [After Kiser (19).]

For the multiple ionization, we may write the equation

$$R + e \longrightarrow R^{k+} + (k + 1)e, \tag{6–11}$$

for which the expression

$$i(V) = K(V - E_c)^k/k! \tag{6–12}$$

is believed to hold in the threshold region [G. H. Wannier (18) and F. H. Dorman and J. D. Morrison (16)]. Here $i(V)$ is the ion current at voltage V, E_c is the ionization potential, and K is the relative electronic transition probability. Taking two points in the threshold region,

$$K = k!\{[(i(V_2)/\gamma_r)^{1/k} - (i(V_1)/\gamma_r)^{1/k}]/[V_2 - V_1]\}^k, \tag{6–13}$$

where γ_r is a modified secondary electron emission coefficient [R. W. Kiser (19)]. From this last expression, we may calculate values of K. Some of these values of K for multiply charged monatomic ions are given in Table 6–1.

TABLE 6–1. RELATIVE ELECTRONIC TRANSITION PROBABILITIES FOR KRYPTON AND XENON*

	Relative Electronic Transition Probability, K	
Charge on Ion	Krypton	Xenon
1+	2.0	2.0
2+	0.04 (0.03)	0.06 (0.09)
3+	5×10^{-6}	$1.5\ (2) \times 10^{-4}$
4+	$60\ (1) \times 10^{-10}$	$10\ (3) \times 10^{-8}$
5+	(2×10^{-13})	$5\ (2) \times 10^{-11}$

*Values in parentheses were determined by F. H. Dorman and J. D. Morrison, *J. Chem. Phys.*, **34**, 578 (1961); other values were determined by R. W. Kiser (19).

TABLE 6–2. RELATIVE ELECTRONIC TRANSITION PROBABILITIES FOR MERCURY, CARBON DIOXIDE, TOLUENE, AND METHYL ISOTHIOCYANATE (20)

	Charge on Ion		
	1+	2+	3+
Mercury	1	1×10^{-2}	3×10^{-5}
Carbon dioxide	1	2×10^{-4}	—
Toluene	1	3×10^{-4}	—
Methyl Isothiocyanate	1	1×10^{-4}	—

In Table 6–2 are given some relative electronic transition probabilities for Hg^{++} and Hg^{3+}, and three polyatomic species, as determined by L. A. Shadoff and R. W. Kiser (20). For comparison, $K = 4 \times 10^{-4}$ for CO_2^{++} and $K = 1 \times 10^{-3}$ for ϕCH_3^{++} have been determined by F. H. Dorman and J. D. Morrison (16).

Recently, Newton (21) has shown the existence of stable states of triply-charged ions of small molecules such as CS_2, COS, and C_2N_2. Newton suggests that small molecules possessing a sufficient number of nonbonding or delocalized electrons may be made to yield stable triply charged ions.

6.7 NEGATIVE IONS

J. J. Thomson was the first to observe a number of simple *negative ions*; in his study he used his parabola apparatus, as described earlier. By suitably reversing the fields in the mass spectrometer, one may use the instrument to detect and study negative ions in a manner similar to the detection and investigation of positive ions.

Under the usual conditions of mass spectrometer operation, few negatively charged *parent ions* are formed, and many fragment ions are formed with kinetic energy. The number of species formed with negative charges is commonly much smaller than for positive ions, and it should also be noted that negative ion intensities are often much smaller than positive ion intensities. However, in the mass spectrum of ClO_3F, ClO_3^- is the most abundant of all of the ions, either positive or negative. $BiCl_2^-$ and $BiCl^-$ have been observed in the mass spectrum of $BiCl_3$.

The various processes by which negative ions are produced will be discussed in more detail in Chapter 8. However, we should note here that there are two main routes for production of negative ions from molecules by electron impact. These are (a) electron capture, and (b) ion-pair production. An example of electron capture is

$$YZ + e \longrightarrow YZ^- \longrightarrow Y + Z^-. \tag{6–14}$$

The formation of YZ^- illustrates simple electron attachment and the formation of $Y + Z^-$ illustrates dissociative electron attachment. An example of an ion-pair production process is

$$YZ + e \longrightarrow Y^+ + Z^- + e. \tag{6–15}$$

Metastable transitions between negative ions have also been observed and studied. B. L. Donnally and H. E. Carr (22) observed the reactions

$$C_2H_5PO_2Cl^- \longrightarrow PO_2Cl^- + C_2H_5Cl$$

and

$$PO_2Cl^- \longrightarrow Cl^- + PO_2.$$

6.8 TOTAL IONIZATION

Total ionization is defined as the sum of all of the ion intensities for all of the ions in the mass spectrum, multiplied by the sensitivity s of the base peak in the mass spectrum. The sensitivity s is in units of current per unit pressure; this will be discussed further and used in our discussion of analytical applications in Chapter 9.

The total ionization, determined in the manner just described, has no significance in the absolute sense, but it is characteristic of the instrument with which it was determined. If the value obtained for a given compound (commonly n-butane) is taken as a standard, the total ionization for other compounds relative to the standard can be calculated. The relative total ionization should be independent of the particular mass spectrometer employed. However, this is not always so in practice.

The total ionization (relative) increases as the number of carbon atoms increases in a given homologous paraffin series. For a series of hydrocarbons which all contain the same number of carbon atoms, the total ionization (relative) increases as the number of hydrogen atoms increases. This indicates that the total ionization (relative) of hydrocarbon isomers should be the same, and this has been found to be so within certain limits.

H. A. Bethe (23) calculated from theoretical grounds that the ionization of an nl atomic electron (having the quantum numbers n and l) is very roughly proportional to the mean square radius of the nl electron shell for very high energy electrons. J. W. Otvos and D. P. Stevenson (24) have since shown that the relative total ionization cross section of atoms are given very nearly by the weighted sum of the valence electrons of the atoms, where the weighting factor employed by Otvos and Stevenson is the mean square radii of the electrons, as calculated for hydrogen-like wave functions of the electrons.

For hydrocarbons, the *principle of additivity* can be given as

$$\sum_i I_i = K'(n_H Q_i^H + n_C Q_i^C), \tag{6–16}$$

where $\sum_i I_i$ is the total ionization, Q_i^H and Q_i^C are the ionization cross sections for hydrogen and carbon atoms, respectively, n_H and n_C are the number of hydrogen atoms and carbon atoms in a given hydrocarbon molecule, and K' is a proportionality constant. Using the relative total ionization cross sections (relative to $Q_i^H = 1.00$) given by Otvos and Stevenson, Equation (6–16) becomes

$$\sum_i I_i = K(n_H + 4.16n_C). \tag{6–17}$$

This additivity concept also is satisfactory for many other types of organic molecules. F. W. Lampe, J. L. Franklin, and F. H. Field (25) have found that this additivity concept applies to hydrocarbons, but that it is not very satisfactory for treatment of inorganic molecules.

The principal use made of total ionization is in analytical standardizations of mass spectra. However, curves of $(I_i/\sum_i I_i)$ as a function of electron energy present some very interesting and useful data, as shall be seen in Chapter 8.

6.9 ION-MOLECULE REACTIONS

A relatively recent field of investigation via mass spectrometry is that of ion-molecule reactions. As implied, these are bimolecular reactions between ions and molecules, and they are studied in the ion source of the mass spectrometer at very high pressures (relative to the usual operation of the mass spectrometer ion source) by means of the various product ions formed. These reactions (actually, the products of these reactions) were first observed by Thomson in 1913, but the recent interest has stemmed more or less from the work of V. L. Tal'roze and A. K. Lyubimova (26) in the Soviet Union and Stevenson and Schissler (27), Field, Franklin, and Lampe (28) and Hamill (29) in the United States. Other workers who have contributed to the study of ion-molecule reactions are Melton, *et al.* (30), Henglein and Muccini (31), and Beynon (32), to name only a few. Hand and von Weyssenhoff (33) have reported a study of ion-molecule reactions with a time-of-flight mass spectrometer and Babeliowsky and Boelrijk (34) recently studied the negative temperature coefficients of ion-molecule reactions.

Consider the reactions

$$P_i^+ + M \xrightarrow{k_{1i}} P_i M^+, \tag{6–18}$$

$$P_i M^+ \xrightarrow{k_{2ij}} S_{ij}^+ + N_{ij}, \tag{6–19}$$

from which can be derived (35), for small extent of reaction, the expression

$$\left(\frac{I_{S_{ij}}}{I_{P_i}}\right) = k_{1i}k_{2ij}(M)\tau \Big/ \sum_j k_{2ij}, \tag{6–20}$$

where $I_{S_{ij}}$ is the ion current of the secondary ions S_{ij}^+, I_{P_i} is the ion current of the primary ion, P_i^+, (M) is the concentration of M, and τ is the *residence time* in the ion source (reaction chamber).

A plot of I_S/I_P versus (M) should give a straight line with a slope of

$$\text{slope} = k_{1i}\tau \left[k_{2ij}\Big/ \sum_j k_{2ij}\right], \tag{6–21}$$

which should pass through the origin. Figure 6–10 shows data determined for the reaction

$$CD_4^+ + CD_4 \longrightarrow CD_5^+ + CD_3$$

[given by Lampe, Franklin, and Field (35)], and it is seen that the data fit the expression given by Equation (6–20).

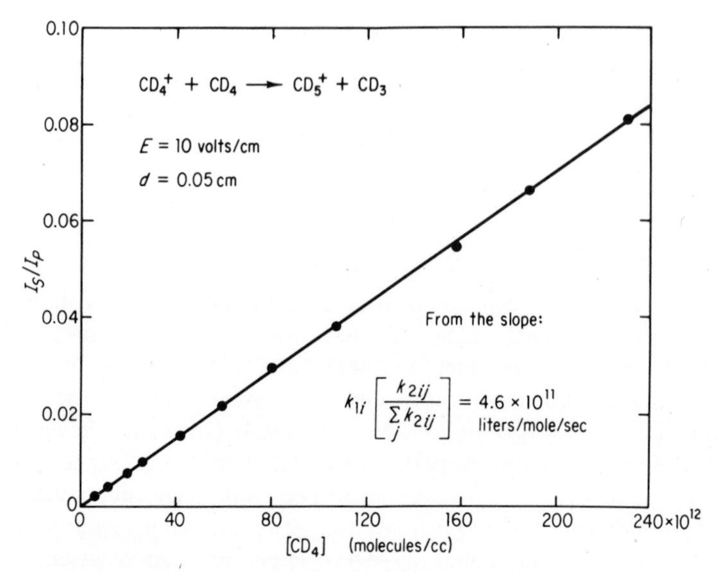

Fig. 6-10. A plot of I_s/I_p for the reaction $CD_4^+ + CD_4 \longrightarrow CD_5^+ + CD_3$. [After Lampe, Franklin, and Field (35).]

Now,

$$\frac{I_{S_j}}{\sum_j I_{S_j}} = \frac{k_{2ij}}{\sum_i k_{2ij}}. \tag{6–22}$$

The term on the left can be measured experimentally, and therefore the slope can be used to yield k_{1i}, if τ is known. The residence time τ is dependent on the ion source (reaction chamber) conditions, and is given by

$$\tau = (2dm_i/eE)^{1/2}, \tag{6–23}$$

where d is the distance from the electron beam to the exit slit in the ion source, m_i is the mass of the primary ion, e is the electronic charge, and E is the field applied to the ion source. Therefore one may determine k_{1i}.

EXAMPLE 6–2. For example, from the data given in Figure 6–10, the residence time in the ion source is

$$\tau = \left(\frac{2 \times 0.05 \times 20 \times 300}{6.024 \times 10^{23} \times 4.8 \times 10^{-10} \times 10}\right)^{1/2}$$
$$= (2.074 \times 10^{-13})^{1/2},$$

or

$$\tau = 4.555 \times 10^{-7} \text{ sec.}$$

Thus, from the slope of the curve given in Figure 6–10,

$$(I_S/I_P) \text{ vs. } (M) = \text{slope} = (0.080)/(2.30 \times 10^{14}) \text{ cc/molecule},$$

so that

$$k_{1i}\left(k_{2ij}\Big/\sum_j k_{2ij}\right) = \left(\frac{0.080 \times 6.024 \times 10^{23}}{2.30 \times 10^{14} \times 4.555 \times 10^{-7} \times 10^3}\right) \text{liter/mole-sec}$$

$$= 4.60 \times 10^{11} \text{ liter/mole/sec.}$$

In the study of the bimolecular ion-molecule reactions it is also convenient to express the rates of the reactions in terms of the reaction cross sections. For reactions that do not have an activation energy (the situation for almost all ion-molecule reactions)

$$k = g_i Q_R, \tag{6–24}$$

where g_i is the speed of the ion, k is the specific rate constant, and Q_R is the reaction cross section. However,

$$\overline{g_i^2} = (3kT/m_i)\cdot(2eEx/m_i), \tag{6–25}$$

where k is the Boltzmann constant, T is the absolute temperature, E is the repeller field strength, and x is the position of the ion in the ionization chamber ($x \equiv 0$ in the electron beam, $x = d$ at the ion-exit slit).

For no electric field,

$$\overline{g_i^2} = 3kT/m_i. \tag{6–26}$$

Substituting this into Equation (6–24), we obtain

$$k = (3kT/m_i)^{1/2}\overline{Q_R}. \tag{6–27}$$

When the contribution of the electric field to the speed of the ion is much greater than the thermal energy contribution,

$$\overline{g_i^2} = 2eEx/m_i. \tag{6–28}$$

Substituting the time-average velocity of the ion into Equation (6–24), we obtain

$$k = (eEd/2m_i)^{1/2}\overline{Q_R}. \tag{6–29}$$

EXAMPLE 6–3. For the data already given in Example 6–2, let us calculate $\overline{Q_R}$ for the reaction data given in Figure 6–10. From Equation (6–29),

$$g_i = (eEd/2m_i)^{1/2}$$

$$= \left(\frac{4.802 \times 10^{-10} \times 10 \times 0.05 \times 6.024 \times 10^{23}}{300 \times 2 \times 20}\right)^{1/2}$$

$$= (1.207 \times 10^{10})^{1/2} = 1.10 \times 10^5 \text{ cm/sec.}$$

Then,

$$\overline{Q_R} = k/g_i = 4.60 \times 10^{11} \times 10^3/(1.10 \times 10^5 \times 6.024 \times 10^{23})$$
$$= 69.5 \times 10^{-16} \text{ cm}^2.$$

In Table 6–3 are summarized a few of the ion-molecule reactions which have been studied. This list is by no means complete, but it does give the specific rate constant and the reaction cross section for a number of different ion-molecule reactions. In addition, heats of formation of the product ions are given as determined from the use of the nonendothermicity of these reactions (see comments above). It should also be noted that the primary ion and secondary ion are determined in a particular reaction by the matching of the appearance potentials of the two ions, since the reactions are non-endothermic. A conversion of phenomenological to microscopic cross sections for ion-molecule reactions has been given by Light (50). In an interesting experiment, Freeman and McIlroy (36) reasoned that since singly charged ions of the noble gases are isoelectronic with the halogens, it might be possible to form a series of ions containing both an alkali metal atom and a noble gas atom; these ions would correspond to the alkali halide salts. Using an isotope separator for their studies, they were able to observe the

TABLE 6–3. SOME ION-MOLECULE REACTIONS AND THEIR RATE CONSTANTS AND CROSS SECTIONS

Ion-Molecule Reaction	$k \times 10^{-10}$ (l/mole/sec)	$Q \times 10^{16}$ (cm²)	ΔH_f^+ (kcal/mole)	References
$H_2^+ + H_2 \longrightarrow H_3^+ + H$	126.	27.4	286–304(311)	35, 39, 45
$H_2^+ + O_2 \longrightarrow HO_2^+ + H$	580.	126.	<304 (271)	27, 35, 38, 41
$(N_2^+)^* + N_2 \longrightarrow N_3^+ + N$			<398 (388)	35, 42, 43, 46
$N_2^+ + D_2 \longrightarrow N_2D^+ + D$	106.	86.3	<307	27, 35, 41
$CO^+ + D_2 \longrightarrow COD^+ + D$	89.	72.5	<245 (203)	27, 35, 38
$CH_4^+ + CH_4 \longrightarrow CH_5^+ + CH_3$	51.1	61.0	218–233	26, 28, 29, 35
$HI^+ + CH_3I \longrightarrow CH_3I_2^+ + H$	21.5	51.	<199, 244	29, 35
$Ar^+ + H_2 \longrightarrow ArH^+ + H$	114.	111.	<312	27, 35, 41
$Kr^+ + H_2 \longrightarrow KrH^+ + H$	30.1	42.5	<271	27, 35, 41
$O^+ + N_2 \longrightarrow NO^+ + N$	600.	2000.	235	38, 44
$H_2O^+ + H_2O \longrightarrow H_3O^+ + OH$	76.	95.0	136–140(125)	35, 40, 48
$CH_3OH^+ + CH_3OH \longrightarrow CH_3OH_2^+ + CH_3O$	66.	79.		49
$H_2S^+ + H_2S \longrightarrow H_3S^+ + SH$	18.	31.	<187	28, 35
$HBr^+ + HBr \longrightarrow H_2Br^+ + Br$	28.	39.	<226	27, 35
$I_2^+ + I_2 \longrightarrow I_3^+ + I$			<222	35, 37
$I_2^- + I_2 \longrightarrow I_3^- + I$			<−68	35, 37
$O^- + CH_3I \longrightarrow OI^- + CH_3$	127.	169.	<−1	31, 35
$O^- + NO_2 \longrightarrow NO_2^- + O$	284.	378.	<−26 (−29)	31, 35, 47
$O^- + I_2 \longrightarrow OI^- + I$	62.	83.	<−1	31, 35

ions $LiAr^+$, $LiKr^+$, and $RbAr^+$ produced in the field free region of the ion-source plasma. Quite possibly other alkali metal-noble gas ions will be observed and studied in the future. Before we leave this brief discussion of ion-molecule reactions, we should note the type of ion source design which Čermák and Herman have suggested for such studies.

V. Čermák and Z. Herman have described a novel ion source design for the study of ion-molecule reactions (51), a schematic diagram of which is shown in Figure 6–11. The elements of this ion source are not greatly different from those of the electron bombardment ion source shown in Figure 3–1. However, the potentials on the various grids are different, as will be described. Electrons are emitted from the filament F and accelerated to plate G_1. The electrons passing plate G_1 are then decelerated toward plate G_2 so that the energies of the electrons passing through the ion chamber C are not sufficient to cause ionization or dissociation of the molecules present in this region. Plates G_2 and G_3 are held at the same potential. Between plates G_3 and G_4 the electrons experience a great acceleration and gain more than sufficient energy to cause ionization and dissociation to occur in molecules in the region bounded by plate G_4. Thus, the primary ions are formed only in the region bounded by plate G_4. Since plate G_3 is quite negative with respect to plate G_4, the primary positive ions are accelerated back through plate G_3 into the ion chamber where the primary ions can then undergo ion-molecule reactions. This brings about the formation of the secondary ions, which are subsequently expelled by the repeller R from the ion chamber into the ion accelerating field between grids (or plates) G_5 and G_7 prior to mass analysis. A significant advantage of the Čermák-Herman ion source is that essentially only the second-

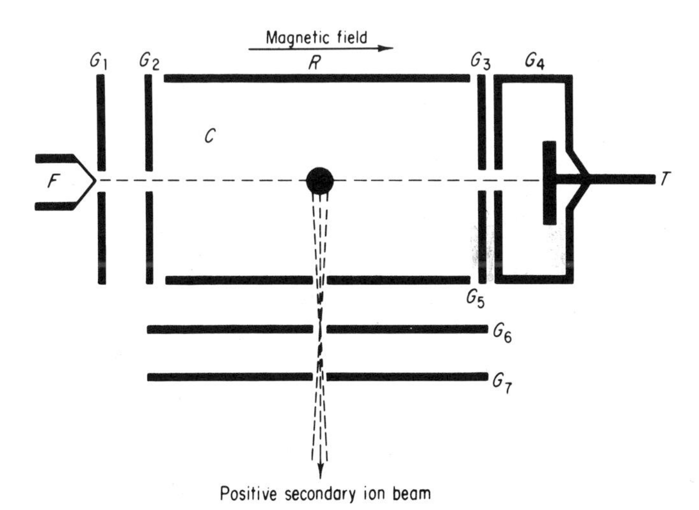

Fig. 6-11. Schematic diagram of a Čermák-Herman (51) ion source for the study of ion-molecule reactions.

ary ions are collected. Therefore, the secondary spectrum and its interpretation are much simplified.

Another obvious means of studying ion-molecule reactions employs the use of tandem mass spectrometers. Little of this type of work has been done until recently, but we may expect confidently to see many more investigations of this type in the future.

REFERENCES

1. J. Franck, *Trans. Faraday Soc.*, **21**, 536 (1926).
2. E. U. Condon, *Phys. Rev.*, **32**, 858 (1928).
3. M. Pahl, *Z. Naturforsch.*, **9B**, 188 and 418 (1954).
4. J. Olmsted, III, K. Street, Jr., and A. S. Newton, *J. Chem. Phys.*, **40**, 2114 (1964).
5. G. Herzberg, *Molecular Spectra and Molecular Structure:* Vol. I, *Spectra of Diatomic Molecules*, 2nd ed., D. Van Nostrand Co., Inc., New York, 1950, pp. 199–201.
6. M. Krauss and V. H. Dibeler, "Appearance Potential Data of Organic Molecules," in *Mass Spectrometry of Organic Ions*, F. W. McLafferty (ed.), Academic Press, New York, 1963, pp. 117–63.
7. R. W. Nicholls and A. L. Stewart, "Allowed Transitions," in *Atomic and Molecular Processes*, D. R. Bates (ed.), Academic Press, New York, 1962, pp. 47–78.
8. R. W. Nicholls, *J. Research Natl. Bureau Standards*, **65A**, 451 (1961).
9. E. G. Bloom, F. L. Mohler, J. H. Lengel, and C. E. Wise, *J. Research Natl. Bureau Standards*, **40**, 437 (1948).
10. J. A. Hipple, R. E. Fox, and E. U. Condon, *Phys. Rev.*, **69**, 347 (1946).
11. N. D. Coggeshall, *J. Chem. Phys.*, **37**, 2167 (1962); **38**, 1786 (1963).
12. R. E. Ferguson, K. E. McCulloh, and H. M. Rosenstock, "Observations of the Products of Collision Processes and Ion Decomposition in a Linear, Pulsed Time-of-Flight Mass Spectrometer," 10th annual meeting of the ASTM Committee E-14 on Mass Spectrometry, New Orleans, La., June 3–8, 1962; see also *J. Chem. Phys.*, **42**, 100 (1965).
13. W. W. Hunt, Jr., R. E. Huffman and K. E. McGee, *Rev. Sci. Instr.*, **35**, 82 (1964); and W. W. Hunt, Jr., R. E. Huffman, J. Saari, G. Wassel, J. F. Betts, E. H. Paufve, W. Wyess and R. A. Fluegge, *ibid.*, **35**, 88 (1964).
14. S. Meyerson and P. N. Rylander, *J. Am. Chem. Soc.*, **79**, 842 and 1058 (1957); and *J. Chem. Phys.*, **27**, 901 (1957).
15. W. Bleakney, *Phys. Rev.*, **35**, 139 and 1180 (1930).
16. F. H. Dorman and J. D. Morrison, *J. Chem. Phys.*, **31**, 1320 and 1335 (1959); **32**, 378 (1960); **34**, 578 and 1407 (1961); **35**, 575 (1961).

17. R. E. Fox, *J. Chem. Phys.*, **32**, 385 (1960); **33**, 200 (1960); **35**, 1379 (1961).

18. G. H. Wannier, *Phys. Rev.*, **100**, 1180 (1956).

19. R. W. Kiser, *J. Chem. Phys.*, **36**, 2964 (1962).

20. L. A. Shadoff and R. W. Kiser, unpublished data, 1963.

21. A. S. Newton, *J. Chem. Phys.*, **40**, 607 (1964).

22. B. L. Donnally and H. E. Carr, *Phys. Rev.*, **93**, 111 (1954).

23. H. A. Bethe, *Ann. Physik*, **5**, 352 (1930).

24. J. W. Otvos and D. P. Stevenson, *J. Am. Chem. Soc.*, **78**, 546 (1956).

25. F. W. Lampe, J. L. Franklin, and F. H. Field, *J. Am. Chem. Soc.*, **79**, 6129 (1957).

26. V. L. Tal'roze and A. K. Lyubimova, *Doklady Akad. Nauk S.S.S.R.*, **86**, 909 (1952).

27. D. P. Stevenson and D. O. Schissler, *J. Chem. Phys.*, **23**, 1353 (1955); **24**, 926 (1956); **29**, 282 (1958); G. Gioumousis and D. P. Stevenson, *ibid.*, **29**, 294 (1958); and D. P. Stevenson, "Ion-Molecule Reactions," in *Mass Spectrometry*, C. A. McDowell (ed.), McGraw-Hill Book Company, New York, 1963, pp. 589–615.

28. F. H. Field, J. L. Franklin and F. W. Lampe, *J. Am. Chem. Soc.*, **79**, 2419, 2665, 4244, and 6129 (1957); **80**, 5583, 5587 (1958); **81**, 3238 and 3242 (1959); **83**, 4509 (1961); *Tetrahedron*, **7**, 189 (1959).

29. W. H. Hamill, *et al.*, *J. Chem. Phys.*, **25**, 790 (1956); *Radiation Research*, **10**, 664 (1959); *J. Phys. Chem.*, **61**, 1456 (1957); **63**, 825 and 877 (1959); **65**, 183 (1961); *J. Am. Chem. Soc.*, **83**, 17 (1961); **84**, 529, 730 and 1134 (1962).

30. C. E. Melton, G. A. Ropp, P. S. Rudolph and G. F. Wells, *J. Chem. Phys.*, **29**, 400 and 968 (1958); *Rev. Sci. Instr.*, **28**, 1065 (1957); *J. Chem. Phys.*, **12**, 586, 700 and 1128 (1960); **35**, 1751 (1961); *J. Phys. Chem.*, **64**, 1577 (1960).

31. A. Henglein and G. A. Muccini, *J. Chem. Phys.*, **31**, 1426 (1959); *Z. Naturforsch.*, **18A**, 98 (1963); **15A**, 584 (1960); **17A**, 452 (1962).

32. J. H. Beynon, *Mass Spectrometry and its Application to Organic Chemistry*, Elsevier Publishing Company, Amsterdam, 1960, pp. 275 ff; *Trans. Faraday Soc.*, **57**, 1259 (1961).

33. C. W. Hand and H. von Weyssenhoff, *Can. J. Chem.*, **42**, 195 (1964).

34. T. P. J. H. Babeliowsky and N. A. I. M. Boelrijk, *Physica*, **29**, 405 (1963).

35. F. W. Lampe, J. L. Franklin, and F. H. Field, "Kinetics of the Reactions of Ions with Molecules," in *Progress in Reaction Kinetics*, Vol. 1, G. Porter (ed.), Pergamon Press, New York, 1961, pp. 67–103.

36. J. H. Freeman and R. W. McIlroy, *Nature*, **201**, 69 (1964).

37. T. R. Hogness and R. W. Harkness, *Phys. Rev.*, **32**, 784 (1928).

38. F. H. Field and J. L. Franklin, *Electron Impact Phenomena and the Properties of Gaseous Ions*, Academic Press, Inc., New York, 1957.

39. H. Eyring, J. O. Hirschfelder and H. S. Taylor, *J. Chem. Phys.*, **4**, 479 (1936).

40. V. L. Tal'roze and E. L. Frankevich, *Doklady Akad. Nauk S. S. S. R.*, **111**, 376 (1956); **93**, 997 (1953); *Izv. Akad. Nauk S. S. S. R.*, **1959**, (7), 1351.

41. D. P. Stevenson, *J. Phys. Chem.*, **61**, 1453 (1957).

42. M. Saporoschenko, *Phys. Rev.*, **111**, 1550 (1958).

43. G. Junk and H. J. Svec, *J. Am. Chem. Soc.*, **80**, 2908 (1958).

44. R. F. Potter, *J. Chem. Phys.*, **23**, 2462 (1955).

45. R. S. Baker, J. C. Giddings and H. Eyring, *J. Chem. Phys.*, **23**, 344 (1955).

46. J. L. Franklin, V. H. Dibeler, R. M. Reese and M. Krauss, *J. Am. Chem. Soc.*, **80**, 298 (1958).

47. H. O. Pritchard, *Chem. Revs.*, **52**, 529 (1953).

48. F. W. Lampe and F. H. Field, *Zhur. Fiz. Khim.*, **33**, 732 (1959).

49. K. R. Ryan, L. W. Sieck and J. H. Futrell, *J. Chem. Phys.*, **41**, 111 (1964).

50. J. C. Light, *J. Chem. Phys.*, **41**, 586 (1964).

51. V. Čermák and Z. Herman, *Nucleonics*, **19**, (9), 106 (1961).

CHAPTER 7

THEORY OF MASS SPECTRA

> There is one aspect of mass spectrometry where the cleavage into laymen and experts does not yet apply. That is, I should like to emphasize, a good thing, because the most live and truly scientific parts of any subject are those which excite the attention of the layman and the expert equally. I am referring now to the fundamental physics and chemistry of the processes by which the ions are formed, and in which they fragment to give the characteristic pattern shown in the mass spectrum of a complex molecule. The whole sequence of events is still in many ways rather a mysterious one, but it is of fundamental interest, and, indeed, the behavior of molecules in this fragmentation is a new and self-contained chapter of chemical kinetics.
>
> Sir Cyril Hinshelwood, in "Opening Remarks" in *Advances in Mass Spectrometry*, J. D. Waldron (ed.), Pergamon Press, New York, 1959, pp. xiii–xiv.

From an examination of the various ions found upon electron impact of a given molecule, one can see that certain fragment ions are formed corresponding to the cleavage of certain bonds in the molecule. To some extent there is a relationship between the strengths of the bonds cleaved and the relative abundances of the ions formed. However, this generalization does not always apply. What is required is a theory that will allow one to predict or to explain the formation of various ions, and the relative quantities of the ions formed at different electron energies.

In 1952 such a theory was advanced for polyatomic molecules, and we shall examine it shortly. Today we know that although the theory is far from perfected, it does give an insight into the production of the ions observed in the mass spectrum of a given compound. We shall describe in this chapter some of the features and assumptions of this quasi-equilibrium theory; and by means of an example, we will show the utility of the theory.

We might first think of the manner in which the various ions are formed. It is believed that many of these ions originate as the result of the unimolecular decomposition of an activated complex of the parent-molecule ion, although some ions may also be formed from the unimolecular decomposition of other product ions.

Let us consider, for purposes of illustration, the mass spectrum of thiacyclobutane shown in Figure 7–1. We see that seven ions compose the major fraction of the mass spectrum of thiacyclobutane. The relative and fractional abundances at 70 ev of five of these seven ions, together with one of the less abundant ions ($C_3H_5S^+$), are tabulated in Table 7–1.

TABLE 7–1. ABUNDANCES OF IONS IN THE MASS SPECTRUM OF THIACYCLOBUTANE [E. J. GALLEGOS AND R. W. KISER (1)]

Ion	70 ev Relative Abundance	70 ev Fractional Abundance
$C_3H_5^+$	11.1	0.047
CHS^+	26.1	0.112
CH_2S^+	100.0	0.428
CH_3S^+	7.9	0.034
$C_3H_5S^+$	2.0	0.009
$C_3H_6S^+$	49.5	0.212
All others	37.3	0.159

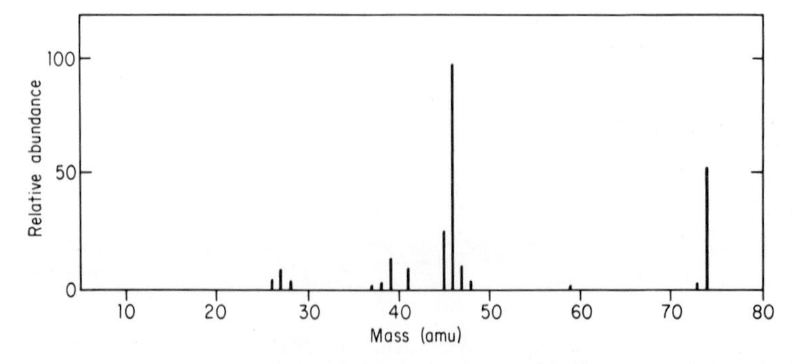

Fig. 7-1. The mass spectrum of thiacyclobutane. [Gallegos and Kiser (1).]

Considering the ions to be formed via a unimolecular decomposition of the parent-molecule ion of thiacyclobutane, we could write:

$$
(C_3H_6S)^+ \; (m/e = 74) \rightarrow
\begin{cases}
C_3H_5^+ & (m/e = 41) \\
CHS^+ & (m/e = 45) \\
CH_2S^+ & (m/e = 46) \\
CH_3S^+ & (m/e = 47) \\
C_3H_5S^+ & (m/e = 73)
\end{cases}
$$

But as pointed out above, it is possible that not all of the ions result directly from the parent-molecule ion; some ions could result from other fragment ions produced. Hence, as another possibility, we could write:

$$
(C_3H_6S)^+ \; (m/e = 74)
\begin{cases}
\xrightarrow{k_1} CH_3S^+ & (m/e = 47) \\
\xrightarrow{k_2} CHS^+ & (m/e = 45) \\
\xrightarrow{k_3} C_3H_5^+ & (m/e = 41) \\
\xrightarrow{k_4} C_3H_5S^+ & (m/e = 73) \xrightarrow{k_5} CH_2S^+ \quad (m/e = 46)
\end{cases}
$$

If one knew or could calculate the rate constants for such a series of unimolecular decompositions, then from the kinetics of the competitive and parallel consecutive reactions of such a scheme, the quantities of each of the species remaining or formed after some time t could be determined, and, hence, the mass spectrum could be calculated.

In the following discussion of the theory and the example calculation of the mass spectrum of a compound, we shall see both how k_i can be determined and the manner in which the kinetic scheme may be employed.

7.1 THE QUASI-EQUILIBRIUM THEORY

As pointed out earlier, the ionization process via electron impact is generally assumed to be a vertical process, following the Franck-Condon principle. The parent-molecule ion formed in the electron impact process will have a certain amount of excitational energy distributed in its electronic and vibrational degrees of freedom. Rosenstock, *et al.*, (2) devised a theory to explain the production of the relative intensities of the various ions from large polyatomic molecules upon electron impact. In this theory it is assumed that the excited parent-molecule ion does not decompose immediately into the various fragment ions and neutral fragments, but rather that the excited parent-molecule ion may undergo several vibrations prior to decomposition. It is also assumed that during these vibrations there is a high probability of radiationless transitions among the many potential surfaces of the parent-molecule ion, which results in a distribution of the excitational energy in a completely random fashion. The molecule-ion therefore decomposes only when sufficient energy has concentrated in the necessary degrees of freedom.

Using a statistical approach, Rosenstock, *et al.*, (2) derived a general unimolecular rate constant for the dissociation of a polyatomic molecule which is given by

$$k(E) = (1/h) \int_0^{E-\epsilon_0} \frac{\rho^{\ddagger}(E, \epsilon_0, \epsilon_t)}{\rho(E)}\, d\epsilon_t, \tag{7–1}$$

where $\rho(E)\,\delta E$ is the number of states of the ion with energies between E and $(E + \delta E)$, and $\rho^{\ddagger}(E, \epsilon_0, \epsilon_t)\,\delta E$ is the number of states of the ion in the activated complex configuration with potential energy ϵ_0 and translational energy ϵ_t in the reaction coordinates.

The state density functions are calculated for internal rotations and vibrations only. The electronic state density functions are assumed to cancel out. Nuclear motions are considered to be the same in all electronic states of a given ion or activated complex. Taking the reactant to be a system of $(N - L)$ weakly coupled harmonic oscillators plus L internal rigid rotators, and the activated complex to be a system of $(N - L^* - 1)$ harmonic oscillators plus L^* internal rotors, Equation (7–1) becomes

$$k(E) = Z(1 - \epsilon_0/E)^p(E - \epsilon_0)^q, \tag{7–2}$$

where

$$p = (N - \tfrac{1}{2}L - L), \tag{7–3}$$

$$q = \tfrac{1}{2}(L - L^*), \tag{7–4}$$

and

$$Z = \sigma(2\pi)^{3q}\left[\frac{\Gamma(N - \frac{1}{2}L)\prod_{i=1}^{L^*}\left(\frac{I_i^{1/2}}{n_i^*}\right)\prod_{k=L+1}^{N}\nu_k}{\Gamma(N - \frac{1}{2}L^*)\prod_{j=1}^{L}\left(\frac{I_j^{1/2}}{n_j}\right)\prod_{l=L^*+1}^{N-1}\nu_l^*}\right], \tag{7–5}$$

where σ is the number of equivalent ways of choosing the reaction coordinate, L is the number of internal rotational degrees of freedom, and N is the total number of internal degrees of freedom. $\Gamma(N)$ is the gamma function of N, and values of $\Gamma(N)$ as a function of N may be found in the common mathematical tables and handbooks. Also, I_i is the reduced moment of inertia for the ith internal rotor, n_i is the number of equivalent positions of the ith internal rotor, ν_i is the frequency of vibration for the ith normal mode, E is the total energy of the molecule, ϵ_0 is the energy of activation for the reaction, and the * superscript indicates the quantity for the activated complex.

If one considers the molecule to be only a collection of N weakly coupled harmonic oscillators and the activated complex to be a collection of $(N - 1)$ similar oscillators, one can simplify Equations (7–2) to (7–5) to the form

$$k(E) = Z^* \sigma[(E - \epsilon_0)/E]^{N-1}, \qquad (7\text{–}6)$$

where $k(E)$ represents the rate constant at total energy E with activation energy ϵ_0 and Z^* is the ratio of the products of the vibrational frequencies of the reactant to the activated complex. Here σ represents again the number of equivalent ways of choosing the reaction coordinates.

Once the $k(E)$ are calculated for the various processes of a chosen fragmentation scheme, a kinetic treatment may be applied to find the number of each kind of ions remaining after some time t. This information then may be used, upon application of an energy distribution, to yield the mass spectrum of the molecule. We shall actually carry through some of these calculations in Section 7.3 to illustrate the methods employed.

A number of workers have applied this theory to simple esters (3), alkyl halides (4), heterocyclics (5, 6), alkanes (7), ethylamine and ethyl mercaptan (4), organic sulfides and disulfides (6), aliphatic alcohols (4, 8), substituted hydrazines (9), ethane and deuteroethane (10), and the most widely studied molecule of all, the one originally treated by Rosenstock, *et al.*, propane (2, 10–15). These various treatments have met with varying degrees of success (16–20). Most often the results of the treatments were partial successes. Commonly the results are only in semi-quantitative agreement with experiment.

W. A. Chupka (16) deduced from a study of metastable ions that only a fraction of the total number of oscillators seem to be accessible to provide the activation energy for the decompositions. The fraction $(N - 1)/2$ or $(N - 1)/3$ has been shown to give better agreement between calculated and experimental mass spectra, but lacks a theoretical foundation. We shall again make note of this point in Section 7.2.

7.2 AN IMPROVED RATE EXPRESSION

> I do not say that physicists always use sound mathematics; they often use unsound steps in their calculations. But previously when they did so it was simply because of, one might say, laziness. They wanted to get results as quickly as possible without doing unnecessary work. It was always possible for the pure mathematician to come along and make the theory sound by bringing in further steps, and perhaps by introducing quite a lot of cumbersome notation and other things that are desirable from a mathematical point of view in order to get everything expressed rigorously but do not contribute to the physical ideas.
>
> P. A. M. Dirac, in "The Evolution of the Physicist's Picture of Nature," *Scientific American*, **208**, 45 (1963).

The integral approximation used (2) to determine the number of quantum states in the development of the original theory has been shown (4, 16–20) to be both a poor approximation at higher electron energies and completely invalid at lower electron energies. This difficulty may be overcome partially by empirically reducing the number of oscillators, as discussed in Section 7.1. However, it would be more satisfying if this could be accomplished on a sound theoretical basis. Vestal, *et al.* (14, 15), have given a new theoretical approach that results in an improved rate expression and produces the desired corrections in the behavior of the calculated rate constants at lower electron energies. This is accomplished, however, at the expense of greater mathematical complexity, although the theory remains basically the same.

The density of states, $\rho(E)$ and $\rho\ddagger(E, \epsilon_0, \epsilon_t)$, are given by

$$\rho(E) = \frac{dW(E)}{dE} \tag{7–7}$$

and

$$\rho\ddagger(E, \epsilon_0, \epsilon_t) = \frac{dW\ddagger(E - \epsilon_0 - \epsilon_t)!}{dE}, \tag{7–8}$$

since in the activated complex there is energy of $(E - \epsilon_0 - \epsilon_t)$ in the remaining $N - 1$ degrees of freedom. In Equations (7–7) and (7–8) $W(E)$ and $W\ddagger(E - \epsilon_0 - \epsilon_t)$ are the totality of the quantum states.

Vestal, *et al.* (15), have derived the following integral approximation for $W(E)$:

$$W(E) = \sum_{P=0}^{K} \binom{N}{P} \frac{1}{P!} \left(\frac{\sigma_P E}{h\bar{\nu}} - \frac{P-1}{2} \right)^P, \tag{7–9}$$

where P is an index varying from 1 to N, N is the vibrational degrees of freedom, $\bar{\nu}$ is the geometric mean frequency,

$$\binom{N}{P} = \frac{N!}{P!(N-P)!} \tag{7–10}$$

is the binomial coefficient, and σ_P is a frequency coefficient, defined by

$$\sigma_P = \left\{ \left[\binom{N}{K} \right]^{-1} A_K \right\}^{1/K}, \tag{7–11}$$

where

$$A_K = \Sigma \left[(-1)^{K+\Sigma P_i} \prod^{i} \frac{1}{P_i!} \left(\frac{S_i}{i} \right)^{P_i} \right] \tag{7–12}$$

and the principal summation is carried over all sets $(P_1, P_2, \ldots, P_K)$ of integers and zeros which satisfy the equation

$$\sum_{j=1}^{K} jP_j = K \tag{7-13}$$

and where

$$S_K = \sum_{i=1}^{N} \chi_i^K, \tag{7-14}$$

$$\chi_i = (\bar{\nu}/\nu_i), \tag{7-15}$$

ν_i is the individual frequency considered, and E is the internal excitation energy.

Substitution of Equations (7–7) to (7–9) into Equation (7–1) yields

$$k(E) = \bar{\nu}\frac{\sum_{Q=1}^{L}\binom{N-1}{Q}\frac{1}{Q!}\left[\frac{\sigma_Q^{\ddagger}(E-\epsilon_0)}{h\bar{\nu}} - \frac{Q-1}{2}\right]^Q}{\sum_{P=1}^{K}\binom{N}{P}\frac{1}{(P-1)!}\left[\frac{\sigma_p E}{h\bar{\nu}} - \frac{P-1}{2}\right]^{P-1}}. \tag{7-16}$$

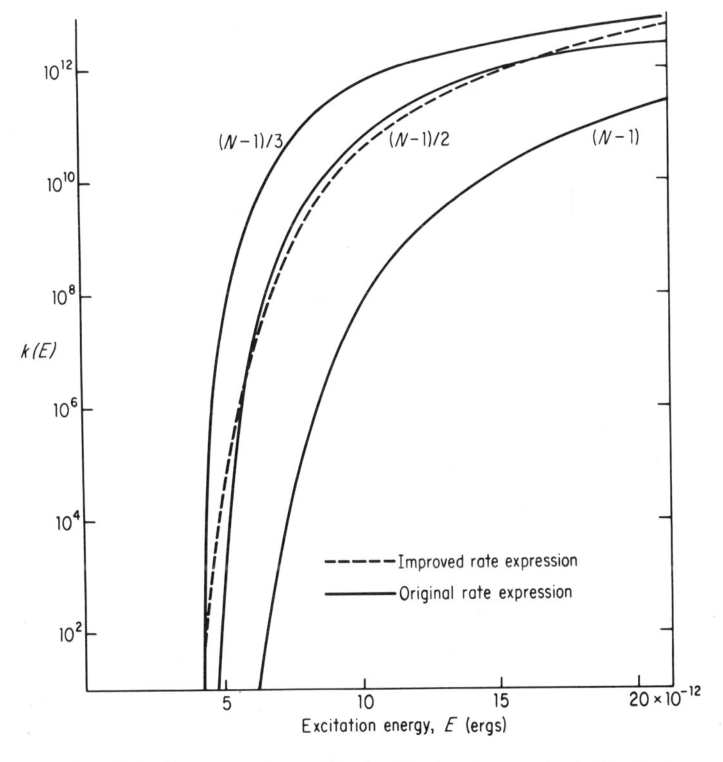

Fig. 7-2. A comparison of calculated rate constants for k_1 in the 2,3-dithiabutane case. [B. G. Hobrock (6).]

Each series will terminate with the last positive term, or when $L = N - 1$ in the numerator, $K = N$ in the denominator.

It is of interest to note how $k(E)$ calculated by means of Equation (7–16) compares to $k(E)$ calculated according to Equation (7–6). Such comparison calculations for the

$$CH_3SSCH_3^+ \xrightarrow{k_1} CH_3SS^+ + CH_3$$

process in 2,3-dithiabutane have been carried out (6) and are summarized in Figure 7–2. It is seen that the desired feature of the rate of change of $k(E)$ with E is brought out in the improved treatment, and, furthermore, that the values of $k(E)$ correspond closely to those calculated from Equation (7–6) using $(N - 1)/2$, as noted in Section 7.1. Vestal first found the improved agreement with the calculations using $(N - 1)/3$ for that case.

The use of the $k(E)$ values in the calculation of the mass spectra of molecules is then the same as that outlined earlier. Let us now turn to illustrations of the use of these theories in calculating mass spectra.

7.3 USE OF THE THEORIES

The quasi-equilibrium theory, as represented in Equations (7–2) to (7–5), is a rather formidable appearing theory. At first glance, even Equation (7–6) does little to dispel the feeling that the use of the theory is beyond one. In order to observe that the use of these mathematical expressions is a fairly simple task, and that it can be of great aid, we shall next consider, in the form of an example, the actual use of the original theory and the evaluation of the equations for a real case. The case we shall choose is the one for which we have already given some of the necessary information: thiacyclobutane.

EXAMPLE 7–1. We shall choose the second of the two decomposition schemes given earlier for thiacyclobutane. (The choice of a particular scheme involves many factors; many of these are discussed in Section 11.3.) To simplify our calculations, let us further choose to employ a modified Equation (7–6) for $k(E)$; this means that we are only considering the molecule and the activated complex to be collections of weakly coupled harmonic oscillators, and that we are neglecting the internal rotors.

From the appearance potential measurements (1) for thiacyclobutane, the energy requirements for each of the processes given by $k_1, k_2, \ldots, k_5$ can be determined. (We will see in Chapter 8 how these energetics are determined from experimental data.) These energetic requirements are given in Table 7–2 as ΔH^*. However, $\Delta E^* \geqslant \Delta H^*$, and we have no simple way of determining the amount of inequality. Without any other information, we shall take $\Delta E^* = \Delta H^*$, except for the process described by k_5. For

TABLE 7–2. HEATS OF REACTION CALCULATED AND ACTIVATION ENERGIES EMPLOYED FOR THE VARIOUS DECOMPOSITION PROCESSES OF THIACYCLOBUTANE

Reactant	k	Products	ΔH* (kcal/mole)	ΔH* (ergs/molecule)	ΔE* (ergs/molecule)
$C_3H_6S^+$	1	$CH_3S^+ + C_2H_3$	79	5.48	5.48
$C_3H_6S^+$	2	$CHS^+ + C_2H_5$	73	5.08	5.08
$C_3H_6S^+$	3	$C_3H_5^+ + SH$	76	5.27	5.27
$C_3H_6S^+$	4	$C_3H_5S^+ + H$	65	4.50	4.50
$C_3H_5S^+$	5	$CH_2S^+ + C_2H_3$	66	4.60	5.40

this latter process, we estimate that $\Delta E_5^* = \Delta H_5^* + 11$ kcal/mole, since this is a consecutive reaction in the scheme we are employing (11 kcal/mole = 0.5 ev = 8×10^{-13} ergs/molecule). Thus, $\Delta E_5^* = \Delta H_5^* + 0.8$, in units of 10^{-12} ergs/molecule. Therefore, the values of ΔE^* that we shall use in our calculations are those given in the last column of Table 7–2. These values of ΔE^* are then the values of the activation energy ϵ_0.

To determine the number of internal degrees of freedom N, we use the relation for a nonlinear molecule,

$$N = 3n - 6, \tag{7–17}$$

where n is the number of atoms in the reactant molecule-ion. For $C_3H_6S^+$, $n = 10$, and therefore $3n = 30$. Thus, values of $N = 24$ and $(N - 1) = 23$ are found. However, in light of the earlier comments made on Chupka's study of metastable ions, we shall only consider one-third of the oscillators as being accessible to provide the activation energy for decomposition. Thus, $(N - 1)/3 = 23/3 = 7.66$, and this then is the number of degrees of freedom for k_1, k_2, k_3, and k_4. For k_5, the reactant ion is $C_3H_5S^+$, which gives $n = 9$, $3n = 27$, $N = 21$, $(N - 1) = 20$, and $(N - 1)/3 = 6.66$. For simplicity, we shall set the symmetry number σ equal to unity. These data are shown in Table 7–3.

Our next step must be to evaluate Z^*. Since the mass spectrum of ethylene sulfide is so very similar to the mass spectrum of thioethanal, we may con-

TABLE 7–3. VALUES OF PARAMETERS USED IN THE CALCULATIONS OF THE MASS SPECTRUM OF THIACYCLOBUTANE

Specific Rate Constant	ϵ_0 (ergs)	Reduced Degrees of Freedom	σ	Z or Z^*	Eqn. No.	Reaction Coordinate
k_1	5.48×10^{-12}	7.66	1	9.0×10^{13}	7–6	C–C
k_2	5.08×10^{-12}	7.66	1	6.0×10^{13}	7–6	C–C
k_3	5.27×10^{-12}	7.66	1	6.0×10^{13}	7–6	C–S
k_4	4.50×10^{-12}	7.66	1	9.0×10^{13}	7–6	C–H
k_5	5.40×10^{-12}	6.66	1	6.0×10^{13}	7–6	C–C

sider this suggestive that the same activated complex is involved in both molecules when bombarded with electrons. Extending this approach to thiacyclobutane, we might also expect that the activated complex in this case be noncyclic. The C–H stretching frequency in CH_3CHS is about 3000 cm^{-1}. Vibrational information about the ion is not known, so we shall estimate it to be similar to that for the neutral molecule. Thus $\nu_4 = 3000\ cm^{-1}$ or $3000 \times 3 \times 10^{10} = 9 \times 10^{13}\ sec^{-1}$. If this becomes translational and the other frequencies remain constant, $\nu_4 = Z_4^*$, so that $Z_4^* = 9 \times 10^{13}\ sec^{-1}$. Similar arguments may be used to estimate Z_i^* for the other processes as well, and they are summarized in Table 7–3.

We now have values for Z^*, σ, ϵ_0, and $(N - 1)/3$, so that $k(E)$ may be calculated by choosing a value of E, and calculating k. Thus, let us calculate k_4 at $E = 15.0 \times 10^{-12}$ ergs/molecule for the process given by k_4.

$$Z^*\sigma = Z^* = 9 \times 10^{13}$$

and

$$[(E - \epsilon_0)/E] = [(15.0 - 4.50)/15.0] = 0.700,$$

so that

$$[(E - \epsilon_0)/E]^{(N-1)/3} = (0.700)^{7.66} = 0.065.$$

Thus,

$$k_4(15.0) = 0.065 \times 9 \times 10^{13}$$

or

$$k_4(15.0) = 5.9 \times 10^{12}.$$

In similar fashion, all other $k_4(E)$ values are calculated. And all other $k_i(E)$ values are also calculated in a like manner. A tabulation of the values of $k_i(E)$ for the thiacyclobutane case is given in Table 7–4.

Now that we have obtained all of the $k_i(E)$ values, we shall need to calculate the quantities of each of the ionic species. For this, we need a couple of kinetic expressions. For a system of j competing unimolecular reactions, the amount of reactant left at time t is given by the expression

$$[\text{reactant}^+] = n_0 \exp\left[-\sum_j k_j t\right], \qquad (7\text{–}18)$$

where n_0 is the amount of the reactant ion present at zero time. For a series of consecutive reactions

$$\begin{array}{cccc} A \xrightarrow{k_1} & B \xrightarrow{k_2} & C \xrightarrow{k_3} & D \\ n_1 & n_2 & n_3 & n_4 \end{array}$$

the amounts of A, B, C, and D, present at time t, are given by

TABLE 7–4. RATE CONSTANTS FOR THE VARIOUS DECOMPOSITIONS AS A FUNCTION OF THE INTERNAL EXCITATION ENERGY FOR THIACYCLOBUTANE

E	k_1	k_2	k_3	k_4	k_5
1	—	—	—	—	—
2	—	—	—	—	—
3	—	—	—	—	—
4	—	—	—	—	—
5	—	—	—	2.0×10^6	—
6	6.3×10^5	2.9×10^7	5.5×10^6	2.2×10^8	1.3×10^7
7	7.2×10^8	2.7×10^9	1.3×10^9	3.3×10^{10}	1.3×10^{10}
8	1.3×10^{10}	2.4×10^{10}	1.6×10^{10}	1.6×10^{11}	3.3×10^{10}
9	1.1×10^{11}	1.3×10^{11}	1.1×10^{11}	5.3×10^{11}	1.8×10^{11}
10	2.1×10^{11}	2.7×10^{11}	2.0×10^{11}	9.3×10^{11}	3.3×10^{11}
11	5.1×10^{11}	5.7×10^{11}	4.4×10^{11}	1.7×10^{12}	7.3×10^{11}
12	8.2×10^{11}	8.9×10^{11}	7.1×10^{11}	2.4×10^{12}	1.1×10^{12}
13	1.5×10^{12}	1.4×10^{12}	1.1×10^{12}	3.5×10^{12}	1.8×10^{12}
14	2.2×10^{12}	2.0×10^{12}	1.8×10^{12}	4.6×10^{12}	2.4×10^{12}
15	3.0×10^{12}	2.7×10^{12}	2.2×10^{12}	5.9×10^{12}	3.1×10^{12}
16	3.7×10^{12}	3.1×10^{12}	2.9×10^{12}	7.1×10^{12}	3.8×10^{12}
17	4.6×10^{12}	3.8×10^{12}	3.5×10^{12}	8.4×10^{12}	4.6×10^{12}
18	5.6×10^{12}	4.6×10^{12}	4.2×10^{12}	9.7×10^{12}	5.5×10^{12}
19	6.6×10^{12}	5.5×10^{12}	5.0×10^{12}	1.1×10^{13}	6.4×10^{12}
20	7.6×10^{12}	6.2×10^{12}	5.7×10^{12}	1.2×10^{13}	7.5×10^{12}

$$n_1 = n_0 \exp[-k_1 t], \tag{7–19}$$

$$n_2 = n_0 \left(\frac{k_1}{k_2 - k_1}\right)\{\exp[-k_1 t] - \exp[-k_2 t]\}, \tag{7–20}$$

$$n_3 = n_0 \{[k_1 k_2/(k_2 - k_1)(k_3 - k_1)(k_3 - k_2)] [(k_3 - k_2)\exp(-k_1 t) + (k_1 - k_3)\exp(-k_2 t) + (k_2 - k_1)\exp(-k_3 t)]\} \tag{7–21}$$

$$n_4 = n_0 \left\{1 + \frac{k_2 k_3 \exp(-k_1 t)}{(k_2 - k_1)(k_1 - k_3)} + \frac{k_1 k_3 \exp(-k_2 t)}{(k_2 - k_1)(k_3 - k_2)} + \frac{k_1 k_2 \exp(-k_3 t)}{(k_3 - k_1)(k_2 - k_3)}\right\}. \tag{7–22}$$

The time t is taken to be about 10^{-5} sec, since this is the approximate time of residence of the ions in the ion source. More complex kinetic schemes may be handled conveniently using Laplace transforms.

Let us calculate the amounts of the various ions at $t = 10^{-5}$ sec at an energy of 10.0×10^{-12} ergs/molecule. From Table 7–4, $k_1 = 2.1 \times 10^{11}$, $k_2 = 2.7 \times 10^{11}$, $k_3 = 2.0 \times 10^{11}$, $k_4 = 9.3 \times 10^{11}$, and $k_5 = 3.3 \times 10^{11}$. Now, from Equation (7–18), one can see that since $k_i t$, where $t = 10^{-5}$, is so very large, $e^{-k_i t} = 0$, and therefore [reactant$^+$] $= 0$. That is, at $E = 10 \times 10^{-12}$ ergs/molecule, $C_3H_6S^+$ decomposes in much less than 10^{-5} sec and is not present at all after 10^{-5} sec. Similarly, one can see from Equation

(7–20) that all of the $C_3H_5S^+$ has decomposed in less than 10^{-5} sec to give the CH_2S^+. What then are the relative amounts of the CH_2S^+, CHS^+, and $C_3H_5^+$ ions?

For competitive reactions

$$n_A = n_0 \left(\frac{k_A}{\sum_j k_j} \right). \tag{7–23}$$

Hence, at 10×10^{-12} ergs/molecule,

$$[CH_3S^+] = 2.1/16.1 = 0.131,$$
$$[CHS^+] = 2.7/16.1 = 0.168,$$
$$[C_3H_5^+] = 2.0/16.1 = 0.124,$$
$$[CH_2S^+] = 9.3/16.1 = 0.578,$$

and these total to unity, since the data have been normalized to unity. One can see that these are actual points on the curve drawn in Figure 7–3.

In this manner one constructs a *breakdown* curve such as that shown in Figure 7–3 by determining the amounts of each species present at a given value of E. Just to add the feeling for how rapidly this can really be done, look at the $k_i(E)$ values in Table 7–4, taking data for $E = 20 \times 10^{-12}$ ergs/molecule. We see immediately that $[CH_2S^+] \gg [CH_3S^+] > [CHS^+] \cong [C_3H_5^+]$. Also we see that at $E = 7 \times 10^{-12}$ ergs/molecule, $[CH_2S^+] \gg [CHS^+] > [C_3H_5^+] > [CH_3S^+]$. These observations can be rapidly checked by referring to Figure 7–3. One additional point must be made before moving on to the final step in the calculations. The *internal energy E* of the ion that is decomposing is not to be confused with the energy of the bombarding electrons. These are not at all the same, as we shall see now.

When 75-volt electrons bombard a molecule, and if all of the energy is transferred in the collision, there is more than sufficient energy to ionize and to cause many dissociations. If all of the energy were transferred in each collision, the calculation of $k_i(E)$ at the appropriate values of E would suffice to calculate the mass spectrum. But we know that the mass spectrum of a compound does not generally change significantly above about 30 ev electron energy, and changes only very slightly above 50 ev, up to, say, 100 ev. Thus, only some fraction of the energy of the electron is transferred to the molecule at higher electron energies, and this fraction varies with the electron energy. We can also conclude that there must be a distribution of the energies transferred to the molecules upon impact. One might estimate that there probably would be more transfers of smaller quantities of energy than of large quantities of energy. One could assume the energy distribution to be somewhat like a Maxwell-Boltzmann distribution.

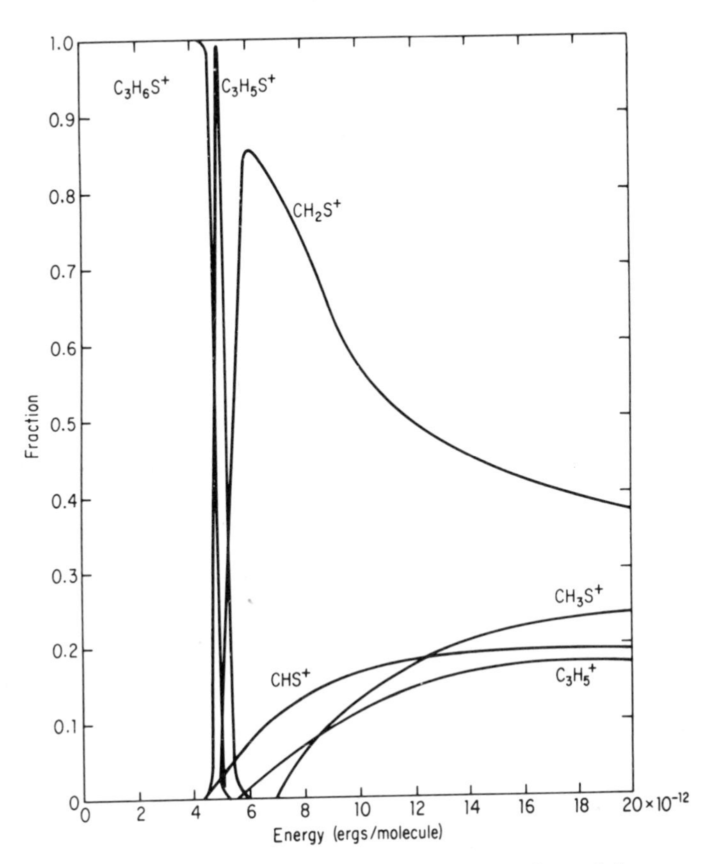

Fig. 7-3. Fractions of the several fragment ions formed from thiacyclobutane in 10^{-5} seconds as a function of the internal excitation energy.

Three different *energy distributions* are shown in Figure 7–4. The broken curve (C) is the first such distribution assumed [Rosenstock, *et al.*, (2)]. Curve A is an approximation made by Vestal, *et al.*, (14, 15) to approximate the experimental findings of Chupka and Kaminsky (21). For the present purposes, we shall use the square distribution (curve C) to treat the data in Figure 7–3 (the breakdown curve). Doing so, one calculates the mass spectrum given in Table 7–5. By comparison to the experimental data listed in this same table, we can see that the theoretical calculation is qualitatively, even semi-quantitatively, correct. But yet not perfect! Certainly one feature in error is the magnitude of the $k(E)$ values, as shown by Vestal, *et al.*, (14, 15). With the improved rate expression, the $k(E)$ values calculated are better.

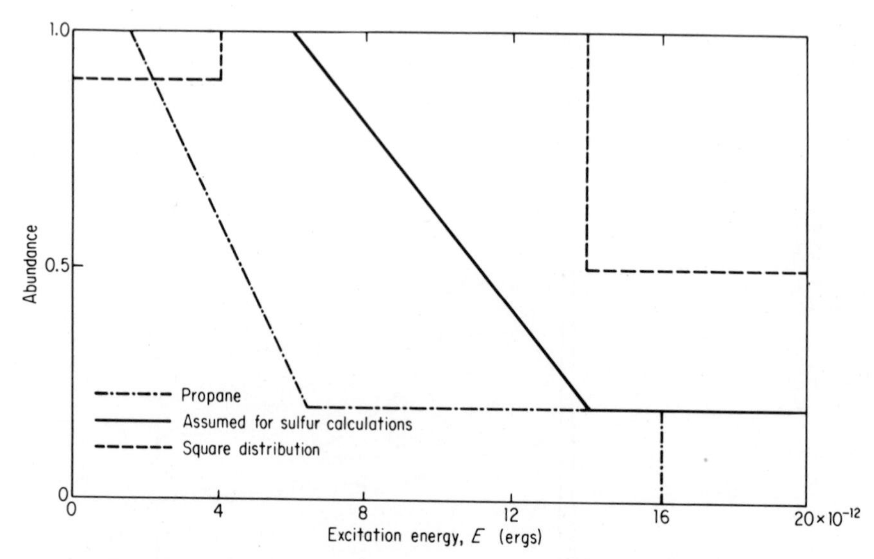

Fig. 7-4. Excitation energy distribution functions employed in mass spectra calculations.

The reader should have noted by now that possibly other fragmentation processes than those given in the second scheme (see page 143) could give as good or even better agreement with experiment. This choice is a salient feature of the entire set of calculations. In practice, one may choose many decomposition schemes and make the appropriate calculations. The scheme that best agrees with the experimental mass spectrum (and the experimental *clastograms*) is generally chosen as the scheme to be employed to describe the system. Additionally, by studying several homologs, in which the fragmentation is expected to occur by similar routes, further credence may be placed in the chosen processes. But good (or even excellent) agreement

TABLE 7–5. COMPARISON OF CALCULATED AND EXPERIMENTAL RESULTS OF THE MASS SPECTRUM OF THIACYCLOBUTANE

Ion	Relative Abundance		Fractional Abundance	
	Calculated	Experimental	Calculated	Experimental
$C_3H_5^+$	19.5	11.1	0.068	0.047
CHS^+	28.9	26.1	0.101	0.112
CH_2S^+	100.0	100.0	0.349	0.428
CH_3S^+	22.4	7.9	0.078	0.034
$C_3H_5S^+$	4.9	2.0	0.017	0.009
$C_3H_6S^+$	65.3	49.5	0.228	0.212
All others	45.3	37.3	0.159	0.159

between the calculations and experiment does not prove that the chosen mechanism is necessarily the correct one.

This use of the quasi-equilibrium theory of mass spectra to deduce reasonable mechanisms for the fragmentation of molecule-ions is, in the opinion of the author, one of the most important applications of the theory for the chemist.

We have seen that the quasi-equilibrium theory calculations using Equation (7–6) were fairly simple to make. The calculations using Equation (7–16) are somewhat more tedious, but no more difficult. Let us now examine the use of the improved rate expression in the framework of the quasi-equilibrium theory by means of another example.

TABLE 7–6. VIBRATIONAL FREQUENCIES ASSIGNED FOR 2,3-DITHIABUTANE (22)

Type	Frequency (cm^{-1})	Type	Frequency (cm^{-1})
CH stretch	2915	CH_3 rock	950
CH stretch	2915	CH_3 rock	950
CH stretch	2985	CH_3 rock	950
CH stretch	2985	CH_3 rock	950
CH stretch	2985	CS stretch	690
CH stretch	2985	CS stretch	690
CH bend	1300	SS stretch	517
CH bend	1300	SSC bend	240
CH bend	1425	SSC bend	240
CH bend	1425	CS torsion	580
CH bend	1425	CS torsion	742
CH bend	1425	SS torsion	116

EXAMPLE 7–2. Let us use 2,3-dithiabutane as our example. Again, we must calculate values of $k(E)$ in order to determine the amounts of the various species present in the mass spectrum. There are several quantities in Equation (7–16) which we must first determine. We shall consider these in order.

The geometric mean frequency $\bar{\nu}$ is determined by multiplying all $3n - 6$ frequencies together and taking the $(3n - 6)$ th root. For 2,3-dithiabutane, the frequencies given by Scott, Finke, Gross, Guthrie, and Huffman (22), and listed in Table 7–6, are used. Thus,

$$\bar{\nu} = (2915 \times 2915 \times \ldots \times 742 \times 116)^{1/24} = 1038 \text{ cm}^{-1}$$

so that $h\bar{\nu}$ is

$$6.625 \times 10^{-27} \times 1038 \times 3 \times 10^{10} = 0.208 \times 10^{-12} \text{ ergs.}$$

The activation energies we shall employ for the processes are given in

Table 7–7 and correspond to the following assumed fragmentation scheme (6):

$$CH_3SSCH_3^+ \xrightarrow{k_1} CH_3SS^+$$
$$CH_3SSCH_3^+ \xrightarrow{k_2} CH_3SCH_2^+ \xrightarrow{k_5} CH_2S^+ \xrightarrow{k_7} CHS^+$$
$$CH_3SSCH_3^+ \xrightarrow{k_3} CH_4S^+ \xrightarrow{k_6} CHS^+$$
$$CH_3SSCH_3^+ \xrightarrow{k_4} CH_3S^+$$

Now we need to calculate values of σ_P (and $\sigma_Q^\ddagger$). First we need to know values of A_K to use in Equation (7–11). We may do this by solving Equation (7–13) for $K = 1, 2, 3 \ldots$, as follows:

$$\sum^{1} jP_j = 1$$

so that

$$A_1 = (-1)^{1+1}(1/1)(S_1/1) = S_1 \tag{7–24}$$

and

$$\sum_{1}^{2} jP_j = 2,$$

which gives

$$A_2 = (-1)^{2+1}(1/0!)(S_1/1)^0(1/1!)(S_2/2)^1 + (-1)^{2+2}(1/2!)(S_1/1)^2(1/0!)(S_2/2)^0$$

or

$$A_2 = (S_1^2 - S_2)/2. \tag{7–25}$$

Similarly,

$$A_3 = (S_1^3 - 3S_1S_2 + 2S_3)/6 \tag{7–26}$$

and

$$A_4 = (S_1^4 - 6S_1^2S_2 + 8S_1S_3 + 3S_2^2 - 6S_4)/24, \tag{7–27}$$

TABLE 7–7. VALUES OF PARAMETERS USED IN THE CALCULATIONS OF THE MASS SPECTRUM OF 2,3-DITHIABUTANE

Rate Constant	Reaction Coordinate	ϵ_0 (ergs)	Z	σ	$(N-1)/3$
k_1	C–S	4.48×10^{-12}	2.07×10^{13}	2	7.67
k_2	S–S	4.23×10^{-12}	1.55×10^{13}	2	7.67
k_3	S–S	4.60×10^{-12}	1.55×10^{13}	2	7.67
k_4	S–S	4.67×10^{-12}	1.55×10^{13}	2	7.67
k_5	C–S	4.70×10^{-12}	2.05×10^{13}	1	5.67
k_6	C–H	10.20×10^{-12}	8.85×10^{13}	4	3.67
k_7	C–H	10.20×10^{-12}	8.85×10^{13}	2	1.67

etc. We insert these results into Equation (7–11) to obtain

$$\sigma_1 = \left[\binom{N}{1}\right]^{-1} S_1,$$

$$\sigma_2 = \left\{\left[\binom{N}{2}\right]^{-1} (S_1^2 - S_2)/2\right\}^{1/2},$$

and

$$\sigma_3 = \left\{\left[\binom{N}{3}\right]^{-1} (S_1^3 - 3S_1 S_2 + 2S_3)/6\right\}^{1/3}.$$

Using Equation (7–17), $N = 24$ for 2,3-dithiabutane. Therefore,

$$\binom{N}{1} = \frac{24!}{23!\,1!} = 24,$$

$$\binom{N}{2} = \frac{24!}{22!\,2!} = \frac{(24)(23)}{(2)} = 276,$$

and

$$\binom{N}{3} = \frac{24!}{21!\,3!} = \frac{(24)(23)(22)}{(2)(3)} = 2024,$$

so that

$$\sigma_1 = S_1/24,$$

$$\sigma_2 = [(S_1^2 - S_2)/552]^{1/2},$$

and

$$\sigma_3 = [(S_1^3 - 3S_1 S_2 + 2S_3)/12{,}144]^{1/3}.$$

Now it is necessary to evaluate S_K using Equations (7–14) and (7–15). Using the data given in Table 7–6, we calculate

$\chi_a = 1038/2985 = 0.348$ (4)
$\chi_b = 1038/2915 = 0.356$ (2)
$\chi_c = 1038/1300 = 0.800$ (2)
$\chi_d = 1038/1425 = 0.729$ (4)
$\chi_e = 1038/950 = 1.092$ (4)
$\chi_f = 1038/690 = 1.505$ (2)
$\chi_g = 1038/517 = 2.010$ (1)
$\chi_h = 1038/240 = 4.33$ (2)
$\chi_i = 1038/580 = 1.790$ (1)
$\chi_j = 1038/742 = 1.400$ (1)
$\chi_k = 1038/116 = 8.95$ (1)

where the values in parentheses show the number of times that frequency of a given χ-value appears. Then,

$$S_1 = 4(0.348) + 2(0.356) + 2(0.800) + 4(0.729) + 4(1.092) + 2(1.505) + 2.010 + 2(4.33) + 1.790 + 1.400 + 8.95 = 36.71.$$

Similarly,

$$S_2 = 140.2 \quad \text{and} \quad S_3 = 910.$$

Therefore,

$$\sigma_1 = 36.71/24 = 1.53,$$
$$\sigma_2 = [(1347.6 - 140.2)/552]^{1/2} = 1.48,$$
$$\sigma_3 = [(49471 - 15435 + 1820)/12144]^{1/3} = 1.43.$$

Other values of σ_P and $\sigma_Q^{\ddagger}$ are calculated in an analogous manner.

We may now use Equation (7–16) to calculate $k(E)$. Let us do this for k_1 at $E = 6 \times 10^{-12}$ ergs. Then

$$k_1(6) = (1038 \times 3 \times 10^{10}) \times \left\{\frac{(23)\left[\frac{1.738(6-4.48)}{0.208}\right] + \frac{(23)(11)}{(2)}\left[\frac{1.670(6-4.48)}{0.208} - 0.5\right]^2 + \cdots}{24 + (23)(12)\left[\frac{1.477(6)}{0.208} - 0.5\right] + (23)(22)(2)\left[\frac{1.433(6)}{0.208} - 1.0\right]^2 + \cdots}\right\}.$$

One can see that there are a large number of tedious, but rather simple, calculations necessary to complete this computation. The numerator can be cut off after 12 terms and the denominator after 18 terms in this case, giving

$$k_1(6) = 3.1 \times 10^{13}\left[\frac{2.5 \times 10^8}{2.2 \times 10^{15}}\right] = 3.5 \times 10^6.$$

Obviously, an electronic computer is the solution to such lengthy calculations. For the 2,3-dithiabutane example, it requires about 2 hr to calculate one $k_i(E)$, using a desk calculator. To complete the calculations for this molecule would require a few hundred hours. After this problem was programmed for an IBM-1410–1401 computer, the calculations were made in about 15 min.

Using the other values of $k(E)$ for 2,3-dithiabutane, the breakdown curve shown in Figure 7–5 is obtained from the kinetic considerations. Using curve B in Figure 7–4, the mass spectra are calculated as presented in Table 7–8. One notes the rather satisfactory agreement found. Certainly the quasi-equilibrium theory provides us with both a qualitative and a semi-quantitative explanation of the origin of mass spectra.

Table 7–8 also compares the 70-ev mass spectra calculated using the original and the improved rate expressions. Although it is not obvious from this table alone, it has been noted (6) that the improved expression offers no tremendous calculational advantage, although it is more satisfying in that it has a more rigorous foundation than the original form. Several other sulfur compounds and heterocyclics have been compared in a similar manner (6).

The breakdown curves are also obtainable by means of a rather unique experimental charge transfer approach due to Lindholm, *et al.*, (23–25).

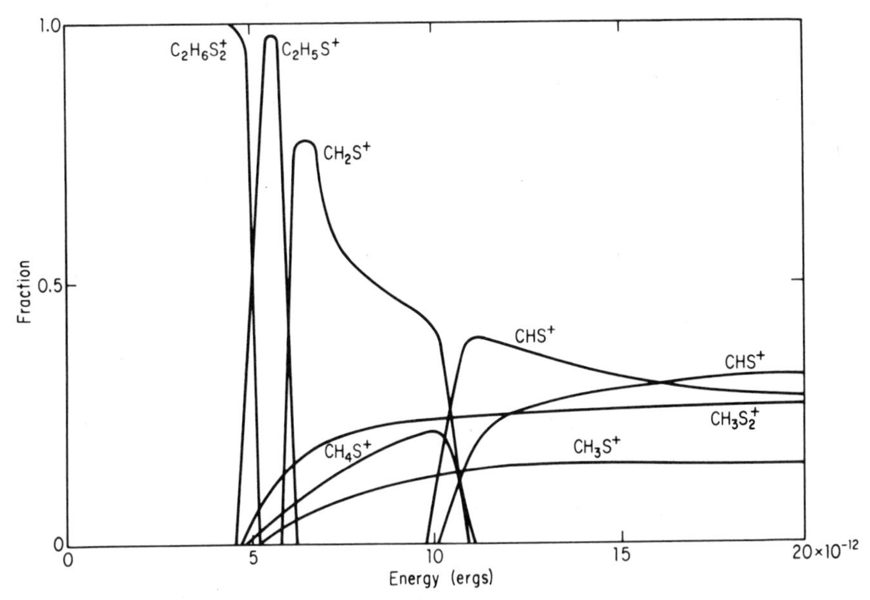

Fig. 7-5. Breakdown graph for a 2,3-dithiabutane, using the improved rate expression. [B. G. Hobrock (6).]

Recently, Chupka and Lindholm (25) have indicated that their tests of the theory with this method have given added weight to the theory.

Other features of the statistical or quasi-equilibrium theory have been brought out by Stevenson (26) and recently Schug (27) has discussed a fragmentation model for *n*-paraffins based on the theory. One can only anticipate many other applications of the theory in the future. Work in the author's laboratory has indicated the usefulness of the theory in choosing

TABLE 7–8. A COMPARISON OF THE CALCULATED AND EXPERIMENTAL MASS SPECTRUM OF 2,3-DITHIABUTANE [B. G. HOBROCK (6)]

	Fractional Abundance		
	Calculated Using		Experimental
Ion	Equation (7–6)	Equation (7–16)	
$C_2H_6S_2^+$	0.213	0.252	0.302
$CH_3S_2^+$	0.195	0.151	0.162
$C_2H_5S^+$	0.042	0.046	0.045
CH_4S^+	0.038	0.044	0.035
CH_3S^+	0.113	0.091	0.071
CH_2S^+	0.094	0.112	0.110
CHS^+	0.204	0.198	0.171
All others	0.101	0.106	0.104

mechanisms to explain the formation of ions in the ion source. It is believed that the use of the theory in establishing the fragmentation processes may take a place beside the labelling techniques and the studies of metastable transitions.

Recently Rosenstock and Krauss (28) have discussed the quasi-equilibrium theory in detail. The interested reader is referred to these reviews and critical discussions for further information.

REFERENCES

1. E. J. Gallegos and R. W. Kiser, *J. Phys. Chem.*, **66**, 136 (1962).
2. H. M. Rosenstock, Doctoral Dissertation, University of Utah, Salt Lake City, Utah, 1952; H. M. Rosenstock, M. B. Wallenstein, A. L. Wahrhaftig, and H. Eyring, *Proc. Natl. Acad. Sci.* (*U.S.*), **38**, 667 (1952).
3. A. B. King and F. A. Long, *J. Chem. Phys.*, **29**, 374 (1958).
4. L. Friedman, F. A. Long, and M. Wolfsberg, *J. Chem. Phys.*, **27**, 613 (1957).
5. E. J. Gallegos, "Mass Spectroscopic Investigation of Saturated Heterocyclics," Doctoral Dissertation, Kansas State University, Manhattan, Kan., 1962.
6. B. G. Hobrock, "Mass Spectrometric Investigations of Mono-, Di-, and Tri-Sulfides," Doctoral Dissertation, Kansas State University, Manhattan, Kan., 1963.
7. F. W. Lampe and F. H. Field, *J. Am. Chem. Soc.*, **81**, 3238 (1959).
8. J. Collin, *Bull soc. roy. sci.* (*Liege*), **7**, 520 (1956).
9. E. J. Gallegos and R. W. Kiser, unpublished data.
10. A. Kropf, Doctoral Dissertation, University of Utah, Salt Lake City, Utah, 1954.
11. M. Krauss, A. L. Wahrhaftig, and H. Eyring, *Ann. Rev. Nucl. Sci.*, **5**, 241 (1955).
12. A. Kropf, E. M. Eyring, A. L. Wahrhaftig, and H. Eyring, *J. Chem. Phys.*, **32**, 149 (1960).
13. E. M. Eyring and A. L. Wahrhaftig, *J. Chem. Phys.*, **34**, 23 (1961).
14. M. Vestal, A. L. Wahrhaftig, and W. H. Johnston, *J. Chem. Phys.*, **37**, 1276 (1962).
15. M. Vestal, A. L. Wahrhaftig, and W. H. Johnston, "Theoretical Studies in Basic Radiation Chemistry," September, 1962. ARL-62–426, Air Force Contract AF-33(616)–7638, Project 7023, Task 7023–03. 180 pp.
16. W. A. Chupka, *J. Chem. Phys.*, **30**, 191 (1959).
17. W. A. Chupka and J. Berkowitz, *J. Chem. Phys.*, **32**, 1546 (1960).
18. R. A. Marcus and O. K. Rice, *J. Phys. & Colloid Chem.*, **55**, 894 (1951).
19. L. Friedman, F. A. Long, and M. Wolfsberg, *J. Chem. Phys.*, **26**, 714 (1957).

20. B. Steiner, C. F. Giese, and M. G. Inghram, *J. Chem. Phys.*, **34**, 189 (1961).

21. W. A. Chupka and M. Kaminsky, *J. Chem. Phys.*, **35**, 1991 (1961).

22. D. W. Scott, H. L. Finke, M. E. Gross, G. B. Guthrie, and H. M. Huffman, J. *Am. Chem. Soc.*, **72**, 2424 (1950).

23. H. von Koch and E. Lindholm, *Arkiv Fys.*, **19**, 123 (1961).

24. E. Pettersson and E. Lindholm, *Arkiv Fys.*, **24**, 49 (1962); **25**, 181 (1963).

25. W. A. Chupka and E. Lindholm, *Arkiv Fysik*, **25**, 349 (1964).

26. D. P. Stevenson, *Radiation Research*, **10**, 6 (1959); D. P. Stevenson and D. O. Schissler, "Mass Spectrometry and Radiation Chemistry," in *Actions Chimiques et Biologiques des Radiations*, Vol. 5, M. Haissinsky (ed.), Masson et C[ie], Paris, 1961, pp. 167–271.

27. J. C. Schug, *J. Chem. Phys.*, **38**, 2610 (1963); and "Simple Fragmentation Models for Hydrocarbons," Symposium on Unimolecular Reactions in the Mass Spectrometer and Related Topics in Chemical Kinetics, Division of Physical Chemistry, American Chemical Society, Salt Lake City, Utah, July 7–10, 1963.

28. H. M. Rosenstock and M. Krauss, "Quasi-Equilibrium Theory of Mass Spectra," in *Mass Spectrometry of Organic Ions*, F. W. McLafferty (ed.), Academic Press, New York, 1963, pp. 1–64; "Current Status of the Statistical Theory of Mass Spectra," in *Advances in Mass Spectrometry*, Vol. 2, R. M. Elliott (ed.), Pergamon Press, Oxford, England, 1963, pp. 251–84.

CHAPTER 8

ENERGETICS OF ELECTRON IMPACT PROCESSES

For approximately 30 years, the measurement of the appearance potentials of the various ions observed in the mass spectra of substances has provided an almost unique general source of information and data on the energies of ions, radicals, and molecules. In this chapter we shall treat of some of the experimental and theoretical methods of obtaining these data on energetics after briefly examining the basics of determining energetic information.

8.1 SOME DEFINITIONS

The *appearance potential* is the minimum energy required to produce a given ion and its accompanying neutral fragments (if any) from a given molecule, ion, or radical. This then considers both ionization and dissociation processes. Of course, it is possible also that the products (neutral or ionic) will be in excited states rather than in their theoretical ground states. Therefore, the experimental values may be somewhat greater than the values corresponding to the theoretical definitions.

For the reaction

$$M + e \longrightarrow F^{+} + N_i + 2e, \qquad (8\text{–}1)$$

where F^+ is a fragment ion and N_i is/are the neutral fragment(s), the appearance potential of F^+ is

$$\text{A.P.}(F^+) = \Delta H_f(F^+) + \sum_i \Delta H_f(N_i) - \Delta H_f(M), \tag{8-2}$$

providing that the appearance potential experimentally determined corresponds to the species in their ground states and that there is no excess kinetic energy involved in the process given by Equation (8–1).

A special case of the appearance potential is the ionization potential, for here only ionization occurs, with no accompanying dissociation. The *ionization potential* of a molecule (or an atom or radical) is defined as the minimum energy required to remove an electron from the neutral molecule, atom, or radical. Theoretically, the reference states are the ground states (lowest vibrational levels) of both the neutral molecule, atom, or radical and the molecule-ion, atomic ions, or radical-ion formed. However, one does not always measure experimentally these ground state - ground state transitions.

For the reaction given in Equation (8–1), if $F^+ \equiv M^+$, there are no neutral fragments, and we write,

$$M + e \longrightarrow M^+ + 2e, \tag{8-3}$$

in which case the appearance potential is also the ionization potential:

$$\text{A.P.}(M^+) = I(M) = \Delta H_f(M^+) - \Delta H_f(M) \tag{8-4}$$

again with the provisions noted following Equation (8–2).

For other possible reactions, such as

$$M + e \longrightarrow F^- + N_i \tag{8-5}$$

and

$$M + e \longrightarrow F_a^- + F_b^+, \tag{8-6}$$

the same terminology applies. However, additional terms for describing these processes are also used; they will be considered in more detail in the discussion of negative ions in Section 8.4.

The determination of ionization and appearance potentials is accomplished experimentally through the interpretation of ionization efficiency curves. We shall first discuss the nature of the ionization efficiency curves and then treat of the interpretative methods employed in dealing with these curves.

8.2 IONIZATION EFFICIENCY CURVES

Typical ionization efficiency curves are shown in Figures 8–1 and 8–2. Such curves are a plot of the ion current of a given m/e as a function of the

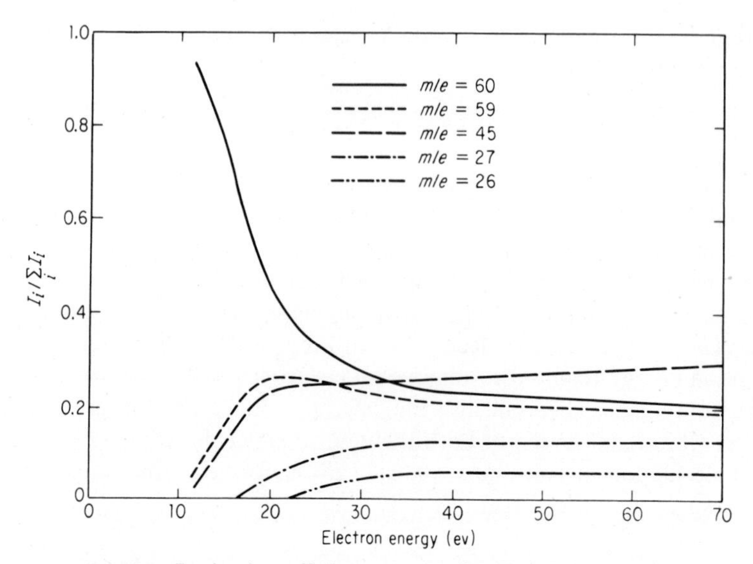

Fig. 8-1. Ionization efficiency curves for Hg^+, N_2^+, and O_2^+.

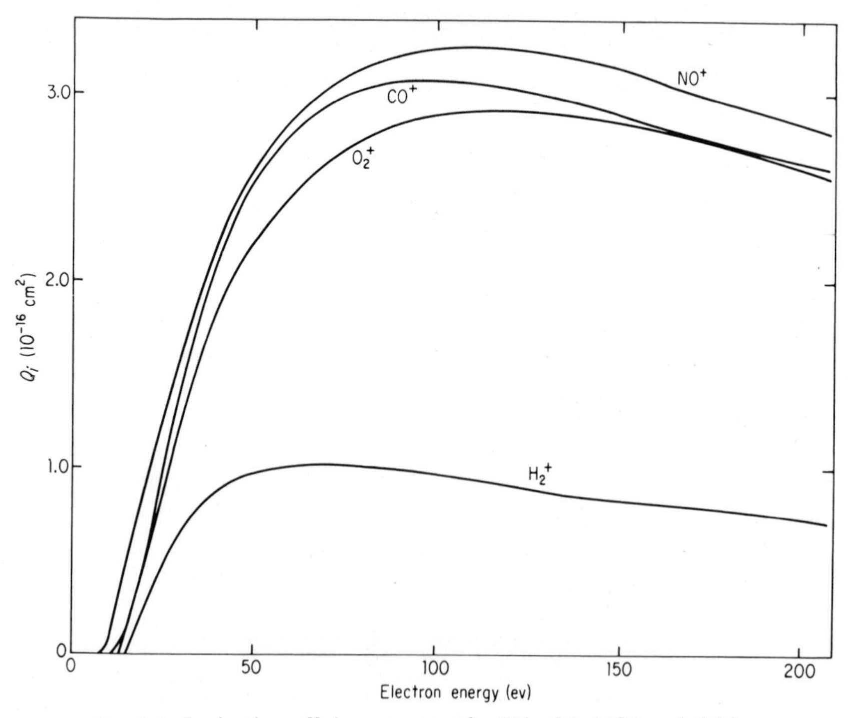

Fig. 8-2. Ionization efficiency curves for H_2^+, O_2^+, NO^+ and CO^+.

energy of the ionizing electron beam. In the case of mercury, a monatomic gaseous molecule, all of the ions produced are ions of mercury. But for oxygen and nitrogen, the curves refer only to the O_2^+ and N_2^+ ions, respectively, and do not include O^+ and N^+. Yet, very similarly shaped curves may also be observed for O^+ and N^+, and these also are commonly termed ionization efficiency curves. This is quite obviously improper terminology when terming such curves for fragment ions "ionization efficiency curves," for more than just simple ionization is involved. Yet through common usage in the field of mass spectrometry, this term has come to be accepted for all such curves, for both parent-molecule ions and fragment ions.

Since the ion current is related to the cross section for ionization, the ordinates of Figures 8–1 and 8–2, which are given in units of 10^{-16} cm², could just as well read in units of microamperes of ion current.

One thing that is noticed immediately from both Figures 8–1 and 8–2 is that the ion current is relatively insensitive to the electron energy in the region of about 50 or 70 volts to about 120 or 150 volts. Therefore, the mass spectra obtained at various voltages in this region will be very nearly the same. For this reason most of the mass spectrometers that are used to record mass spectra (generally for analytical purposes) operate their electron bombardment ion sources with electron energies of 50, 70, or 75 volts. In general most mass spectra are reported for an electron energy of 70 volts.

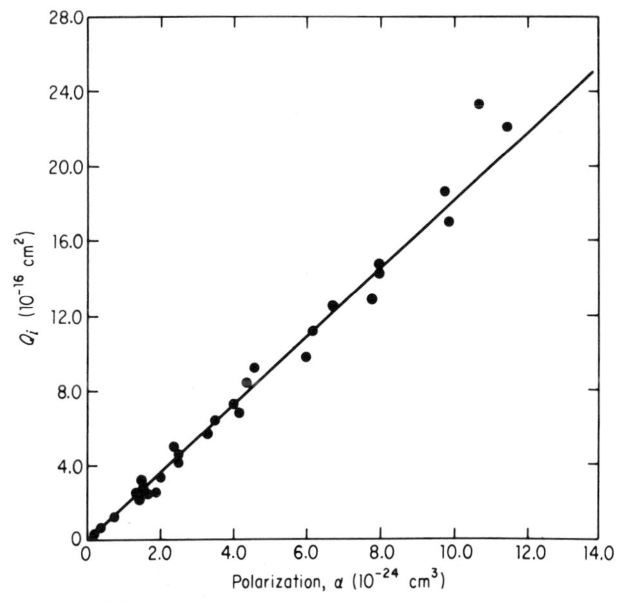

Fig. 8-3. Total ionization cross section versus polarizability. [After F. W. Lampe, J. L. Franklin, and F. H. Field (2).]

It should be noted in passing that ionization cross sections may be determined by means of a mass spectrometer. J. W. Otvos and D. P. Stevenson (1) and F. W. Lampe, J. L. Franklin, and F. H. Field (2) have measured a number of these. A tabulation of ionization cross sections for 75-ev electrons is to be found in Appendix III, which includes values from the above-mentioned sources as well as from the listings of H. S. W. Massey and E. H. S. Burhop (3). Lampe, Franklin, and Field (2) observed an interesting relation between ${}_{75}Q_i$ and the polarizability, α, as shown in Figure 8–3.

8.3 IONIZATION POTENTIALS

The true or *adiabatic ionization potential* of a molecule is by definition the energy difference between the ground vibrational level of the lowest electronic state of the molecule and the ground vibrational level of the molecule ion. We are here restricting our discussion to the first ionization potential. If, however, the potential energy curves for the molecule and the molecule ion have minimums at appreciably different internuclear distances, the turning point for the $v = 0$ level of the molecule ion may lie outside the effective *Franck-Condon* region for the molecule, in which case the 0–0 vibrational transition (and thus the adiabatic ionization potential) generally would not be observed by electron impact methods. Relatively small displacements of the potential energy curves for the molecule and the molecule ion will prevent one from observing the adiabatic ionization potential for a molecule. Thus it isn't surprising that ionization potential values as determined by electron impact methods are often higher than the adiabatic values (as determined spectroscopically). In fact, the electron impact values of ionization potentials are usually considered to constitute upper limits to the adiabatic values.

EXPERIMENTAL DETERMINATIONS

In practice the methods of determining the ionization potentials, and appearance potentials as well, of various ions in different molecules is to compare the ionization efficiency curve of the ion with the unknown appearance potential with the ionization efficiency curve for some other molecule. The reference molecule is very often a noble gas atom whose ionization potential has been accurately determined by other methods, such as by fitting spectroscopic data with a Rydberg series. It is also essential, because of the unknown nature of the contact potentials in the ion source, that both the known or noble gas calibrant, and the unknown sample being studied, be present together in a mixture of the gases. A further advantage is also obtained when the ionization potentials of the two molecules (i.e., the calibrant molecule and the unknown molecule) are of very nearly the same magnitude. In principle then, if these generalizations are observed, one may reasonably accurately determine the unknown appearance potentials of the ions from a given molecule. However, although in principle these determinations are reasonably simple, we will see that the determination of appearance potentials in practice becomes a difficult, somewhat complicated problem.

The electron beam is not usually homogeneous in energy, but rather has an energy distribution due to the thermionic emission of the electrons from the hot filament. While in principle the energies would be given by a Maxwell-Boltzmann distribution function, we find that the problem of correcting for the energy spread in the electron beam is a very difficult one. We shall put off discussion of this particular point on energy spread until later (see Section 8.4) and at this point look at the various methods by which one may practically determine these ionization and appearance potentials.

Experimentally, then, the procedure is to employ a mixture of the material under study for which an ionization potential is desired and a material whose ionization potential is known and will serve as the reference for establishing the energy scale. The electron beam energy is varied, and, as a result, one obtains a variation in the parent-molecule ion current. A plot of such data provides one with an *ionization efficiency curve*. Now, when one has experimentally determined the necessary ionization efficiency curves, the problem becomes one of evaluating these curves to yield the desired information. There are a number of methods by which one interprets the ionization efficiency curves, and we shall next discuss these in turn. It should be noted, however, that all of these methods are essentially empirical, and even the better of these have definite shortcomings.

All of the procedures given below involve a calibrant gas molecule in order to establish the electron energy scale. Recently, however, Asundi and Kurepa (4) have given a method, based on an experimental evaluation of the contact potential and an analysis of the electron energy distribution, for an absolute calibration of the electron energy scale which should prove useful for positive ions, and particularly useful for negative ions.

Direct Determinations

By obtaining the ionization efficiency curves as described above, and then by applying the appropriate means to interpret the data, one may make a direct determination of the ionization potential, providing the ionization efficiency curve for the parent-molecule ion is employed. To obtain the ionization potential by means of subsequent thermochemical calculations is not a direct method, but rather is indirect, and will be discussed in a later section.

Linear Extrapolation. A method that was introduced by R. H. Vought (5), which is no longer used for the accurate determination of appearance potentials (but is still used to obtain an upper limit for ionization and appearance potentials), is the method of *linear extrapolation*. In this method, the linear portion of the ionization efficiency curve is extrapolated back to zero ion current, as shown in Figure 8–4. The intersection on the energy axis is the ionization potential of the unknown, and comparing this to the linear extrapolation value of the reference material, gives the value of the ionization potential of the unknown. It turns out that in practically all cases the ionization potential so determined is higher than the true ionization potential. Now, this does provide one with an upper limit, and is useful in this sense, but the accuracy obtained by this method is generally rather poor. However, this method does have the feature of being very simple in its interpretation.

Initial Break Method. The early means of determination of ionization potentials from the ionization efficiency curves was one of determining the *initial break*. That is, the problem was one of extrapolating the ionization efficiency curve back to its intersection with the energy axis. This method is not very satisfactory, for on the "foot" of the ionization efficiency curve

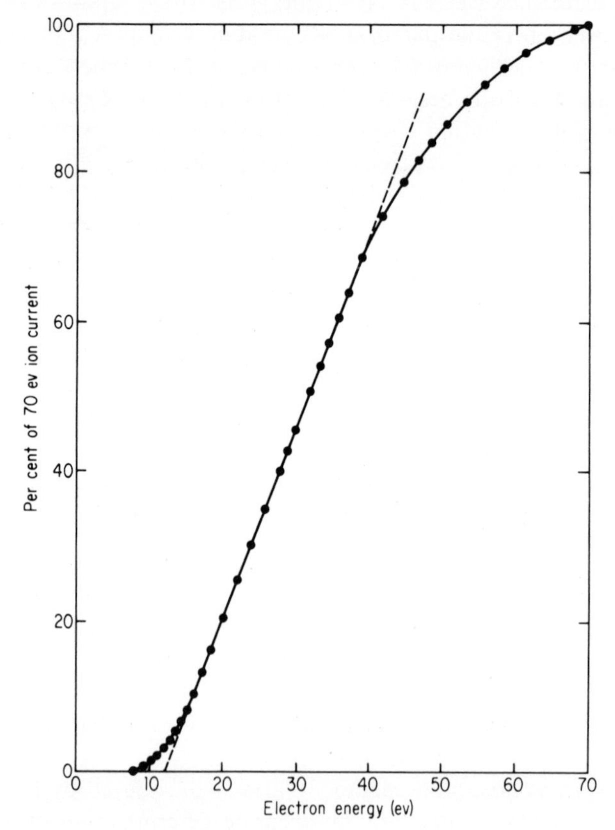

Fig. 8-4. Ionization efficiency curve for the production of M^+ from M, illustrating the near linear rise, and the method of linear extrapolation to obtain the ionization potential.

there are very low sensitivities. Also, in the "foot" of the ionization efficiency curve the ion current is approaching the energy axis very nearly asymptotically, which makes a determination of the initial break quite difficult. There is no sharp break; so, one has some difficulty in deciding where the initial break actually occurs. In addition, Waldron and Wood in 1952 experimentally showed that the value of the ionization potential determined by the initial break method decreases as the sample pressure in the ion source is increased; i.e., the ionization potential that one would determine from the initial break method is dependent upon the sample pressure. Although there are other objections to this method, it will suffice to say that the initial break method is, in general, not the most satisfactory method of determining either ionization potentials or appearance potentials.

Extrapolated Voltage Differences Method. The extrapolated voltage differences method, proposed by J. W. Warren (6), has been used by a number of workers and has been found to be reasonably satisfactory. We find in our laboratories that it is one of the more reliable of the interpretative techniques. A calibrating gas and the gaseous sample under investigation are intimately mixed, and the mixture is admitted to the ion source. The ionization efficiency curves of the various ions from the sample and the ion from the calibrant gas are determined. The ion current scale of either the sample ion or the calibrant ion is arbitrarily adjusted to make the linear portions of the ionization efficiency curves *parallel*. Now the voltage differences ΔV at various values of i_+ are determined from the curves. Finally, a new plot of ΔV versus i_+ is prepared, and the curve is linearly extrapolated to $i_+ = 0$. The value of ΔV at $i_+ = 0$, ΔV_0, is taken as the difference between the appearance potentials of the calibrant ion and the sample gas ion under study. This method gives good results both for ionization potential and appearance potential determinations if the ions have an abundance of greater than about 3% of the base peak in the mass spectrum, for the extrapolations are normally made over the range of 0.05 to 2.0% of the 50-ev ion current.

Figures 8-5A, 8-5B, 8-5C, and 8-5D illustrate the extrapolated voltage difference method, described just above. It can readily be observed that this method is a variation on the vanishing current method, but certainly it is less subjective than is the vanishing current (initial break) method. The asset of the *vanishing current* method (i.e., that the values determined approach the adiabatic ionization potentials at least as closely as any other electron impact method) is retained in the extrapolated voltage differences method.

Semi-Logarithmic Plot Method. F. P. Lossing, A. W. Tickner and W. A. Bryce (7) found that plots of the logarithm of the ion current versus electron energy for parent molecule-ions of many substances were parallel in the region of about 1% of the 50 ev ion current. Values stated to be reproducible to ± 0.01 ev were obtained. In our laboratories we find that the reproducibility is often more like about 0.05–0.10 ev and that the region of parallelism

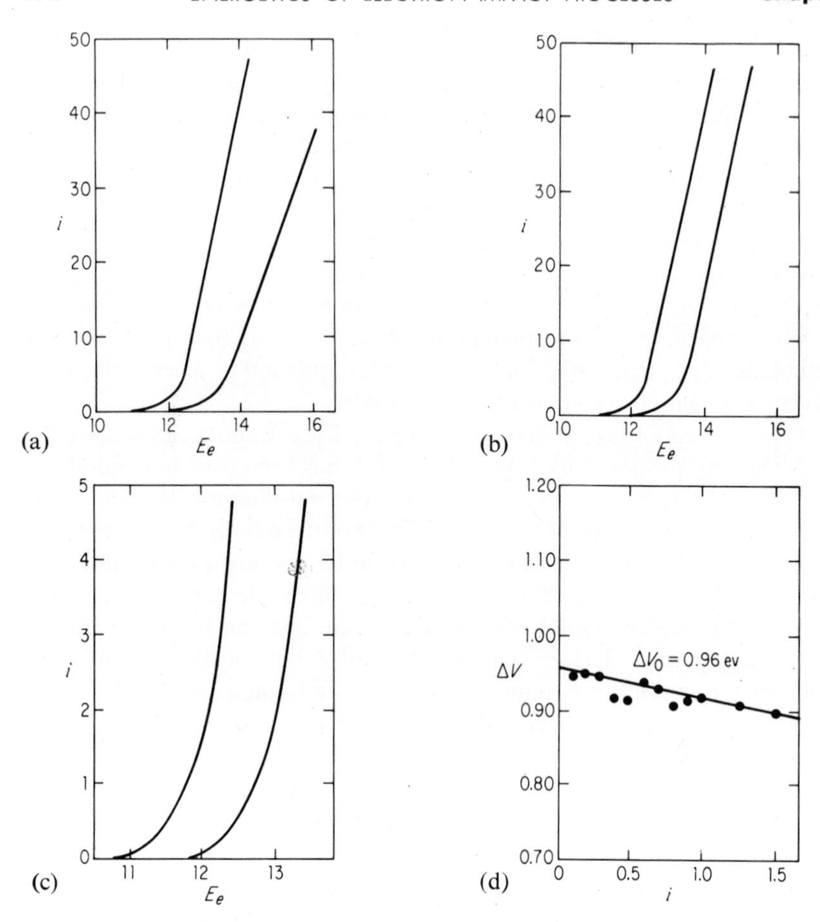

Fig. 8-5. Illustration of the Warren method of interpreting ionization efficiency curves (a). Curve b is multiplied by 1.75 to cause the linear rising portions to be parallel (b). From the expanded portion of the foot of the curve (c), the voltage differences, ΔV, are determined and plotted (d) as a function of the current, *i*.

often extends from 2 or 3% to about 0.1% of the 50 ev ion current. By using a mixture of the sample and the calibrant gas, good results are obtained for ionization potentials and oftentimes for appearance potentials as well [providing the appearance potentials are not too high or the ion intensities at 70 ev (or 50 ev) are not too low]. The effect of curve shape at low ion currents (about 10^{-12} amp) can render this method inoperable. An example of this method is shown in Figure 8–6.

At 4%, the difference in voltages between the two curves is 1.63 volts, at 2%, the difference is 1.64 volts, at 1% the difference is 1.62 volts, and at 0.6% the difference is 1.63 volts. This is also readily observable from noting

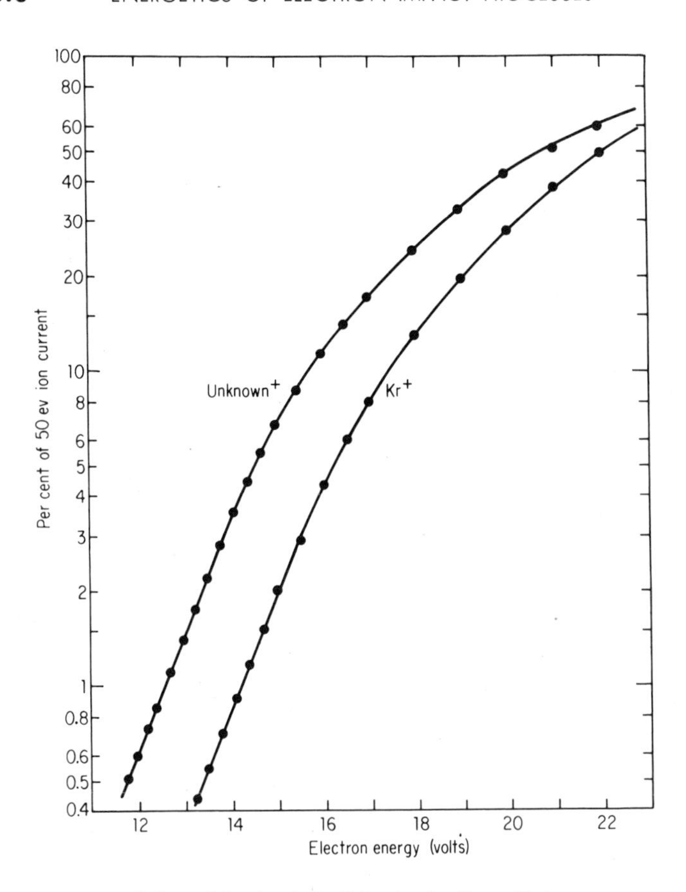

Fig. 8-6. A logarithmic plot of the ionization efficiency curves.

the parallelism between the two curves across the region of 0.4% to about 4%. Since the known ionization potential of Kr (to give Kr^+) is 14.00 ev, we see that the ionization potential of the unknown (to give unknown$^+$) is $14.00 - 1.63 = 12.37$ ev.

The Critical Slope Method. R. E. Honig (8) devised a method, termed the *critical slope* method, for determining the ionization potentials of molecules. Honig assumed that the probability of ionization (for ionization potentials) was proportional to the square of the *excess electron energy* above the critical (ionization) potential. He obtained the relationship

$$\ln N_i(V) = \ln [(V_c - V) + 3kT] - \left(\frac{\phi + V_c - V}{kT}\right) + C, \qquad (8\text{–}7)$$

where $N_i(V)$ is the number of ions produced per second at an energy of V, V_c is the ionization potential, k is the Boltzmann constant, T is the absolute temperature, C is a constant, and ϕ is the work function of the filament from which the electrons are emitted in the ion source. At small voltages, a plot of ln $N_i(V)$ versus E yields a straight line of slope λ, given by

$$\lambda = (1/kT) - [1/(V_c - V + 3kT)]. \quad (8\text{–}8)$$

At $V = V_c$,

$$\lambda = (1/kT) - (1/3kT) = (2/3kT). \quad (8\text{–}9)$$

Using a first power dependence of the ionization probability on the electron energy *in excess* of the ionization potential,

$$\lambda = 1/2kT. \quad (8\text{–}10)$$

Thus, one determines the ionization potential from a semi-logarithmic plot, such as shown in Figure 8–6, by determining at what voltage a line of slope $1/2kT$ or $2/3kT$ becomes tangent to the curve on the semi-logarithmic plot.

The method has been found to give rather satisfactory results for the determination of ionization potentials, and for many appearance potentials as well. Certainly this method is better than the linear extrapolation method, but this author has found it to be less satisfactory than the Warren extrapolated differences method in the determination of many different appearance potentials.

Energy Compensation Technique. A method of obtaining approximate ionization and appearance potentials has been developed and employed in the author's laboratory [R. W. Kiser and E. J. Gallegos, (9)], using a Bendix time-of-flight mass spectrometer. Using this new method, which has been termed the *energy compensation technique*, ionization and appearance potentitals can be obtained usually in less than 1 min. The energy compensation technique follows the concept of the logarithmic plot method described just above. The energy compensation technique, being instrumental in character, eliminates the necessity of obtaining the complete ionization efficiency curve in the determination of ionization and appearance potentials. A similar method, termed *simplified procedure*, was employed by Lossing, Tickner, and Bryce (7) to determine ionization potentials. Using the *energy compensation technique*, the ion currents of the calibrating gas and the gas being studied are measured at 50 ev and recorded on separate channels of a dual-channel recorder. The sensitivity of the two amplifiers (one for each ion output) is increased 100-fold (or, if desired, other convenient factors between 100-fold and 1000-fold), and the electron energy is decreased until the ion current intensity reads the same for each ion as previously at 50 ev. The difference in the voltages is taken as the difference in the appearance potentials of the calibrating gas and the gas under study. Although Kiser and Gallegos (9) used this technique only with a time-of-flight instrument for appearance potential determinations, they indicate that it should also prove suitable for use with other types of mass spectrometers.

Table 8–1 gives some comparisons of results of ionization potentials determined by the energy compensation technique and various other interpretative methods. Xenon was employed as the calibrating gas; its ionization potential is 12.13 ev. In general, values of ionization and appearance potentials can be determined to within about ± 0.2 ev.

Indirect Determinations

Ionization potentials may also be determined experimentally by indirect methods. We previously gave, in Equation (8–3), the process for ionization of a molecule, and in Equation (8–4) the relation between the ionization potential of the molecule, the heat of formation of the molecule, and the heat of formation of the ion. It is readily observed that if one knows the heat of formation of the ion, or if we may determine this quantity experimentally

TABLE 8–1. A COMPARISON OF IONIZATION POTENTIALS OBTAINED USING VARIOUS METHODS OF INTERPRETING IONIZATION EFFICIENCY CURVES AND THOSE OBTAINED USING THE ENERGY COMPENSATION TECHNIQUE

	Ionization Potential (ev)*				
Molecule	L. E.	L. P.	E. D.	E. C.	Lit.†
Methyl ethyl sulfide	9.2	8.7	8.70	8.7	
Methyl *n*-propyl sulfide	9.1	8.75	8.80	8.7	
Ethylene sulfide	9.1	8.7	8.87	8.9	
Trimethylene sulfide	9.2	9.1	8.9	8.9	
Tetrahydrothiophene	8.7	8.5	8.57	8.4	
Tetrahydrothiapyran	9.0	8.6	8.5	8.5	
Trimethylene oxide	9.9	9.9	9.85	9.7	
Tetrahydrofuran	9.5	9.2	9.45	9.3	
Tetrahydropyran	9.6	9.6	9.53	9.7	
Azetidine	9.1	9.2	9.1	8.9	
Pyrrolidine	9.2	9.1	9.0	8.9	
Piperidine	8.8	9.0	8.9	8.7	
Tetramethylsilicon	10.0	10.1	9.80	9.8	
Tetramethyltin	8.9	8.0	8.25	8.4	
2-Fluoroethanol	11.0	10.9	10.8	11.1	
Benzene				9.7	9.25
Krypton (II)				24.2	24.56
Nitrogen				15.7	15.6
Oxygen				12.5	12.2
Ammonia				10.3	10.15–10.50
Phosphine			10.2	10.3	10.1

*L. E. = linear extrapolation; L. P. = logarithmic plot; E. D. = extrapolated voltage difference; E. C. = energy compensation.

†A comparison to literature values is made only for those molecules where comparisons to L. E., L. P., and E. D. were not made. For a summary of literature values, see R. W. Kiser, "Table of Ionization Potentials," TID-6142, U.S. Atomic Energy Commission, June 20, 1960 and supplements.

in some manner, we may couple this information with the value of the heat of formation of the molecule, and thereby calculate the ionization potential of the molecule. This is an indirect determination of the ionization potential of the molecule.

EXAMPLE 8–1. The appearance potential (see Section 8.4 for further information about appearance potentials) of the $HSSH^+$ ion from 3,4-dithiahexane has been determined to be 12.2 ± 0.2 ev (10), and the heat of formation of H_2S_2 is known to be +4 kcal/mole. Calculate the ionization potential of H_2S_2.

$$C_2H_5SSC_2H_5 \longrightarrow HSSH^+ + 2C_2H_4 \qquad \text{A.P.} = 12.2 \pm 0.2 \text{ ev.} \qquad (8\text{–}11)$$

But $\Delta H_f(C_2H_4) = 12.5$ kcal/mole and

$$\Delta H_f(C_2H_5SSC_2H_5) = -17.4 \text{ kcal/mole.}$$

Therefore $\Delta H_f(HSSH^+) = 239$ kcal/mole.

$$H_2S_2 \longrightarrow H_2S_2^+ \qquad I(H_2S_2) = \Delta H_f(H_2S_2^+) - \Delta H_f(H_2S_2)$$

so that

$$I(H_2S_2) = 239 - 4 = 235 \text{ kcal/mole}$$

or

$$I(H_2S_2) = 235/23.061 = 10.2 \text{ ev.}$$

EXAMPLE 8–2. In a similar manner, determine the heat of formation of the $HNCS^+$ ion from the appearance potential (11) of this ion from ethyl isothiocyanate (11.38 ± 0.15 ev); then from this information and the heat of formation of HNCS, calculate the ionization potential of HNCS.

$$C_2H_5NCS \longrightarrow HNCS^+ + C_2H_4 \qquad \text{A.P.} = 11.38 \pm 0.15 \text{ ev.} \qquad (8\text{–}12)$$

Since $\Delta H_f(C_2H_4) = 12.5$ kcal/mole and $\Delta H_f(C_2H_5NCS) = 22$ kcal/mole, we find that $\Delta H_f(HNCS^+) = 272$ kcal/mole. Since $\Delta H_f(HNCS) = 27$ kcal/mole, $I(HNCS) = 272 - 27 = 245$ kcal/mole $= 10.6$ ev.

It is worth noting from the two examples above that in certain cases one may derive information concerning inorganic species and ions from electron impact studies of organic molecules. Another significant use of this method is in the determination of the ionization potentials of free radicals from appearance potential data. However, further discussion of free radicals will be reserved for Chapter 10.

Reliability of Measurements

One certainly wishes to know the reliability or degree of accuracy of measurements of appearance potentials and ionization potentials by electron impact methods using the mass spectrometer. Although we shall not explore them all in detail here, there are numerous factors that enter into the reliability of experimental values. However, most often the exact magnitudes of these factors are not known, so that estimates of accuracies are difficult, if not impossible, to state.

Most mass spectroscopists list some limits of uncertainty for the values of appearance potentials. Often these error limits are average or standard deviations of replicate determinations. In some cases, the error limits may only be guesses. Thus, the limits of uncertainty commonly given describe something of the precision and nothing of the accuracy.

Comparison of the appearance potential for a given ion determined by a number of different workers allows one, in general, to develop some basis for predicting the accuracy of measurements. Table 8–2 gives the values of the ionization potential of methyl alcohol determined by various workers. For comparison purposes, photoionization and spectroscopic results are also given. From an examination of Table 8–2 one may draw several conclusions:

(a) It is not uncommon to observe values apparently in error by more than the limits given. In this connection, there are numerous instances recorded in the literature where very small error limits are associated with grossly erroneous values of ionization and appearance potentials.

(b) Numerous determinations by different workers will generally allow one to decide upon a "best" value. For example, if one discards the value of 11.36 ev for the ionization potential of CH_3OH, the remaining electron impact values average nearly 10.9 ev, suggesting that 10.86 ± 0.05 ev is probably the "best" value here. This value may be compared to the values of 10.85 ± 0.02 ev determined by photoionization and 10.8 ± 0.1 ev determined spectroscopically.

(c) Other methods are not entirely free of error, as evidenced by the two

TABLE 8–2. IONIZATION POTENTIAL OF METHANOL

Ionization Potential (ev)	Year of Work	Reference
By electron impact:		
10.8	1940	12
10.95	1952	13
10.86 ± 0.05	1953	14
10.97 ± 0.05	1955, 1956	15
11.36 ± 0.08	1956	16
10.9	1957	17
By photoionization:		
10.52 ± 0.03	1953	18
10.85 ± 0.05	1954	19
10.85 ± 0.02	1957, 1959	20
By spectroscopy:		
10.8 ± 0.1	1941	21

different values of 10.52 ± 0.03 ev and 10.85 ± 0.02 ev determined by photoionization.

To put much weight in such conclusions from observing the few data presented in Table 8–2 would be rather unreasonable. However, there are many similar examples in the literature (22, 23), and these conclusions are generally valid.

Therefore, we may generalize, perhaps a bit incautiously, that, if the parent ion is rather abundant, electron impact determinations of ionization potentials will usually have error limits of 0.1 to 0.2 ev. Furthermore, for fragment ions, appearance potentials may have limits of about 0.2 to 0.5 ev, and often the greater the value of the appearance potential and/or the greater the difference in the shape of the ionization efficiency curve in the threshold region from that of the calibrating gas, the greater the uncertainty limits. Of course, if the abundance of the ion being studied is very small, the error limits may well be larger than usual.

Much greater accuracy is possible using methods which provide for electron beams homogeneous in energy. The retarding potential difference method of R. E. Fox, W. M. Hickman, D. J. Grove, and T. Kjeldaas (24) and those of P. Marmet and L. Kerwin (25) and P. Marmet and J. D. Morrison (26) provide such homogeneous energy electron beams, as will be described below. These methods ensure that the electrons producing ionizations in the threshold region come from the same region of the electron energy distribution. This also aids in removing much of the subjectiveness in interpreting ionization efficiency curves in the threshold region.

Field and Franklin, in their book, state that, ". . . with present techniques no appearance potential (and to a somewhat lesser extent, ionization potential) can be considered as well established until several reasonable concordant values have been obtained by different workers." There is really no alternative but to agree with this statement. The literature amply supports this view.

THEORETICAL CALCULATIONS

Ionization potentials are one of the most important properties of a molecule, being indicative of electronegativity, bond order, and bond energy. They are also important in determining charge transfer spectra. When available, ionization potentials may give considerable information about the molecular structures of chemical compounds.

Yet the determination of ionization potentials is not a mean task, and requires laborious measurements and data processing, as we have just observed. For these reasons it is desirable to have means of calculating ionization potentials. Purely theoretical calculations of ionization potentials are extremely complex for such monatomic molecules as neon and argon (the calculation for helium is not too difficult; calculations for helium by the various approximative methods are included in most elementary texts on quantum mechanics). For diatomic and polyatomic molecules such calculations approach the impossible, so that one turns to semi-empirical methods. Two such semi-empirical methods are the equivalent orbital method and the group orbital method. Let us look at these and two other methods in some detail by employing examples of the use of these methods to calculate ionization potentials.

The Equivalent Orbital Method

G. G. Hall (27) and J. Lennard-Jones and G. G. Hall (28) have treated the ionization process with their equivalent orbital method. Since the mathematical treatment is lengthy and involved, only a summary with some examples will be given here.

These authors have shown that removal of an electron from a molecular orbital distributed over the entire molecule, without altering the remaining orbitals, results in ionization. There are, therefore, ionization potentials corresponding to each of the various molecular orbitals of the molecule. These ionization potentials are equal to the negative of the energies of the molecular orbitals, the lowest ionization potential corresponding to the orbital of highest energy.

The molecular orbitals may be expressed in terms of equivalent orbitals by means of the secular equation

$$|e_{mn} - E\delta_{mn}| = 0, \tag{8–13}$$

where e_{mn} refers to electrons in the various bonds and lone pairs of the molecule and E is the energy associated with the corresponding orbital. It is necessary to determine the various parameters from experimental results, which thereby requires a self-consistent set of ionization potentials for various compounds.

In Appendix IV is given a fairly comprehensive set of ionization potentials, listing values for many atoms, molecules, ions, and radicals which have been obtained in various ways: electron impact, emission spectroscopy, vacuum ultraviolet spectroscopy, photoionization measurements, and others. However, for the purposes at hand, we shall consider these listings as a self-consistent set of ionization potentials.

In the treatment by Hall of the ionization potentials of the normal alkanes, a large determinental equation conveniently reduces to give

$$\begin{vmatrix} c - E - 2e\cos(\pi/s + 1) & 1.414d \\ 1.414d & (g + b) - E \end{vmatrix} = 0, \tag{8–14}$$

where s is the number of C—C linkages in the alkane. From experimental values of the ionization potentials for the normal alkanes given by R. E. Honig (8), Hall found the "best values" of the constants in Equation (8–14) to be

$$(g + b) = -12.0000$$
$$c = -13.2486$$
$$d = \pm\ 0.4678$$
$$e = -\ 1.4785.$$

EXAMPLE 8–3. Calculate the ionization potential of propane, $CH_3CH_2CH_3$.

$$\begin{vmatrix} c - E - 2e\cos(\pi/3) & 1.414d \\ 1.414d & (g + b) - E \end{vmatrix} = 0.$$

Then,

$$(-13.2486 - E - 2e\cos 60°)(-12.0000 - E) = 2.000d^2$$

or

$$(-13.2486 + 2 \times 1.4785 \times 0.500 - E)(-12.0000 - E) = 2.000(0.4678)^2.$$

so that

$$(11.770 + E)(12.0000 + E) - 0.4377 = 0.$$

Putting this into quadratic form, we obtain

$$E^2 + 23.770E + 140.804 = 0,$$

and solving by the quadratic equation, we find

$$E = -11.885 \pm \sqrt{141.255 - 140.804}$$

or

$$E = -11.885 \pm \sqrt{0.451},$$

so that

$$E = -11.214, \quad \text{and} \quad E = -12.556 \text{ ev.}$$

Since $-E = I$, we have

$$I(C_3H_8) = 11.214 \text{ and } 12.556 \text{ ev.}$$

The lowest value corresponds to the first ionization potential, i.e., 11.214 ev. This value for propane and the calculated values of the ionization potentials for other n-alkanes are compared to Honig's experimental values in Table 8–3.

TABLE 8–3. CALCULATED AND EXPERIMENTAL IONIZATION POTENTIALS

n-Alkane	Ionization Potential (ev)	
	Calculated	Experimental
CH_4	13.04	13.04
C_2H_6	11.78	11.78
C_3H_8	11.214	11.21
C_4H_{10}	10.795	10.80
C_5H_{12}	10.554	10.55
C_6H_{14}	10.412	10.43
C_7H_{16}	10.323	10.35
C_8H_{18}	10.265	10.24
C_9H_{20}	10.224	10.21
$C_{10}H_{22}$	10.194	10.19

The Group Orbital Method

For branched-chain paraffins and substituted paraffins, the above treatment becomes quite involved. Lennard-Jones and Hall (28) showed that for planar molecules which have an orbital antisymmetric in the plane of the molecule, the secular equation reduces to

$$| e_{rs} - E\delta_{rs} | = 0, \qquad (8\text{–}15)$$

where the terms refer now to characteristic groups. This greatly simplifies the calculations. Consider the substituted ethylene molecule, $R_2C{=}CR_2$:

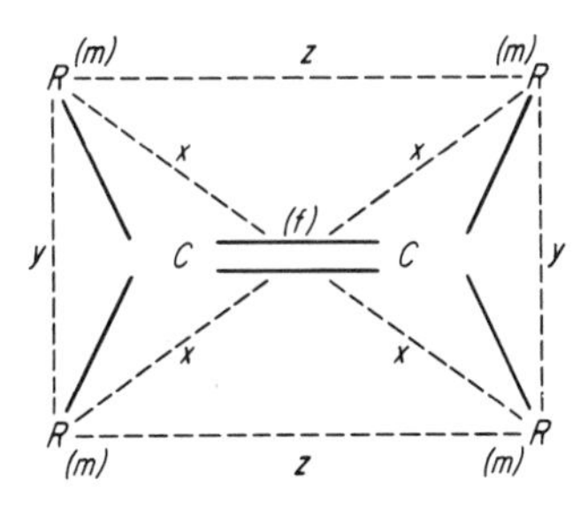

where m is the ionization potential of RH,

f is the ionization potential of $CH_2{=}CH_2$,

x is the R—(C=C) interaction parameter,

y is the R—R interaction parameter (on same carbon atom), and

z is the R—R interaction parameter (on adjacent carbon atoms).

Then the general determinant may be written as

$$\begin{vmatrix} m-E & y & x & 0 & 0 \\ y & m-E & x & 0 & 0 \\ x & x & f-E & x & x \\ 0 & 0 & x & m-E & y \\ 0 & 0 & x & y & m-E \end{vmatrix} = 0. \qquad (8\text{–}16)$$

Note that in Equation (8–16), we have disregarded second-order interactions, i.e., we have set $z = 0$. Such a treatment generally greatly simplifies the calculations.

To make any calculations, it is necessary to know m, f, x, and y. $m = I(\text{RH})$; $f = I(C_2H_4) = 10.515$ ev, and x and y must be determined.

EXAMPLE 8–4. Let us consider the methyl-substituted ethylenes ($R = CH_3$). Then, $m = I(CH_4) = 12.98$ ev and $f = 10.515$ ev. Note that throughout the following calculations numerical values different from those employed by Hall are being used by this author.

Now, for propylene,

$$\begin{array}{l} CH_3\diagdown \quad\; H \\ \qquad C{=}C \\ \qquad H \;\; H \end{array} \qquad I_{\text{exptl}} = 9.73 \text{ ev}; \; E = -9.73.$$

Since

$$\begin{vmatrix} -12.98 - E & x \\ x & -10.515 - E \end{vmatrix} = 0,$$

we have

$$\begin{vmatrix} -12.98 + 9.73 & x \\ x & -10.515 + 9.73 \end{vmatrix} = 0.$$

Therefore,

$$x^2 = (-3.25)(-0.785) = 2.551$$

and

$$x = \pm 1.60.$$

Consider now the case of 2-methylpropene:

$$\begin{array}{l} CH_3\diagdown \quad\; H \\ \qquad\; C{=}C \\ CH_3\diagup \quad\; H \end{array} \qquad I_{\text{exptl}} = 9.23 \text{ ev}; \; E = -9.23,$$

for which we write the determinant

$$\begin{vmatrix} m-E & y & x \\ y & m-E & x \\ x & x & f-E \end{vmatrix} = 0.$$

Therefore,

$$(-12.98 - E)(-12.98 - E)(-10.515 - E) + 2x^2y - 2x^2(-12.98 - E) - y^2(-10.515 - E) = 0$$

or

$$(3.75)^2(1.285) + 5.102y - (5.102)(3.75) - y^2(1.285) = 0,$$

which in quadratic form is

$$y^2 - 3.970\,y - 0.826 = 0$$

and yields

$$y = 0.22$$

as a solution from the quadratic equation.

Having calculated x and y when $R = CH_3$, and knowing m and f, we may calculate now the ionization potentials of the other methyl-substituted ethylenes. Let us do so for 2-butene

$$\begin{matrix} CH_3 & & CH_3 \\ & \diagdown\ \ \diagup & \\ & C{=}C & \\ & H\ \ H & \end{matrix}$$

(we shall not here differentiate between *cis* and *trans* forms), for which we write the determinant

$$\begin{vmatrix} m - E & x & 0 \\ x & f - E & x \\ 0 & x & m - E \end{vmatrix} = 0$$

or

$$(m - E)^2(f - E) - 2x^2(m - E) = 0.$$

One root of this equation is given by $(m - E) = 0$, so $E = -12.98$ or $I = 12.98$ ev. The other two roots are given by

$$(f - E)\,(m - E) = 2x^2.$$

Substituting our determined parameters,

$$(-10.515 - E)(-12.98 - E) = 2(2.551)$$

or

$$E^2 + 23.495E + 131.383 = 0,$$

so that

$$\begin{aligned} E &= -11.747 \pm \sqrt{137.992 - 131.383} \\ &= -11.474 \pm \sqrt{6.609} \\ &= -11.747 \pm 2.571 \\ &= -9.18 \text{ ev and } E = -14.32 \text{ ev.} \end{aligned}$$

Thus, the three roots are

$$E = -9.18 \quad \rightarrow \quad I = 9.18 \text{ ev}$$

$$E = -12.98 \quad \rightarrow \quad I = 12.98 \text{ ev}$$

$$E = -14.32 \quad \rightarrow \quad I = 14.32 \text{ ev},$$

and therefore, since 9.18 ev is the lowest value, the ionization potential of 2-butene is calculated to be 9.18 ev. The experimental value is 9.13 ev, and we observe that the comparison is quite satisfactory.

In Table 8–4 is presented a summary of the parameters for the methyl-substituted ethylenes and a comparison of the calculated and experimental values of the ionization potentials. (Values in parentheses were used in the evaluation of the necessary parameters.)

TABLE 8–4. PARAMETERS AND IONIZATION POTENTIALS OF METHYL-SUBSTITUTED ETHYLENES

	Calculated (ev)	Experimental (ev)
f	10.515	
m	12.98	
x	1.60	
y	0.22	
$CH_2{=}CH_2$	(10.515)	10.515
$CH_3CH{=}CH_2$	(9.73)	9.73
$(CH_3)_2C{=}CH_2$	(9.23)	9.23
$CH_3CH{=}CHCH_3$	9.18	9.13
$CH_3CH{=}C(CH_3)_2$	8.80	8.67
$(CH_3)_2C{=}C(CH_3)_2$	8.39	8.30

Franklin (29) extended the group orbital calculation of ionization potentials to olefins, alkyl benezenes, aldehydes, amines, alkyl halides, alcohols and ethers, carboxylic acids and esters, cycloparaffins, ketones, and paraffins. The ionization potentials of free radicals may be calculated also by this method. Even for nonplanar compounds, a requirement in the Hall approach, the results of the calculations agreed very well with experimental values. [Readers are referred to the original paper by Franklin (29) for additional details.] However, in Table 8–5 is given a Franklin extension of the Hall approach in a few examples calculated and taken from the recent literature (30).

From Table 8–5, we see that, in general, the agreement is quite good. Extreme faith is not to be placed in the results of the calculations by the group orbital method, but the method is very useful in attempting to approximate an as-yet-undetermined ionization potential. Commonly the calculated values will agree within 0.2–0.3 ev with experimental values.

TABLE 8–5. A COMPARISON OF SOME EXPERIMENTAL AND CALCULATED IONIZATION POTENTIALS OF VARIOUS SULFUR COMPOUNDS (VALUES ARE LISTED IN UNITS OF ELECTRON VOLTS)

	Parameters	
$I(CH_4)$	13.31	
$I(H_2S)$	10.46	
C—C	1.55	
C—S	1.99	
	Calculated	Experimental
CH_3SH	(9.44)	9.44
CH_3CH_2SH	9.30	9.29
n-$CH_3CH_2CH_2SH$	9.28	9.195
CH_3SCH_3	8.73	8.684, 8.73
$CH_3SCH_2CH_3$	8.65	8.55
$CH_3CH_2SCH_2CH_3$	8.58	8.43, 8.48
CH_2CH_2S (ring)	9.08	8.87
$CH_2CH_2CH_2S$ (ring)	8.43	8.64
CH_3CHCH_2S (ring)	9.02 (8.38, 8.51)*	8.6
$CH_2CH_2CH_2CH_2S$ (ring)	8.62	8.48
$CH_2CH_2CH_2CH_2CH_2S$ (ring)	8.54	8.36

*Calculated by other methods; see Reference (30).

Exceptions to this, e.g., the case of cyclopropane, however, are known. (See the discussion of this problem by Field and Franklin in their book, pp. 124–25.)

The Use of δ_K Values

Kaufman and Koski (31) have proposed the use of a set of constants, termed the δ_K values, to calculate quantitatively the change in the ionization potentials of free radicals and molecules with substitution of the parent molecule or radical. The δ_K values are additive within a given series. This method possesses the quality that the calculations are quite simple to make. Kaufman (32) has recently extended the calculations of ionization potentials with δ_K values to many different classes of compounds; additionally, she has noted that these δ_K values may have wider applicability than just for the prediction of ionization potentials. Let us examine the use of δ_K values in connection with the calculation of ionization potentials.

Three types of δ_K values are employed: $\delta_K^{(x)}$, $\delta_K^{(x-y)}$ and $\delta_{K\text{-Me}}^{(x)}$. These are defined in the following paragraphs. The first type is

$$\delta_{K,A}^{(x)}(R) = I[AH_n] - I[(R)_x AH_{n-x}]. \tag{8–17}$$

That is, $\delta_{K,A}^{(x)}(R)$ is the difference in the ionization potentials caused by substituting x identical R groups for H atoms about a central atom A. Taking the amines as an example, we see that

$$\delta_{K,N}^{(1)}(\mathrm{Me}) = I[\mathrm{NH_3}] - I[\mathrm{CH_3NH_2}],$$

$$\delta_{K,N}^{(2)}(\mathrm{Me}) = I[\mathrm{NH_3}] - I[(\mathrm{CH_3})_2\mathrm{NH}],$$

and

$$\delta_{K,N}^{(3)}(\mathrm{Et}) = I[\mathrm{NH_3}] - I[(\mathrm{C_2H_5})_3\mathrm{N}],$$

where Me is the symbol for methyl and Et is the symbol for ethyl.

The second type is

$$\delta_{K,A}^{(x-y)}(R) = I[R_y A\mathrm{H}_{n-y}] - I[(R)_x A\mathrm{H}_{n-x}]. \tag{8–18}$$

Thus, $\delta_{K,A}^{(x-y)}(R)$ values are the difference in ionization potentials between the molecules at various stages in the substitution by R. Taking the aliphatic sulfides to illustrate this, we find that

$$\delta_{K,S}^{(1-0)}(\mathrm{Me}) = I[\mathrm{H_2S}] - I[\mathrm{CH_3SH}],$$

$$\delta_{K,S}^{(2-1)}(\mathrm{Me}) = I[\mathrm{CH_3SH}] - I[\mathrm{CH_3SCH_3}],$$

and

$$\delta_{K,S}^{(2-1)}(\mathrm{Et}) = I[\mathrm{C_2H_5SH}] - I[\mathrm{C_2H_5SC_2H_5}].$$

The third type of δ_K values are those which represent the changes effected in the ionization potential when substituting x other R' groups for methyl groups. That is,

$$\delta_{K\text{-Me},A}^{(x)}(R') = I[R_x A\mathrm{H}_{n-x}] - I[(R')_x A\mathrm{H}_{n-x}]. \tag{8–19}$$

Let us look at three examples of this, using the aliphatic amines again for purposes of illustration.

$$\delta_{K\text{-Me},\mathrm{N}}^{(1)}(\mathrm{Et}) = I[\mathrm{CH_3NH_2}] - I[\mathrm{C_2H_5NH_2}],$$

$$\delta_{K\text{-Me},\mathrm{N}}^{(2)}(\mathrm{Et}) = I[(\mathrm{CH_3})_2\mathrm{NH}] - I[(\mathrm{C_2H_5})_2\mathrm{NH}],$$

and

$$\delta_{K\text{-Me},\mathrm{N}}^{(3)}(n\text{-Pr}) = I[(\mathrm{CH_3})_3\mathrm{N}] - I[(n\text{-}\mathrm{C_3H_7})_3\mathrm{N}],$$

where n-Pr is the symbol for the n-propyl group. An additional relation which has been found to hold true for some types of molecules is (32)

$$\delta_{K\text{-Me},A}^{(x)}(R') = x[\delta_{K\text{-Me},A}^{(1)}(R')]. \tag{8–20}$$

Example 8–5. Let us calculate the ionization potential of methyl ethyl ether. We begin by constructing a table of data using Equations (8–17) to (8–19), and the photoionization data of Watanabe, Nakayama, and Mottl (20). The results are as shown in Table 8–6. From this table we may now calculate the ionization potential of methyl ethyl ether. Thus,

TABLE 8–6. TABLE OF SOME δ_K VALUES

Molecule	I.P. (ev)	$\delta_{K,0}^{(x)}(R)$	$\delta_{K,0}^{(x\text{-}y)}(R)$	$\delta_{K\text{-Me},0}^{(x)}$	
H_2O	12.59			$x = 1$	$x = 2$
			1.74		
CH_3OH	10.85	$1.74\begin{pmatrix} x = 1 \\ R = \text{Me} \end{pmatrix}$		0	
			0.85		
CH_3OCH_3	10.00	$2.59\begin{pmatrix} x = 2 \\ R = \text{Me} \end{pmatrix}$			0
			2.11		
C_2H_5OH	10.48	$2.11\begin{pmatrix} x = 1 \\ R = \text{Et} \end{pmatrix}$		0.37	
			0.95		
$C_2H_5OC_2H_5$	9.53	$3.06\begin{pmatrix} x = 2 \\ R = \text{Et} \end{pmatrix}$			0.47

$$
\begin{aligned}
I[CH_3OC_2H_5] &= I[H_2O] - \delta_{K,0}^{(2)}(\text{Et}) + \delta_{K\text{-Me},0}^{(1)}(\text{Et}) \\
&= 12.59 - 3.06 + 0.37 \\
&= 9.90 \text{ ev},
\end{aligned}
$$

which is equivalent to

$$I[CH_3OC_2H_5] = I[H_2O] - \delta_{K,0}^{(1)}(\text{Me}) - \delta_{K,0}^{(2\text{-}1)}(\text{Et}).$$

An alternative calculation would be

$$
\begin{aligned}
I[CH_3OC_2H_5] &= I[H_2O] - \delta_{K,0}^{(1)}(\text{Me}) - \delta_{K\text{-Me},0}^{(1)}(\text{Et}) \\
&= 12.59 - 2.59 - 0.37 \\
&= 9.63 \text{ ev},
\end{aligned}
$$

which is equivalent to

$$I[CH_3OC_2H_5] = I[H_2O] - \delta_{K,0}^{(1)}(\text{Et}) - \delta_{K,0}^{(2\text{-}1)}(\text{Me}).$$

Thus, taking the average of the two results, we find that $I(CH_3OC_2H_5) = 9.76$ ev. An experimental value of 9.81 ev has been reported for this molecule (14).

Similar calculations and correlations have been carried out for alkyl and cycloalkyl radicals, aliphatic amines and azacycloalkanes, ethers and alcohols, sulfides and mercaptans, and oxacyclo- and thiacyclo-alkanes (32). Unfortunately, the δ_K values change for different central atoms, A, so that large tables of values for the different types of molecules become necessary.

It has been noted by the author that using values of $\delta_{K\text{-Me},N}^{(1)}$ from aliphatic amines and $I(CH_3COOH)$, the ionization potentials of the RCOOH series can be predicted, but that this will not work for the aldehydes. Another point to be made is that these constants, in their present forms, cannot be utilized to calculate the ionization potential of a molecule like $CH_2CH_2OCH_2CH_2S$, whereas the group orbital method will allow such a calculation. Note also that the interaction parameters in the group orbital method are constant, and can be used with varying types of molecules.

This method will likely continue to be useful in estimating ionization potentials which have not been determined experimentally.

The ω-Technique

Molecular orbital calculations of the ionization potentials of organic compounds using the ω-technique have been carried out for a large number of molecules by Streitwieser (33). The approach is to use the Hückel molecular orbital method, similar to that expressed in Equation (8–15), but modified by introducing a parameter ω, to obtain agreement with experiment. It has been found experimentally that $\omega = 1.4$ is satisfactory (33, 34). Using the Hückel MO method, a charge distribution on each carbon atom can be calculated and then used to calculate a new Coulomb integral. This result gives a new charge distribution which again is employed in similar fashion. The reiteration is continued until the system is self-consistent, and gives the energy of the positive ion.

Streitwieser found that the difference in bonding energy in the neutral molecule and the parent-molecule ion χ could be correlated to the electron impact ionization potentials of a large number of compounds by (33, 34)

$$I = 9.878 - 2.110\chi. \tag{8–21}$$

For the aliphatic hydrocarbons and $\omega = 1.4$ (33, 34),

$$\chi = -\left[0.2 + \left(\frac{2.8}{n+1}\right)\sin^2\left(\frac{n\pi}{n+1}\right)\right], \tag{8–22}$$

where n is the number of carbon atoms. Thus, for $n = 1$, $\chi = -1.600$; for $n = 2$, $\chi = -0.900$; for $n = 3$, $\chi = -0.550$; etc. Thus,

$$I(CH_4) = 9.878 + (2.110)(1.600) = 9.878 + 3.376 = 13.25 \text{ ev},$$

and

$$I(C_3H_8) = 9.878 + (2.110)(0.550) = 9.878 \times 1.161 = 11.04 \text{ ev}.$$

If the constant 9.878 were changed to 9.67, much better agreement could be obtained between calculated values and experimental values determined by photoionization methods.

8.4 APPEARANCE POTENTIALS

In discussing energetics and molecular ion dissociations we shall first restrict ourselves to the discussion of molecular ion dissociations involving only positive ions, and then we will treat separately the case of negative ion formations and their appearance potentials. At sufficiently high electron energies, one may ionize the molecules introduced into the electron beam in the ion source. (Again, the comments made earlier in Chapter 6 concerning the fact that there are some molecules which do not yield parent-molecule ions, should be kept in mind.) If the energy of the impacting electrons is increased sufficiently, both ionization and dissociation processes may occur in the molecule. As we continue to increase the energy of the electron beam we should observe a variation in the quantities of the various ions which are formed. We will discuss this in somewhat more detail shortly. However, we can say that at sufficiently high energies, various processes occur when an electron impacts a molecule, thereby producing various ionic fragments, various neutral fragments, and two or more electrons. The problem of determining the specific molecular ion dissociation for any one case is one of determining the appearance potential for the process, and of utilizing heats of formation of the various product ions, neutral fragments, and the orginal molecule, as may be seen from Equation (8–2) and similar equations. From this, the heat of formation of the positive ion produced may be determined; or, alternatively, one may make reasonably intelligent estimates as to the nature of the molecular-ion dissociation which has occurred to give rise to the observed positive ion.

We have already discussed under the general topic of ionization potentials the methods one may employ in order to interpret ionization efficiency curves. At least in principle, these same methods of interpretation should also apply to the ionization efficiency curves for fragment ions, and thereby allow one to accurately determine the appearance potentials of the various ions. But it was noted earlier that not all of the methods are satisfactory in this regard; those methods which are generally satisfactory in the determination of appearance potentials have already been pointed out in the earlier discussion.

POSITIVE IONS

As has already been discussed in Chapter 6, many different types of positive ions are produced in the ion source and make up the observed mass spectrum for a given sample. We have already seen in this chapter the method by which one may determine appearance potentials and ionization potentials from ionization efficiency curves. For a given positive ion produced in accordance with Equation (8–1), we may employ Equation (8–2) to study the energetics, providing there is no excess energy involved. Because of lack of information, it is nearly always necessary to assume that the processes involve no excess energy.

If we can select for study an ion that can be formed in only one way, so that the process of formation cannot be in doubt, then the experimental data may be made to yield information concerning the heat of formation of the ion, a bond dissociation energy, or other types of similar information. On the other hand, if the process by which the ion is formed is open to question, then the experimentally determined energetics may be employed in an effort to decide the process by which the ion is formed in the threshold region. Note that the specification "in the threshold region" has been included. One cannot say that this may be the only possible process, or indeed, the only possible ion, at, say, 70 ev. These two points can be seen much more clearly by means of several examples.

EXAMPLE 8–6. The appearance potential of the $m/e = 31$ ion from methanol, CH_3OH, has been determined by C. S. Cummings and W. Bleakney (35) to be 11.9 ± 0.1 ev. There is only one possible process to write for such a reaction; namely,

$$CH_3OH \rightarrow CH_3O^+ + H + e, \qquad \text{A.P.} = 11.9 \text{ ev},$$

although one might question whether the ion of $m/e = 31$ has the structure CH_3O^+ or CH_2OH^+. Since A.P. $= 11.9$ ev $= 274.5$ kcal/mole $= \Delta H_{\text{reaction}}$, we can write

$$\Delta H_{\text{reaction}} = 274.5 = \Delta H_f(CH_3O^+) + \Delta H_f(H) - \Delta H_f(CH_3OH)$$

or

$$\Delta H_f(CH_3O^+) = 274.5 + \Delta H_f(CH_3OH) - \Delta H_f(H).$$

And since the heats of formation of methanol (g) and the hydrogen atom are known to be -48.1 and $+52.1$ kcal/mole, respectively, we see that

$$\Delta H_f(CH_3O^+) = 274.5 + (-48.1) - 52.1$$

or

$$\Delta H_f(CH_3O^+) = 174 \text{ kcal/mole}.$$

Now, although we know the heat of formation of the CH_3O^+ ion, we do not know the structure. But, from examination of numerous alcohols, we find that, in general, the $m/e = 31$ ion intensity is very strong. If this is the same ion in all of these alcohols—a reasonable assumption—then it is suggestive that the ion has the structure of CH_2OH^+; if the structure were CH_3O^+, rearrangements in all of the alcohols of molecular weight greater than that of methanol would be required to form the CH_3O^+ ion. Thus, although this does not consitute proof of the structure of the ion, it is reasonably good evidence for such a structure. An additional point that aids in the matter of deciding the structure of the CH_3O^+ ion is to examine a number of other compounds which might contain the methoxy group, CH_3O^+, and to see if the same ΔH_f^+ is determined. If the two ions should have different ΔH_f^+, one might well anticipate that $\Delta H_f(CH_3O^+) > \Delta H_f(CH_2OH^+)$. If one examines the summarization of a large number of appearance potentials and the ionic heats of formation, as given by Field and Franklin in their book (22), one finds that the determinations of $\Delta H_f(CH_3O^+)$ from a number of different alcohols gives the same values; namely, 170–174 kcal/mole. However, the $\Delta H_f(CH_3O^+)$ determined from a study of CH_3ONO is found to be 235 kcal/mole. These data provide additional support for the conclusion that the $m/e = 31$ ion from the alcohols is the CH_2OH^+ ion, and that $\Delta H_f(CH_2OH^+) = 172$ kcal/mole.

EXAMPLE 8–7. The lowest appearance potential of CH_2^+ from CH_4 is 15.3 $\pm$ 0.2 ev (36). The appearance potential of CH_2^+ from methyl radicals is 15.29 $\pm$ 0.05 ev (37). Now, is the process by which the CH_2^+ ion is formed from methane in the threshold region best described by

$$CH_4 \longrightarrow CH_2^+ + 2H + e \tag{8–23}$$

or by

$$CH_4 \longrightarrow CH_2^+ + H_2 + e? \tag{8–24}$$

From the experimental information for the methyl radical study, one sees that the only possible reaction is

$$CH_3 \longrightarrow CH_2^+ + H + e,$$

and therefore

$$\Delta H_f(CH_2^+) + \Delta H_f(H) - \Delta H_f(CH_3) = 15.29 \text{ ev} = 352.7 \text{ kcal/mole}$$

or

$$\Delta H_f(CH_2^+) = 352.7 + \Delta H_f(CH_3) - \Delta H_f(H).$$

And since $\Delta H_f(CH_3) = 32$ kcal/mole, we see that

$$\Delta H_f(CH_2^+) = 352.7 + 32 - 52,$$

and, thus,

$$\Delta H_f(CH_2^+) = 333 \text{ kcal/mole}.$$

Now, for the process given by Equation (8–23), we have

$$\Delta H_f(CH_2^+) = (15.3 \times 23.067) - 2\Delta H_f(H) + \Delta H_f(CH_4),$$

and since $\Delta H_f(CH_4) = -17.9$ kcal/mole,

$$\Delta H_f(CH_2^+) = 352.9 - 104.2 - 17.9$$

or

$$\Delta H_f(CH_2^+) = 231 \text{ kcal/mole}.$$

And, for the process given by Equation (8–24), we have

$$\Delta H_f(CH_2^+) = 352.9 - 0 - 17.9$$

or

$$\Delta H_f(CH_2^+) = 335 \text{ kcal/mole.}$$

We can conclude, therefore, that the process occurring in the threshold region in methane, leading to the $m/e = 14$ ion, is that described by Equation (8–24), and that $\Delta H_f(CH_2^+) = 334$ kcal/mole.

EXAMPLE 8–8. The appearance potential of the $m/e = 28$ ion from ethylene oxide, CH_2CH_2O, has been reported by E. J. Gallegos and R. W. Kiser (38) to be 12.6 ± 0.4 ev. Is this ion due to $C_2H_4^+$ or to CO^+?

Field and Franklin list $\Delta H_f(C_2H_4^+) = 255$ kcal/mole and $\Delta H_f(CO^+) = 297$ kcal/mole in their book. Also,

$$\Delta H_f(O) = 59.1, \qquad \Delta H_f(C_2H_4) = 12.5,$$

and

$$\Delta H_f(C_2H_4O) = -12 \text{ kcal/mole.}$$

If the process is

$$C_2H_4O \longrightarrow C_2H_4^+ + O + e, \tag{8–25}$$

then

$$\Delta H_f(C_2H_4^+) = (12.6 \times 23.067) - \Delta H_f(O) + \Delta H_f(C_2H_4O)$$

and thus,

$$\Delta H_f(C_2H_4^+) = 290.6 - 59.1 - 12$$

or

$$\Delta H_f(C_2H_4^+) = 220 \text{ kcal/mole.}$$

And, if the process is

$$C_2H_4O \longrightarrow CO^+ + CH_4 + e, \tag{8–26}$$

we see that

$$\Delta H_f(CO^+) = 290.6 - \Delta H_f(CH_4) - 12$$

so that

$$\Delta H_f(CO^+) = 278.6 + 17.9$$

or

$$\Delta H_f(CO^+) = 297 \text{ kcal/mole.}$$

From these two possibilities, one concludes that the ion observed at $m/e = 28$ is the CO^+ ion in the threshold region, and that the process for its formation is that given by Equation (8–26). This conclusion is in agreement with the findings of J. H. Beynon (39) from the high-resolution mass spectrum of ethylene oxide at electron energies of the order of 70 ev.

Before leaving the subject of positive ions to consider the negative ions, we should add a few comments about certain additional information that can be obtained in studies of positive ions. If one records the entire mass spectrum at various voltages between the ionization potential and 70 ev, one may observe how the fractional abundances of the various ions change with electron energy. Such a fragmentation curve, or *clastogram* as we have termed it in our laboratories, provides certain useful information. The example given in Figure 8–7 shows the clastogram of ethylene sulfide. From Figure 8–7, one observes that the $m/e = 59$ ion is formed and then further fragments as the electron energy is continually increased. The parent-molecule ion, $m/e = 60$, is observed to continually decrease as the electron energy is increased, as would be anticipated from the quasi-equilibrium theory. Also, as expected, other ions "grow in" as the electron energy increases. These latter ions are commonly the smaller fragment ions which are fairly stable and undergo little further fragmentation. It should also be noted that this clastogram shown in Figure 8–7 is in agreement with the predictions of the quasi-equilibrium theory as to which ions are fragmenting and forming other ions.

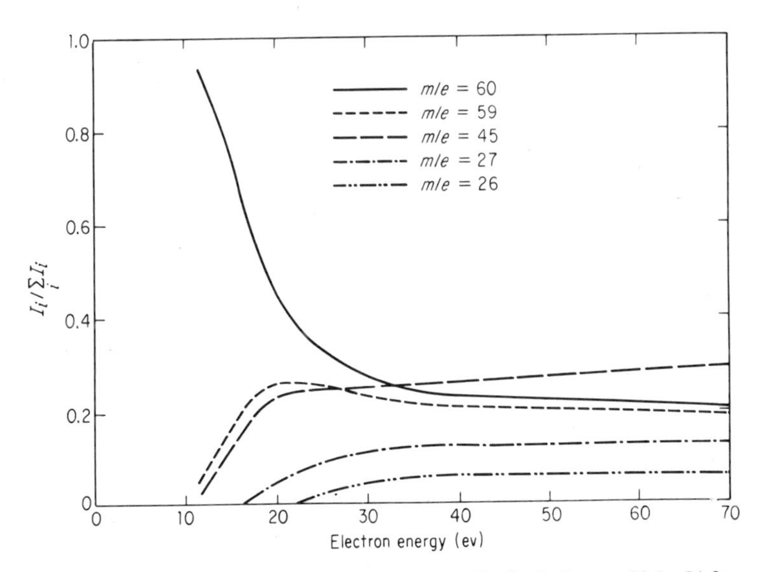

Fig. 8-7. Fragmentation curve or "clastogram" of ethylene sulfide. [After E. J. Gallegos (39).]

NEGATIVE IONS

In the study of ionization and dissociation processes, it is necessary in many cases to study the negative ion mass spectrum and the appearance potentials of negative ions in order to fully understand the processes. Negative ion currents from electron impact are much less intense (by a factor of about 1000) than are the positive ions currents, and this fact creates some difficulty in the study of negative ions. In addition, it is difficult to calibrate the energy scale for the determination of appearance potentials of negative ions. One cannot simply calibrate the energy scale with known positive ions (such as Xe^+ or Kr^+) and then reverse the fields, for the source conditions may be greatly changed, in which case the calibration would be meaningless. A third problem encountered in working with negative ions is that some negative ion ionization efficiency curves can be much different in shape from those for positive ions. However, as mentioned above, studies of the negative ions are often necessary, and the difficulties just discussed can be and are overcome in order to provide the desired information.

As stated above, reversal of the ion repeller (or drawout) potential and the ion accelerating potential are necessary in the study of negative ions, and this may cause variations between the electron energy scale calibrations for positive ions and for negative ions. Furthermore, the variations may be somewhat different at different electron energies.

There are no spectroscopic standards for the energies of negative ions as there are for the positive ions (e.g., Xe^+, Kr^+, Ar^+). Therefore, the electron energy scale must be calibrated ultimately by means of positive ions. Tate and Lozier used an apparatus in which the ions are formed in a region free from electric fields; in such an apparatus an energy scale calibration based on positive ions should also be applicable for negative ions. From this a negative ion calibrant for the electron energy scale may be obtained. The results obtained by Lozier of 9.6 ev for A.P. (O^-) in the resonance capture in CO is often taken as the standard.

Appearance potential measurements of negative ions may be made using the vanishing current method. Use of the retarding potential difference method to obtain a nearly homogeneous energetic beam of electrons is to be recommended. Energy scale calibrations may be made using the O^- ion produced by resonance capture in CO (occurring at 9.6 ev) for the higher energy regions, and by using the SF_6^- ion produced by resonance capture in SF_6 (the energy corresponding to the peak maximum is 0.08 ev) for the low-energy regions.

Negative ions may be formed from a molecule in two ways: (a) through resonant electron capture, and (b) through ion pair production. These two processes may be written as shown in the following two equations:

$$AB + e \longrightarrow AB^-, \qquad \text{(resonance capture)} \qquad (8\text{–}27a)$$

$$AB + e \longrightarrow A + B^-, \qquad \text{(dissociative attachment)} \qquad (8\text{–}27b)$$

and

$$AB + e \longrightarrow A^{+} + B^{-} + e. \quad \text{(ion pair production)} \tag{8–28}$$

Notice that in Equation (8–27b) two particles are produced. In the process depicted by Equation (8–27a), there are no product electrons to carry away excess energy, and therefore the capture process is a resonance process and will occur only within a relatively narrow range of impacting electron energies, e.g., $SF_6 + e \longrightarrow SF_6^-$.

However, the process given in Equation (8–28) will not be a resonance process; the product electron here can carry off excess energy since the kinetic energy of an electron is not quantized. Therefore, the ionization efficiency curves for ion pair formation processes resemble more closely those encountered in positive ion studies.

An example of a case wherein both of these processes result in the production of negative ions is shown in Figure 8–8. Writing the process for the resonance peak with an appearance potential of 9.6 ev (see also Chapter 2),

$$CO + e \longrightarrow C + O^-,$$

we may determine the energetics in either of two ways:

$$\text{A.P.}(O^-) = D(CO) + \text{E.A.}(O) \tag{8–29}$$

or

$$\text{A.P.}(O^-) = L(C) + \Delta H_f(O^-) - \Delta H_f(CO). \tag{8–30}$$

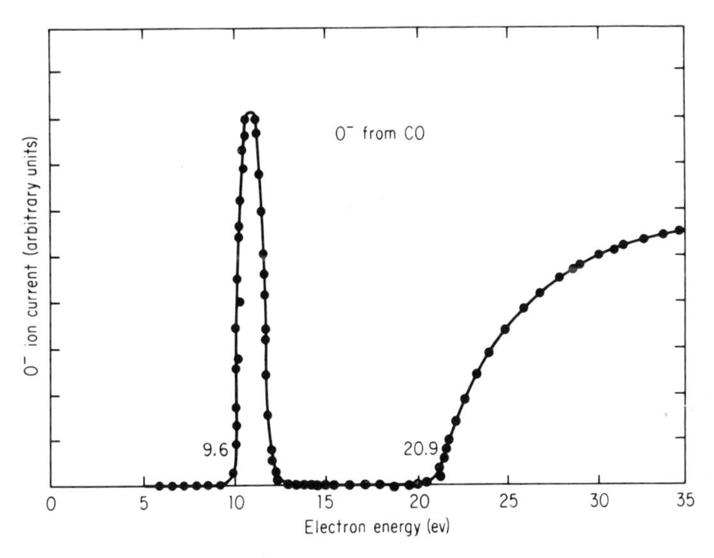

Fig. 8-8. Ionization efficiency curve for the formation of O^- from CO.

Taking $L(C) = 170$ kcal/mole, $\Delta H_f(O) = 59.1$ kcal/mole, and $\Delta H_f(CO) = -27$ kcal/mole, we see that $D(CO) = 256$ kcal/mole $= 11.1$ ev. From the data from the Lozier tube in Chapter 2, $D(CO) = 11.26 \pm 0.08$ ev $= 260$ kcal/mole. Use of these data together with A.P.$(O^-) = 9.6$ ev leads to E.A.(O) $= 35$ kcal/mole by means of either Equation (8–29) or (8–30). The value of the electron affinity of oxygen of 35 kcal/mole (or 1.5 ev) is in agreement with the value of 33 kcal/mole determined by Smith and Branscomb (40) from the onset of photodetachment and the value of 41 kcal/mole (or 1.8 ev) determined from the data given in Section 2.2.

For the ion pair production,

$$CO + e \longrightarrow C^+ + O^-,$$

the appearance potential of 20.9 ev together with $I(C) = 11.26$ ev and the relation

$$\text{A.P.}(O^-) = D(CO) + I(C) + \text{E.A.}(O) \tag{8–31}$$

leads to

$$\text{E.A.}(O) = 482 - 256 - 260$$

or

$$\text{E.A.}(O) = -34 \text{ kcal/mole}.$$

One may also determine from the Lozier tube data presented in Section 2.2 that the electron affinity of carbon is -1.6 ev $= -37$ kcal/mole.

The width of the electron capture resonance peak is partly due to inhomogeneities in the energy of the electron beam and partly due to the nature of the transition involved in the formation of the ions. Hickam and Fox (41) have observed that the SF_6^- resonance capture peak had a half-width of about

TABLE 8–7. SOME ELECTRON CAPTURE PROCESSES

Process	Appearance Potential (ev)	Reference
$H_2O \longrightarrow OH + H^-$	4.1 ± 0.5	42, 43
$CO \longrightarrow C + O^-$	9.6 ± 0.2	44, 45, 46
$SO_2 \longrightarrow SO + O^-$	3.5	47
$PH_3 \longrightarrow PH_2 + H^-$	6.4	47
$NH_3 \longrightarrow H + NH_2^-$	6.0 ± 0.5	43
$C_2N_2 \longrightarrow CN + CN^-$	4.4 ± 0.2	48
$HF \longrightarrow H + F^-$	8.85	49
$HCl \longrightarrow H + Cl^-$	0.8 ± 0.3	50
$HBr \longrightarrow H + Br^-$	0.6 ± 0.3	50
$Br_2 \longrightarrow Br + Br^-$	-1.8	51
$CS_2 \longrightarrow CS + S^-$	3.2	47
$H_2S \longrightarrow H + SH^-$	2.2	47
$SO_2 \longrightarrow O + SO^-$	3.9	47
$H_2Se \longrightarrow H + SeH^-$	1.8	47
$SF_6 \longrightarrow SF_6^-$	0.08	41

0.1 ev, and that this was exactly the half-width of the energy distribution of the ionizing electrons using their retarding potential difference method.

Relative intensities of the various negative ions are often dependent upon the energy homogeneity of the electron beam. Therefore, the retarding potential difference method is very useful for negative ion studies.

Some additional resonance electron capture processes and some additional ion pair production processes, together with their appearance potentials, are listed in Tables 8–7 and 8–8, respectively.

TABLE 8–8. SOME ION PAIR PRODUCTION PROCESSES

Process	Appearance Potential (ev)	Reference
$O_2 \longrightarrow O^+ + O^-$	16.95 ± 0.15	52
$NO \longrightarrow N^+ + O^-$	19.9 ± 0.3	44
$CO \longrightarrow C^+ + O^-$	20.9	53
$CH_3F \longrightarrow CH_3^+ + F^-$	10.8 ± 0.5	54
$CH_3Cl \longrightarrow CH_3^+ + Cl^-$	$10. \pm 0.1$	54
$TiCl_4 \longrightarrow TiCl_3^+ + Cl^-$	12.6 ± 0.3	55
$HCl \longrightarrow H^+ + Cl^-$	13.6 ± 0.5	50
$HBr \longrightarrow H^+ + Br^-$	13.4 ± 0.5	50

ELECTRON ENERGY SPREAD

One source of error in the determination of appearance potentials and ionization potentials is electric field penetration into the ionization chamber region. It is very difficult to make this region entirely field-free. Slits must be employed to allow the electrons to enter the ionization chamber region and to allow the positive ions to exit from this region of ionization. In addition to this, a weak field of some sort is normally provided to either repel the positive ions from the ion source or to draw these positive ions from the ion source into the main accelerating region of the mass spectrometer. Thus we normally must accept the presence of some small electric field as well as some electric field penetration.

One may minimize some of these difficulties by observing the following generalizations. First, the electron trap in the ionization chamber should be maintained at essentially the same potential; unfortunately this causes a considerable lowering in the sensitivity of the instrument. Therefore, it is usually essential to collimate the electron beam energetically in order to obtain the necessary sensitivity for the detection. In this respect, sector instruments have an advantage over other types of instruments, because the different positive ion beams may be studied by varying the magnetic field, leaving the potentials in the ion source unchanged during the course of the study. This same advantage is also exhibited by the time-of-flight mass spectrometer. If one changes the accelerating potential in order to vary the mass of the ions being collected in a sector instrument, this advantage, of course, is lost.

It is obvious that, if one is to determine meaningful appearance and ionization potentials, the electron energy should be homogeneous. The inhomogeneity of the electron beam is another significant source of error in the determination of appearance potentials and ionization potentials. We shall first note some of the reasons for these inhomogeneities and then investigate the method due to Fox, *et al.*, (24) of obtaining an electron beam homogeneous in energy.

One of the main reasons for an electron energy distribution is that the electrons that are emitted from the heated filament have appreciable thermal energies. This source of inhomogeneity has an electron distribution which is essentially Maxwellian in nature, and may be taken [as was done by R. E. Honig, (8)] as

$$dN(U) = (4\pi mA/h^3)\cdot U\cdot \exp[-(\phi + U)/kT]dU, \qquad (8\text{–}32)$$

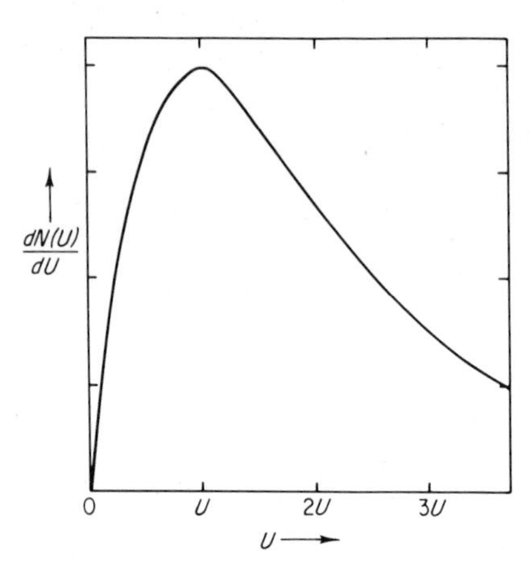

Fig. 8-9. The number of electrons in the energy interval between U and $(U \pm dU)$ as a function of U, assuming a Maxwellian distribution, θ=4.50 ev, and T=2500°K, emitted from a filament 1 cm long with a 5 mil diameter.

where $dN(U)$ is the number of electrons of energy between U and $(U + dU)$ emitted from the heated filament per second, U is the thermal energy of the electrons of mass m, h is Planck's constant, k is Boltzmann's constant, A is the surface area of the filament with a work function of ϕ, and T is the absolute temperature of the filament. The general shape of this distribution is shown in Figure 8–9. One can see that for a temperature of 2500° K, where $kT = 0.215$ ev, the thermal energy spread of the emitted electrons may be 0.2 to 0.4 ev.

An additional reason for the appearance of the "foot" of the ionization efficiency curves is due to possible states lying close in energy to the ground state. In these cases, ionization may also occur from a state which may be thermally populated. Another reason for the energy distribution in the electron beam is that some gaseous molecules affect the work function of the filament and thereby cause a change in the electron energy distribution. This effect of various materials in the ion source is rather irregular, is difficult to predict, and may even be difficult to repeat. Contact potentials in the ion source and particularly the voltage on the ion repeller plate (grid) also may affect the electron energy distribution. An aid in reducing some of these effects upon the determined appearance potentials is obtained if the masses of the ions being studied (i.e., the ions of the substance, with the appearance potential to be determined, and the ions of the calibrating gas) are kept as similar as possible and if the electron beam and repeller are pulsed.

R. E. Fox, W. M. Hickam, D. J. Grove, and T. Kjeldaas, Jr., (24) devised a method for reducing the electron energy spread, and thereby made possible the very precise determination of appearance potentials. Their method, known as the *method of retarding potential differences*, employs a modified type of electron bombardment ion source, such as that shown in Figure 8–10. Note that the ion source in Figure 8–10 is very similar to that given earlier in Figure 3–1, except that additional grids have been added.

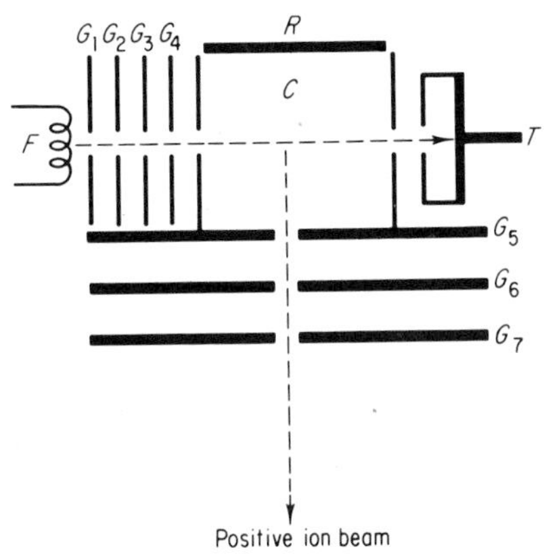

Fig. 8-10. Schematic diagram of an electron bombardment ion source utilizing a Fox-type gun assembly.

The retarding potential differences method works as follows. To grid G_3 is applied a voltage V_r which is negative with respect to the filament F. The voltage V_r is adjusted to some level such that it will prevent electrons from the lower portion of the electron energy distribution (such as that shown in Figure 8–9) from entering the ionization chamber. Now, if V_r is decreased by some small amount ΔV_r, of the order of 0.1 volt, and if the potential on the filament is maintained constant, those electrons in the energy distribution between with energies between V_r and $(V_r - \Delta V_r)$ will pass grid G_3 and enter the ionization chamber C. The observed ion current will increase by an amount that is due to the increase in the electron current, and which is homogeneous in energy to within ΔV_r. Because of the potential difference between the repeller electrode R and grid G_5, the ionization chamber is not an equipotential volume, and will cause some additional spread in the electron energy. Therefore, a pulsing voltage of about 10^5 cps is applied between R and grid G_2; this causes the electrons to enter the ionization chamber only when the potential on R is zero, and then, after the electrons enter C, the potential on G_2 prevents more electrons from entering the ionization chamber when the positive ions which have just been formed are being repelled out of C by the potential on R. Thus, the ions are formed in a field-free region.

The ionization efficiency curves are obtained by measuring the differential ion current as a function of the potential on grid G_4, keeping V_r constant. The differential ion current vanishes at the appearance potential. Recall that

ΔV_r is commonly about 0.1 volt. The data obtained are extrapolated to the intercept on the energy axis, corresponding to A.P. + $(\Delta V_r/2)$. Thus, the appearance potential can be determined quite accurately.

Fox, *et al.*, originally used their retarding potential differences method with a Westinghouse magnetic mass spectrometer, but the method is also usable with other instruments. Their method would appear to be very suitable for use with the already-pulsed electron beam of a linear time-of-flight mass spectrometer. Glick and Llewellyn (56), and Melton and Hamill (57) have described such modifications recently.

Recently, Morrison (58) has developed a deconvolution operation using Fourier transforms which can be applied to experimental ionization efficiency curves. This deconvolution reduces the effective electron energy spread by a factor of four or five and also removes noise from the ionization efficiency curve. Morrison notes that this technique allows the extraction of much more information from a typical ionization efficiency curve than by use of other interpretative methods.

8.5 HEATS OF FORMATION OF IONS

Using Equation (8–2), the heat of formation of the fragment ions F_i may be determined if the other quantities in Equation (8–2) are known or may be calculated (or estimated reasonably accurately). We have already seen in Examples 8–1 and 8–2, as well as Examples 8–6 to 8–8, the calculations of the heats of formation of a number of ions. This information can sometimes aid in attempting to understand the structure of an ion. An illustration of this is given in the following example, taken from the results of R. W. Kiser and B. G. Hobrock (59).

EXAMPLE 8–9. Two complementary reactions brought about by electron impact with cyclopropyl cyanide are

$$C_3H_5CN \longrightarrow C_3H_5^+ + CN + e \tag{8–33}$$

and

$$C_3H_5CN \longrightarrow CN^+ + C_3H_5 + e. \tag{8–34}$$

The appearance potential for the reaction given by Equation (8–33) was 12.70 ± 0.15 ev, and that for the reaction given by Equation (8–34) was 19.5 ± 0.4 ev. Therefore, ΔH for the reaction

$$CN^+ + C_3H_5 \longrightarrow CN + C_3H_5^+ \tag{8–35}$$

is $(12.70 - 19.5) = -6.8$ ev. Since the ionization potential of CN is known to be 14.55 ev, the ionization potential of C_3H_5 is 7.8 ± 0.4 ev.

Although no experimental value of ΔH_f (cyclopropyl cyanide) is yet available, Kiser and Hobrock have estimated that it is 43 kcal/mole. [A very useful method of estimating heats of formation for compounds where experimental data is lacking has been reported by J. L. Franklin (60), using a group approach; additional methods have been cited by Janz (61).] From this estimation, the measured appearance potentials, and known heats of formation of the N_i [in Equation (8–2)], values of

$$\Delta H_f(C_3H_5CN^+) = 301, \qquad \Delta H_f(C_3H_4CN^+) = 298,$$
$$\Delta H_f(C_3H_5^+) = 246, \quad \text{and} \quad \Delta H_f(C_3H_5) = 68 \text{ kcal/mole}$$

were calculated.

Since ΔH_f (allyl$^+$) = 200 kcal/mole, it appears that the ion studied by Kiser and Hobrock was the cyclopropyl ion and not the allyl ion formed by rearrangement. Also, the higher value of $\Delta H_f(C_3H_5) = 68$ kcal/mole [ΔH_f (allyl) = 30 kcal/mole] indicates the cyclopropyl radical. Lossing has measured I(cyclopropyl) = 8.05 ev (see Appendix IV-C), which leads to $\Delta H_f(C_3H_5)$ = 60 kcal/mole using $\Delta H_f(C_3H_5^+) = 246$ kcal/mole. Hence, Kiser and Hobrock concluded from their studies that the intense ion (100% relative abundance at 70 ev) of $m/e = 41$ was the cyclopropyl ion and not the allyl ion.

A very important rule to be considered when studying complementary reactions is *Stevenson's rule* (62). Let us consider a molecule that may be ionized and dissociated either by the process

$$R_1R_2 \longrightarrow (R_1R_2)^+ \longrightarrow R_1^+ + R_2 \tag{8–36}$$

or by the process

$$R_1R_2 \longrightarrow (R_1R_2^*)^+ \longrightarrow R_2^+ + R_1. \tag{8–37}$$

Stevenson (62) has stated that only when $I(R_1) < I(R_2)$ will the fragments generally be found in their lowest states or without kinetic energy. Only very few exceptions have been noted to this rule for complementary reactions, and these exceptions have been restricted to either small molecules or molecules of high symmetry. Certainly this rule is to be related to the theory of mass spectra.

Many values for the heats of formation of various ions have been determined and reported in the literature. The interested reader is referred to the comprehensive listings and summaries given by Field and Franklin in their book (22). It is very desirable to continue such compilations, and it is understood that the National Bureau of Standards is currently investigating the feasibility of undertaking the problem of maintaining an up-to-date compilation of appearance potentials and ionic heats of formation.

8.6 BOND DISSOCIATION ENERGIES AND PROTON AFFINITIES

Another type of information that can be gleaned from electron impact studies with a mass spectrometer is that of bond dissociation energies. Consider a general reaction, similar to that given by Equation (8–1),

$$AB \longrightarrow A^+ + B + e, \qquad (8\text{–}38)$$

for which we may write the energetic requirements to be

$$\text{A.P.}(A^+) = \Delta H_{\text{reaction}} = \Delta H_f(A^+) + \Delta H_f(B) - \Delta H_f(AB) \qquad (8\text{–}39)$$

even as we did in Equation (8–2). However, these energetics may also be written as

$$\text{A.P.}(A^+) = \Delta H_{\text{reaction}} = D(A\text{—}B) + I(A), \qquad (8\text{–}40)$$

so that if the ionization potential of A, $I(A)$, is known and the appearance potential of A^+ is determined experimentally, the bond dissociation energy, $D(A\text{—}B)$, may be calculated.

EXAMPLE 8–10. Consider the reaction

$$H_2O \longrightarrow OH^+ + H + e, \qquad (8\text{–}41)$$

for which the appearance potential has been determined by M. M. Mann, A. Hustrulid, and J. T. Tate (43) to be 18.8 ± 0.2 ev. Therefore,

$$D(\text{HO—H}) + I(\text{OH}) = 18.8 \text{ ev}.$$

But $I(\text{OH}) = 13.53$ ev. Therefore,

$$D(\text{HO—H}) = 18.8 - 13.5 = 5.3 \text{ ev}$$

or

$$D(\text{HO—H}) = 122 \text{ kcal/mole},$$

which may be compared to the value of 117.5 kcal/mole listed by T. L. Cottrell (63).

EXAMPLE 8–11. Recently, G. S. Paulett and R. Ettinger (64) determined the appearance potential of CH_2^+ from diazomethane to be 12.3 ± 0.1 ev, which compares with 12.7 ± 0.3 ev determined by Langer, Hipple, and Stevenson (36). G. Herzberg (65) has determined $I(CH_2) = 10.39$ ev. What is the value of $D(CH_2\text{—}N_2)$, the C—N bond dissociation energy in diazomethane?

Taking a weighted mean value of A.P.(CH_2^+) from CH_2N_2, as for the reaction

$$CH_2N_2 \longrightarrow CH_2^+ + N_2 \qquad \text{A.P.}(CH_2^+) = 12.4 \text{ ev} \qquad (8\text{–}42)$$

and combining it with the relation

$$\text{A.P.}(CH_2^+) = D(CH_2\text{—}N_2) + I(CH_2),$$

we obtain

$$D(CH_2\text{—}N_2) = \text{A.P.}(CH_2^+) - I(CH_2),$$

which, upon substitution of the numerical values, yields

$$D(CH_2\text{—}N_2) = 12.4 - 10.39 = 2.0 \text{ ev}$$

or

$$D(CH_2\text{—}N_2) = 46 \text{ kcal/mole}.$$

Paulett and Ettinger have used this result as one argument to indicate that structure (I), below, is the dominant form in the two principal resonance contributions:

$$\overset{\delta^-}{C}H_2\text{—}\overset{\delta^+}{N}{\equiv}N: \longleftrightarrow CH_2{=}\overset{\delta^+}{N}{=}\overset{\delta^-}{\underset{\cdot\cdot}{N}}:$$

(I) (II)

To indicate that mass spectrometric studies may also be used to determine heats of formation of molecules, let us continue with the data from Example 8–11. Recently, H. Prophet (66) concluded that $\Delta H_f(CH_2) = 95 \pm 5$ kcal/mole. Now, for the reaction

$$CH_2N_2 \longrightarrow CH_2 + N_2 \tag{8–43}$$

we can write the energetics as

$$\Delta H_{\text{reaction}} = D(CH_2\text{—}N_2) = \Delta H_f(CH_2) - \Delta H_f(CH_2N_2)$$

or

$$\Delta H_f(CH_2N_2) = \Delta H_f(CH_2) - D(CH_2\text{—}N_2)$$
$$= 95 - 46,$$

which gives

$$\Delta H_f(CH_2N_2) = 49 \text{ kcal/mole},$$

as found by Paulett and Ettinger (64) for diazomethane. Giese and Maier (67) have reported a method which they suggest may be good for determining dissociation energies to perhaps 0.1 ev.

In addition to bond dissociation energies obtained from mass spectrometric data, it is possible in some cases to determine proton affinities (the energy liberated when a H^+ ion reacts with a species to give the protonated species) of various molecules. This may be accomplished in two different ways, one of which sets an upper limit to the proton affinity.

From appearance potential studies for ion-molecule reactions, such as those discussed in Section 6.9, it may be possible to determine upper limits to the proton affinities. For the formation of a secondary ion, as shown in the reactions given by Equations (6–18) and (6–19), $\Delta H < 0$. For those processes in which the reactions producing the secondary ions can be established, the law of Hess may be used to calculate proton affinities. From heats of formation of MH^+ species calculated, and if $\Delta H_f(M)$ is known, the proton affinity (P.A.) for M, shown as

$$M + H^+ \longrightarrow MH^+ \tag{8–44}$$

can be found by

$$\text{P.A.}(M) = -\Delta H_{\text{reaction}} = \Delta H_f(M) + \Delta H_f(H) - \Delta H_f(MH^+). \tag{8–45}$$

Lampe, Franklin, and Field (68) have tabulated proton affinities for a number of molecules determined by this method for a number of molecules.

However, values of proton affinities may also be determined directly from mass spectrometric appearance potentials for the MH^+ ion. The author has found that compounds of the type $(C_2H_5)_nX$ often yield XH_n^+ and XH_{n+1}^+ ions by the processes

$$e + (C_2H_5)_nX \longrightarrow n(C_2H_4) + XH_n^+ + 2e \tag{8–46}$$

and

$$e + (C_2H_5)_nX \longrightarrow (n-1)C_2H_4 + C_2H_3 + XH_{n+1}^+ + 2e. \tag{8–47}$$

If $\text{A.P.}(XH_{n+1}^+)$ for the process shown in Equation (8–47) can be determined, and if $\Delta H_f[(C_2H_5)_nX]$ is known, $\Delta H_f(XH_{n+1}^+)$ can be calculated. Now, XH_n can be identified with M of Equation (8–44) and XH_{n+1}^+ with MH^+. Therefore, the proton affinity of XH_n can be obtained from the mass spectrometric data.

EXAMPLE 8–12. The heat of formation of H_2S is -4.8 kcal/mole. Appearance potentials for the formation of H_3S^+ from various sulfides have been determined experimentally (69). These values, together with the heats of formation of the molecules from which the $\text{A.P.}(H_3S^+)$ was determined are given Table 8–9. The resulting value calculated for $\Delta H_f(H_3S^+)$ in each case is also given. Determine the proton affinity of hydrogen sulfide.

TABLE 8–9. APPEARANCE POTENTIALS FOR H_3S^+ FROM SELECTED MOLECULES

Molecule	$\text{A.P.}(H_3S^+)$ (ev)	$\Delta H_f(M)$ (kcal/mole)	$\Delta H_f(H_3S^+)$ (kcal/mole)
$CH_3SC_2H_5$	15.1 ± 0.2	-14.22	160
$CH_3SC_3H_7$	15.6 ± 0.3	-19.51	174
$CH_3SCH_2CH{=}CH_2$	14.8 ± 0.2	10	163
$C_2H_5SC_2H_5$	15.6 ± 0.4	-19.77	160

We may take a "best value" of $\Delta H_f(H_3S^+) = 161$ kcal/mole. Then for the reaction

$$H_2S + H^+ \longrightarrow H_3S^+$$

we see that

$$\text{P.A.}(H_2S) = \Delta H_f(H^+) + \Delta H_f(H_2S) - \Delta H_f(H_3S^+),$$

so that

$$\text{P.A.}(H_2S) = 367 - 4.8 - 161$$

or

$$\text{P.A.}(H_2S) = 201 \text{ kcal/mole}$$

in agreement with a lower limit of 175 kcal/mole given by Lampe, Franklin, and Field (68).

The reader may see from these few examples the great usefulness of mass spectrometric and electron impact studies, for much thermochemical data may be obtained from such investigations. Franklin (70) has recently summarized many of these features.

REFERENCES

1. J. W. Otvos and D. P. Stevenson, *J. Am. Chem. Soc.*, **78**, 546 (1956).
2. F. W. Lampe, J. L. Franklin, and F. H. Field, *J. Am. Chem. Soc.*, **79**, 6129 (1957).
3. H. S. W. Massey and E. H. S. Burhop, *Electronic and Ionic Impact Phenomenon*, Oxford at the University Press, London, 1952, pp. 38 and 265.
4. R. K. Asundi and M. V. Kurepa, *J. Sci. Instr.*, **40**, 183 (1963).
5. R. H. Vought, *Phys. Rev.*, **71**, 93 (1947).
6. J. W. Warren, *Nature*, **165**, 810 (1950).
7. F. P. Lossing, A. W. Tickner, and W. A. Bryce, *J. Chem. Phys.*, **19**, 1254 (1951).
8. R. E. Honig, *J. Chem. Phys.*, **16**, 105 (1948).
9. R. W. Kiser and E. J. Gallegos, *J. Phys. Chem.*, **66**, 947 (1962).
10. R. W. Kiser and B. G. Hobrock, *J. Phys. Chem.*, **66**, 1214 (1962).
11. R. C. Shenkel, B. G. Hobrock, and R. W. Kiser, *J. Phys. Chem.*, **66**, 2074 (1962).
12. C. S. Cummings and W. Bleakney, *Phys. Rev.*, **58**, 787 (1940).
13. J. D. Morrison and A. J. C. Nicholson, *J. Chem. Phys.*, **20**, 1021 (1952).
14. B. C. Cox, Ph. D. Thesis, University of Liverpool [reported by J. D. Craggs and H. S. W. Massey, *Handbuch der Physik*, **37**, (I), 314 (1959)], and B. C. Cox and C. A. McDowell, unpublished [reported by J. D. Craggs and C. A. McDowell in *Reports on Progress in Physics*, **18**, 374 (1955)].

15. I. Omura, H. Baba, and K. Higasi, *Bull. Chem. Soc. Japan*, **28**, 147 (1955); **29**, 501 and 504 (1956).

16. S. S. Friedland and R. E. Strakna, *J. Phys. Chem.*, **60**, 815 (1956).

17. L. Friedman, F. A. Long, and M. Wolfsberg, *J. Chem. Phys.*, **27**, 613 (1957).

18. E. C. Y. Inn, *Phys. Rev.*, **91**, 1194 (1953).

19. K. Watanabe, *J. Chem. Phys.*, **22**, 1564 (1954).

20. K. Watanabe, *J. Chem. Phys.*, **26**, 542 (1957); K. Watanabe, T. Nakayama, and J. R. Mottl, *J. Quant. Spectroscopy & Rad. Transfer*, **2**, 369 (1962).

21. T. M. Sugden, A. D. Walsh, and W. C. Price, *Nature*, **148**, 373 (1941).

22. F. H. Field and J. L. Franklin, *Electron Impact Phenomena and the Properties of Gaseous Ions*, Academic Press, Inc., New York, 1957.

23. R. W. Kiser, "Tables of Ionization Potentials," *TID-6142*, U.S. Department of Commerce, June 20, 1960 and supplements.

24. R. E. Fox, W. M. Hickman, D. J. Grove, and T. Kjeldaas, *Rev. Sci. Instr.*, **26**, 1101 (1955); *Phys. Rev.*, **84**, 859 (1951).

25. P. Marmet and L. Kerwin, *Can. J. Phys.*, **38**, 787 and 972 (1960).

26. P. Marmet and J. D. Morrison, *J. Chem. Phys.*, **35**, 746 (1961).

27. G. G. Hall, *Proc. Roy. Soc.*, (*London*), **205A**, 541 (1951); *Trans. Faraday Soc.*, **49**, 113 (1953).

28. J. Lennard-Jones and G. G. Hall, *Proc. Poy. Soc.*, **213A**, 102 (1952).

29. J. L. Franklin, *J. Chem. Phys.*, **22**, 1034 (1954).

30. B. G. Hobrock and R. W. Kiser, *J. Phys. Chem.*, **66**, 1551 (1962).

31. J. J. Kaufman and W. S. Koski, *J. Am. Chem. Soc.*, **82**, 3262 (1960).

32. J. J. Kaufman, *J. Am. Chem. Soc.*, **85**, 1576 (1963); **84**, 4393 (1962); *J. Phys. Chem.*, **66**, 2269 (1962).

33. A. Streitwieser, Jr., *J. Am. Chem. Soc.*, **82**, 4123 (1960); A. Streitwieser, Jr., and P. M. Nair, *Tetrahedron*, **5**, 149 (1949); see also S. Ehrenson, *J. Chem. Phys.*, **37**, 455 (1963).

34. A. Streitwieser, Jr., *Molecular Orbital Theory for Organic Chemists*, John Wiley and Sons, Inc., New York, 1961.

35. C. S. Cummings and W. Bleakney, *Phys. Rev.*, **58**, 787 (1940).

36. A. Langer, J. A. Hipple, and D. P. Stevenson, *J. Chem. Phys.*, **22**, 1836 (1954).

37. J. D. Waldron, *Trans. Faraday Soc.*, **50**, 102 (1954).

38. E. J. Gallegos and R. W. Kiser, *J. Am. Chem. Soc.*, **83**, 773 (1961).

39. J. H. Beynon, "High Resolution Mass Spectrometry of Organic Materials," in *Advances in Mass Spectrometry*, J. D. Waldron (ed.), Pergamon Press, London, 1959, pp. 328–54.

40. S. J. Smith and L. M. Branscomb, *J. Research Nat'l. Bureau Standards*, **55**, 165 (1955); *Phys. Rev.*, **98**, 1127 (1955).

41. W. M. Hickam and R. E. Fox, paper presented before the 3rd annual meeting of the ASTM Committee E-14 on Mass Spectrometry, San Francisco, May, 1955; *Phys. Rev.*, **98**, 557 (1955).

42. W. W. Lozier, *Phys. Rev.*, **36**, 1417 (1930).

43. M. M. Mann, A. Hustrulid, and J. T. Tate, *Phys. Rev.*, **58**, 340 (1940).

44. H. D. Hagstrum, *Rev. Mod. Phys.*, **23**, 185 (1951).

45. W. W. Lozier, *Phys. Rev.*, **46**, 268 (1934).

46. A. L. Vaughan, *Phys. Rev.*, **38**, 1687 (1931).

47. H. Neuert and O. Rosenbaum, *Naturwiss.*, **41**, 85 (1954); *Z. Naturforsch.*, **9A**, 990 (1954).

48. C. A. McDowell and J. W. Warren, *Trans. Faraday Soc.*, **48**, 1084 (1952).

49. J. F. Burns, *Doctoral Dissertation*, University of Tennessee, August, 1954.

50. H. Neuert, *Z. Naturforsch.*, **9A**, 335 (1954).

51. J. P. Blewett, *Phys., Rev.*, **49**, 900 (1936).

52. J. Marriott, quoted by R. Thorburn in "Atomic Ions Produced in Oxygen by Electron Bombardment," in *Applied Mass Spectrometry*, The Institute of Petroleum, London, 1954, p. 185.

53. H. D. Hagstrum and J. T. Tate, *Phys. Rev.*, **55**, 1136 (1939); **59**, 354 (1940).

54. V. H. Dibeler and R. M. Reese, *J. Research Nat'l. Bureau of Standards*, **54**, 127 (1955).

55. J. Marriott, R. Thorburn, and J. D. Craggs, *Proc. Phys. Soc.* (*London*), **B67**, 437 (1954).

56. R. E. Glick and J. A. Llewellyn, "Electron Impact Studies on Simple Gaseous Molecules," *FSU-2690-14*, Division of Biology and Medicine, U.S. Atomic Energy Commission, May 1, 1964.

57. C. E. Melton and W. H. Hamill, *J. Chem. Phys.*, **41**, 546 (1964); S. Tsuda, C. E. Melton, and W. H. Hamill, *J. Chem. Phys.*, **41**, 689 (1964); C. E. Melton, and W. H. Hamill, *J. Chem. Phys.*, **41**, 1469 and 3464 (1964).

58. J. D. Morrison, *J. Chem. Phys.*, **39**, 200 (1963); "Some Recent Developments in the Study of Ionization Processes," 12th annual meeting of the ASTM Committee E-14 on Mass Spectrometry, Montreal, Canada, June 7–12, 1964.

59. R. W. Kiser and B. G. Hobrock, *J. Phys. Chem.*, **66**, 957 (1962).

60. J. L. Franklin, *Ind. Eng. Chem.*, **41**, 1070 (1949).

61. G. J. Janz, *Estimation of Thermodynamic Properties of Organic Compounds*, Academic Press, Inc., New York, 1958, 211 pp.

62. D. P. Stevenson, *Disc. Faraday Soc.*, **10**, 35 (1951).

63. T. L. Cottrell, *The Strengths of Chemical Bonds*, second edition, Butterworth's Scientific Publications, London, 1958, p. 271.

64. G. S. Paulett and R. Ettinger *J. Chem. Phys.*, **39**, 825 (1963).

65. G. Herzberg, *Can. J. Phys.*, **39**, 1511 (1961).

66. H. Prophet, *J. Chem. Phys.*, **38**, 2345 (1963).

67. C. F. Giese and W. B. Maier, II, *J. Chem. Phys.*, **39**, 197 (1963).

68. F. W. Lampe, J. L. Franklin, and F. H. Field, "Kinetics of the Reactions of Ions with Molecules," in *Progress in Reaction Kinetics*, vol. 1, G. Porter (ed.), Pergamon Press, New York, 1961, pp. 67–103.

69. B. G. Hobrock and R. W. Kiser, *J. Phys. Chem.*, **66**, 1648 (1962); **67**, 648 and 1283 (1963).

70. J. L. Franklin, *J. Chem. Ed.*, **40**, 284 (1963).

CHAPTER 9

ANALYTICAL APPLICATIONS

The largest use of mass spectrometers is in analytical determinations. In this area, the various types of applications of the mass spectrometer are so numerous as to preclude the possibility of discussing even a major portion of them, much less all of them. However, there are some basic applications on which much of the instrument time is spent, and these we shall discuss with a few examples included to illustrate the manner of application.

Briefly, we will first examine how the sample to be analyzed is introduced to the mass spectrometer. Then, we shall discuss some of the qualitative determinations that can be made with the mass spectrometer. Next, we shall discuss the quantitative applications. In the latter topic we shall study in detail the composition analyses of multi-component mixtures. The great and special utilities of low-voltage mass spectrometry are also considered. The chapter is concluded with an expansion on qualitative analysis, with particular emphasis on the determination of molecular structure by means of mass spectrometry and an examination of some of the helpful correlations between mass spectra and molecular structure.

9.1 SAMPLE INTRODUCTION

The sample must be admitted to the ionization chamber in the gaseous or vapor state. Since many samples are gases or liquids at room temperature, a sample-handling system and a leak arrangement to the ion source is usually required. In general, one desires to produce ion beams that are characteristic of the sample.

Smoluchowski (1) determined that the molecular flow of gas through cylindrical tubes at low pressures is given by

$$Q_m = 3810(D^3/L)(T/M)^{1/2}(P_1 - P_2), \tag{9–1}$$

where Q_m is the molecular gas flow through the opening in dyne-cm/sec; D is the diameter of the opening in centimeters; L is the length of the tube in centimeters; T is the absolute temperature; M is the molecular weight of the gas; and P_1 is the pressure on the low pressure side of the leak in dynes /cm^2. Flow through a circular opening in a thin plate is given by Knudsen's expression (1):

$$Q_m = 2860\, D^2(T/M)^{1/2}(P_1 - P_2), \tag{9–2}$$

where the symbols are the same as defined for Equation (9–1). Note that the coefficient in Equation (9–2) is just $\frac{3}{4}$ of that in Equation (9–1). These two equations hold as long as the mean free paths of the molecules λ are large compared to both the diameter of the leak opening (i.e., $\lambda \gg D$) and the distance in which considerable change occurs in the density of the gas. Usually λ should be about 20 times as great as D. It is also assumed that the cylindrical tube is very long so that terms for end corrections may be neglected. In practice, for Knudsen flow, foils about 0.0025 cm thick with holes 0.0002–0.005 cm in diameter may be used.

From Equations (9–1) and (9–2), it can be seen that the rate of admission of molecules of gas of molecular weight M is proportional to $1/\sqrt{M}$. Such a molecular flow leak may consist of a very small hole, or a number of small holes in a diaphragm. Even a sintered glass disc or porous plug containing many fine small channels will allow molecular flow. If the gases are also pumped from the ion source at a rate proportional to $1/\sqrt{M}$, the composition of the sample in the ion source will be the same as that in the reservoir behind the leak. It is also obvious from the above that if the flow rates of gases of different molecular weight are different, the composition of the sample in the reservoir preceding the leak to the ion source will change with time; the lower molecular weight gases will escape more rapidly than the higher molecular weight gases.

A long, thin capillary leak through which viscous flow occurs may also be placed between the reservoir and the ion source of the mass spectrometer. For higher pressures ($\lambda \ll D$), gas flow is viscous and follows Poiseuille's law (1):

$$Q_v = (\pi D^4/256\eta L)(P_1 + P_2)(P_1 - P_2), \tag{9–3}$$

where Q_v is the viscous gas flow, in dyne-cm/sec, through a capillary of length L, in centimeters, and η is the viscosity of the gas, in poises. Note that in

Equation (9–3) there is no molecular weight term, so that fractionation of the sample cannot occur when the flow is purely viscous. That is, the composition of the gas in the reservoir does not change with time as the gas flows through the capillary leak. However, in a viscous flow leak, there must be a region where the viscous flow changes to molecular flow.

Of course it is possible to have leaks that are between purely viscous and purely molecular flow. Then, however, the details of the fractionation are obscured, and unknown mass discrimination effects are introduced into the analytical results. It is best to use an inlet system with a purely molecular leak into the ionization chamber; but in all cases, the flow out of the ionization chamber must be molecular flow. If one uses a viscous flow system when determining isotopic abundances, a correction for $\sqrt{M}$ must be applied. In practice, capillary leaks may be about 5 in. long and about 0.005 in. in diameter. This then allows pressures of the order of several millimeters (Hg) on the high-pressure side of the leak.

One should note that both types of leaks, both molecular flow and viscous flow, of proper design are used in mass spectrometer sample introduction systems. In general, then, mass spectrometers are operated with continuous pumping and a constant flow of gaseous sample passes through the ion source (and, to a lesser extent, through the other portions of the mass spectrometer). This flow of gases in the mass spectrometer usually occurs at very low pressures, of the order of 10^{-5} to 10^{-7} mm (Hg). Therefore, the system will be similar to most high-vacuum systems of this size, with the added problem that residual gases cannot be tolerated in the mass spectrometer system because of the extreme sensitivity of this instrument.

Certain oil diffusion pumps can give rise to various hydrocarbon fragments through thermal decomposition of some of the oil. Recently, oils for diffusion pumps have been developed with very low vapor pressures and with greater stability towards heat; so, this is less of a problem than in previous years. Mercury diffusion pumps are commonly employed in many instruments; they give rise to background ions at $m/e = 198 - 204$ (due to Hg^+) and $m/e = 99 - 102$ (due to Hg^{++}), and if the electron beam energy is sufficiently great, even to very small amounts of $m/e = 66 - 68$ (due to Hg^{3+}). This is not always a disadvantage, for one can use these ions and their relative abundance to provide a "mass marker" for the m/e scale. It is obvious from the discussion above that, in the mass spectrometer system and in the associated pumping lines, molecular flow predominates.

The exact type of inlet system one employs depends largely on the type of problem being solved with the instrument, and the nature of the materials being studied. Some inlet systems may be made entirely of glass; others entirely of metal. And combinations are possible. Greases used for stopcocks may be of the hydrocarbon type, such as the "Apiezon" greases; or of silicone type, such as the Dow Silicone greases; or of inert fluorocarbons, such as the "Kel-F" grease. An example of a fairly simple system that can be em-

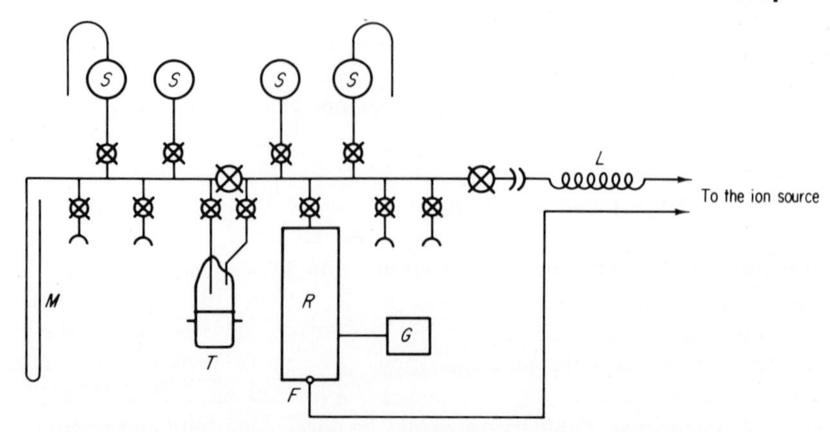

Fig. 9-1. A schematic diagram of one style of vacuum inlet system. M=manometer; T=Toepler pump; R=reservoir; G=vacuum gauge; F=molecular flow leak; L=capillary leak; s=storage bulb; ⊠=stopcocks; ⅄=ball or ₸ joints.

ployed for many common uses is shown in Figure 9–1. It is, of course, not necessary in all cases that the stopcocks be of the type that employ greases. In fact, in many instances lubricated stopcocks cause contamination and annoying memory effects which will outweigh objections to the use of an all-metal introduction system. Mercury "Stock" valves may also be used, or sintered glass supporting gallium seals, or even possibly vacuum-lock type metal seals.

Sampling methods may also be of different types. A common type of

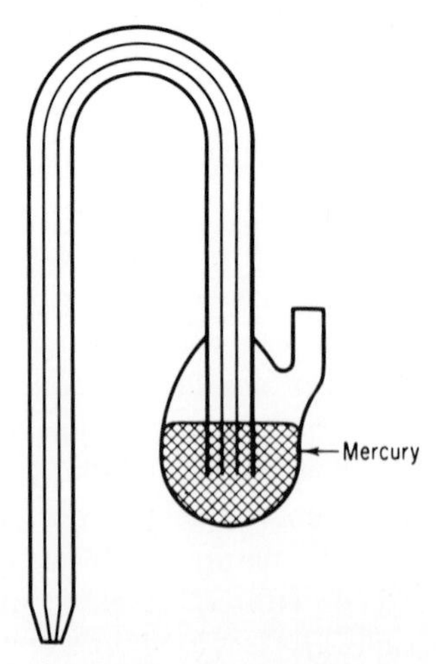

Fig. 9-2. Mercury-sealed constant volume gas pipette. (Courtesy of Consolidated Electrodynamics Corporation, Pasadena, California)

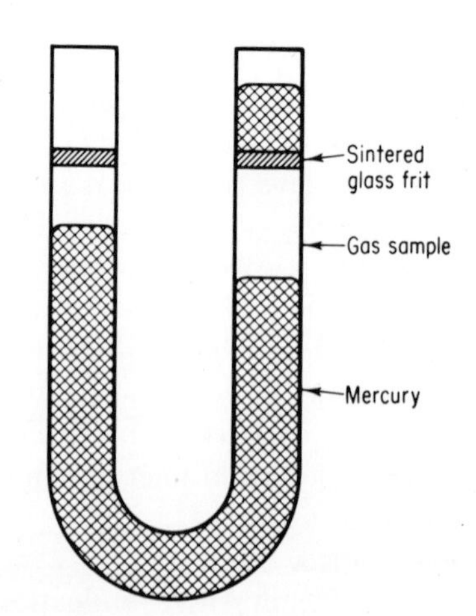

Fig. 9-3. Mercury-sealed gas-storage system. (Courtesy of Consolidated Electrodynamics Corporation, Pasadena, California)

such a gas pipette is shown in Figure 9–2, and a commercially available type of gas-storage system is shown in Figure 9–3. Many other types, far too numerous to describe here, have been and are being used with mass spectrometers. The few mentioned here are commonly termed *external sampling and inlet systems*. Although some solids may be warmed using heated inlet systems to give sufficient vapor pressures for analysis (see some more comments on heated inlets in Section 9.5), many of the inorganic solids cannot be studied mass spectrometrically with external systems. Therefore, one turns to *internal sampling systems*.

To produce a molecular beam of solids directly within the vacuum system can be a simple matter of heating a solid sample in a crucible to a sufficiently high temperature. This method is employed in practice, although its experimental features are somewhat complex. A sample of the material is placed within a crucible (such as a tantalum crucible) and a tight-fitting lid containing a small hole (molecular leak) is placed onto the crucible. The crucible is then heated (induction heating can be used as well as resistance heating), and the sample effuses through the hole in the lid into the ionization chamber, after being defined by a series of slits. This type of molecular-beam inlet is commonly termed a *Knudsen cell outlet*. By sighting the crucible with an optical pyrometer, the temperature of the crucible may be determined. Vapor pressures, heats of vaporization, types of species present in the vapor, and bond dissociation energies may be determined with this internal sampling method. We shall discuss some of the high-temperature chemistry accomplished with such sources in Section 10.2.

Another internal sampling method is that of placing the sample onto electrodes, as in the spark source, and then causing the sample to be vaporized directly in the ionization chamber. Also, the field ionization ion source may be considered an internal inlet system. Other types of special inlets may be used with other types of molecular beams. Inlets for use with free radical studies and shock-wave investigations can be varied greatly, dependent upon the specific application.

9.2 QUALITATIVE ANALYSIS

One readily apparent application of the mass spectrometer, which is quite useful in making a qualitative analysis, is the determination of molecular weights. Particular advantage is gained in such determinations by using low-energy electron beams (see Section 9.4). Generally speaking, the determination of molecular weights is a fairly straightforward process involving the location of the ion of the largest m/e in the mass spectrum (neglecting isotopic contributions) and the determination of its exact m/e value. For example, in Figure 9–4, the largest m/e value that is still obviously not an isotope peak is $m/e = 74$ in all three cases. Thus, we can readily determine that the molecular weight of each of these three compounds is 74. This is not always reliable, however. For example, applying this same approach to the

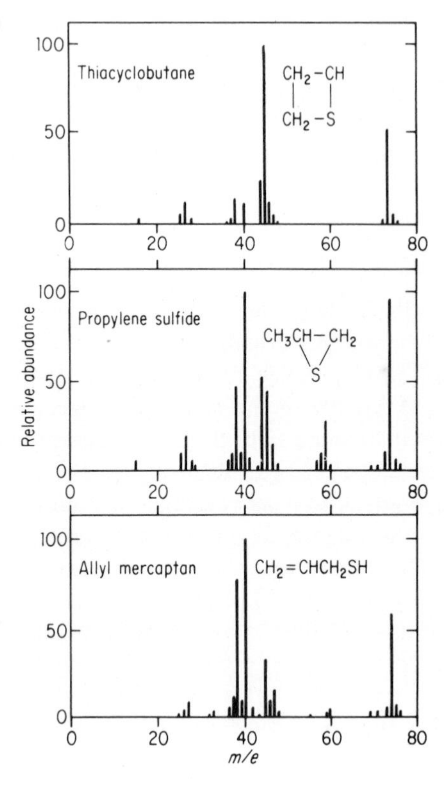

Fig. 9-4. 70 ev mass spectra of three different isomers of C_3H_6S, showing the effects of molecular structure.

mass spectrum of CCl_4, we would determine the molecular weight to be about 117, 119, or 121, since these are the last three abundant ions in the spectrum as we go to higher masses. CCl_4 gives only an extremely minute parent ion peak, if, indeed, any at all. However, even here, if one determined the spectrum, the isotopic abundances of the Cl^+, CCl^+, CCl_2^+, and CCl_3^+ ions should indicate that the parent was either $CHCl_3$ or CCl_4. And since the protonated ions are absent, one could show that the sample was CCl_4. But not from the "apparent" molecular weight.

From the spectra presented in Figure 9–4, one could also determine the unknown molecule if a catalog of the spectra of such compounds were available. Such catalogs are available to those working in mass spectrometry. One of these, and the one most widely referred to, is the American Petroleum Institute Project 44 catalog of *Mass Spectral Data* (2). Another is the newer Manufacturing Chemists Association's *Mass Spectral Data* (3), which contains spectra for many types of compounds in addition to the hydrocarbons. A third type of catalog, not as readily available and from which one may not quote data without permission of the contributing laboratory, but which proves to be extremely useful, is the ASTM Committee E–14 on mass spectrometry's *File of Uncertified Mass Spectra* (4). Between these catalogs, the mass spectra of probably close to 5000 compounds are listed.

However, even without the catalogs of mass spectral data, one can determine something further about each of the compounds whose mass spectra are shown in Figure 9–4.

EXAMPLE 9–1. If we knew the three compounds in Figure 9–4 were thiacyclobutane, propylene sulfide, and allyl mercaptan, we could determine which spectrum was which.

In the first spectrum, the $m/e = 46$ ion is quite intense; this is the CH_2S^+

ion, and its isotopic peaks are visible in the spectrum. Only small $m/e = 39$ and 41 peaks are present.

In the second spectrum, the $m/e = 45$ and 46 ions are intense, as well as the $m/e = 39$ and 41 peaks. Also, a fairly intense ion at $m/e = 59$ is visible; this is the $(p - 15)^+$ ion, suggesting a methyl group in the molecule. This spectrum then could tentatively be identified as the propylene sulfide, since it is the only one of these molecules directly containing a methyl group. The three carbons in propylene sulfide could readily give rise to the $m/e = 39$ and 41 peaks, and the cleavage of C–S and C–C bonds could lead to CH_2S^+, observed at $m/e = 46$, as well as the CHS^+ ion at $m/e = 45$.

In the third spectrum, we see that the $m/e = 59$ ion is very weak, and that the $m/e = 39$ and 41 ions are indeed very intense. However, here the ions of $m/e = 45$, 46, and 47 are much less intense. The ions of $m/e = 39$ and 41 again suggest that the three carbons are in a chain, and their great intensity strongly suggests that the allyl structure is already present. Thus, we could tentatively identify the third spectrum as due to the allyl mercaptan. The small amounts of $m/e = 34$ and 35 visible in this spectrum, due to H_2S^+ and H_3S^+, agree with this conclusion.

Then we would surmise that the first spectrum was due to the thiacyclobutane. Since this molecule could allow the rupture of the bonds as shown here

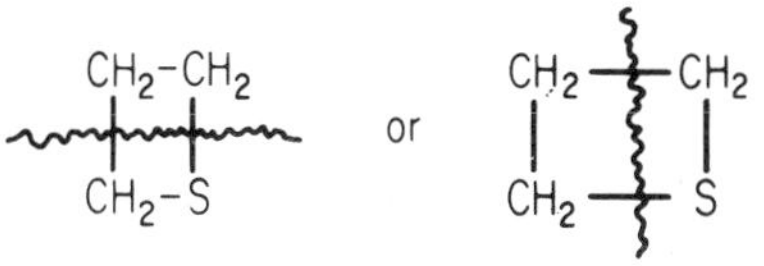

$$\begin{matrix} CH_2-CH_2 \\ CH_2-S \end{matrix} \quad \text{or} \quad \begin{matrix} CH_2 & CH_2 \\ | & | \\ CH_2 & S \end{matrix}$$

we could readily understand the large abundance of the CH_2S^+ ion in the mass spectrum of this compound, and the relatively small abundance of the ions of $m/e = 39$ and 41.

Thus, we are led to conclude that the first spectrum is due to the thiacyclobutane, the second spectrum is due to the propylene sulfide, and the third spectrum is due to the allyl mercaptan. These conclusions agree with the facts (see Figure 9–4).

In addition to the three catalogs of mass spectra indicated earlier, there have appeared in the scientific literature a number of other tabulations of mass spectra by types of compounds. In most cases these tabulations also attempt to correlate the mass spectra and the molecular structures of a group or class of compounds. A further discussion of these summaries and articles will be deferred until we discuss mass spectra and molecular structure in Section 9.5.

It should be noted that the mass spectrum changes with the energy of the electron beam, and this change is rather drastic below about 25 ev. We shall examine this point in more detail when we discuss the technique of low-voltage mass spectrometry.

The relative concentrations of isotopes also affects the mass spectrum of a given compound. For example, the ion corresponding to BCl_3^+ shows up at the masses indicated in Table 9–1, with the experimental relative abundances listed. [The calculated relative abundances were found (5) by using simple probability theory and the following isotopic abundances: B^{10} = 19.6%; B^{11} = 80.4% and Cl^{35} = 75.5%, Cl^{37} = 24.5%.] Similar, but not identical, results would be found for the other ions, BCl_2^+, BCl^+, Cl^+, and B^+.

The number of ways of picking any x atoms of the same kind from a large number N of isotopically different atoms is

$$C_x = \frac{N!}{x!(N-x)!}\,. \tag{9–4}$$

TABLE 9–1. THE BCl_3^+ ION IN THE MASS SPECTRUM OF BORON TRICHLORIDE (5)

m/e	Ionic Species	Relative Abundance	
		Experimental	Calculated
115	$B^{10}Cl_3^{35}$	25.1	25.1
116	$B^{11}Cl_3^{35}$	100.0	100.0
117	$B^{10}Cl_2^{35}Cl^{37}$	23.9	24.6
118	$B^{11}Cl_2^{35}Cl^{37}$	96.0	98.2
119	$B^{10}Cl^{35}Cl_2^{37}$	7.8	7.9
120	$B^{10}Cl^{35}Cl_2^{37}$	30.8	32.2
121	$B^{10}Cl_3^{37}$	0.9	0.9
122	$B^{11}Cl_3^{37}$	3.5	3.5

For example, with the Cl_2^+ ion, we would have $(Cl^{35}Cl^{35})^+$, $(Cl^{35}Cl^{37})^+$, and $(Cl^{37}Cl^{37})^+$ ions. Then,

$$\frac{C_2^a}{(C_1^aC_1^b)} = \frac{\left[\dfrac{N!}{2!(N-2)!}\right]}{\left[\dfrac{N!}{1!(N-1)!}\right]\left[\dfrac{N!}{1!(N-1)!}\right]} = \frac{(N-1)!(N-1)!}{2!(N-2)!N!}$$
$$= \frac{1}{2}\left[\frac{N-1}{N}\right],$$

so that in the limit, as $N \longrightarrow \infty$,

$$\frac{C_2^a}{(C_1^aC_1^b)} = \frac{1}{2}\,.$$

It can be seen similarly that $(C_2^a/C_2^b) = 1$. And therefore the ratios expected are 1: 2: 1 for 35—35: 35—37: 37—37 combinations, if the number of Cl^{35} and Cl^{37} atoms are the same. However, we know that this is not so; rather, Cl^{35} is 75.77% and Cl^{37} is 24.23% of all chlorine in nature (see Appendix I). Thus, we must also include the fractional abundance f of each chlorine isotope:

$$C_2^a \times f_a^2 = 1 \times (0.7577)^2 = 0.5741,$$
$$C_1^a C_1^b \times f_a f_b = 2 \times (0.7577)(0.2423) = 0.3672,$$
$$C_2^b \times f_b^2 = 1 \times (0.2423)^2 = 0.0587,$$

so that the total is unity. The relative abundances then would be R.A.$(Cl^{35}Cl^{35})^+ = 100.0$; R.A.$(Cl^{35}Cl^{37})^+ = 64.0$; and R.A.$(Cl^{37}Cl^{37})^+ = 10.2$.

EXAMPLE 9–2. What are the expected relative abundances of the CCl_3^+ ions (mentioned at the beginning of this Section), taking the relative abundance of the $m/e = 117$ ions as the reference (i.e., as 100.0)?

For the CCl_3^+ ion we would expect fractional abundances of

$$m/e = 117\text{:} \quad 1 \times (0.7577)^3 = 0.4350,$$
$$m/e = 119\text{:} \quad 3 \times (0.7577)^2(0.2423) = 0.4173,$$
$$m/e = 121\text{:} \quad 3 \times (0.7577)(0.2423)^2 = 0.1335,$$
$$m/e = 123\text{:} \quad 1 \times (0.2423)^3 = 0.0142,$$

and hence, for the CCl_3^+ ions, R.A.(117) = 100.0; R.A.(119) = 95.9; R.A.(121) = 30.7; and R.A.(123) = 3.3. Further details of calculating expected relative abundances for more complex isotopically labeled compounds are given by Margrave and Polansky (5).

The presence of these various isotope peaks can often be used to advantage in qualitative analyses of various fragment ions. For example, in the mass spectrum of $C_2H_5SSC_2H_5$, there is an ion peak of fair abundance at $m/e = 66$ and, at $m/e = 68$, there is another ion peak that is 9.0% of the abundance of the ion at $m/e = 66$. These ions at $m/e = 66$ and 68 must therefore be isotope peaks of sulfur for a fragment ion containing two sulfur atoms (since the isotopic abundance of sulfur-34 in nature is 4.5%). Therefore the ions of $m/e = 66$ and 68 are identified as $(H_2S_2^{32})^+$ and $(H_2S^{32}S^{34})^+$, respectively. Of course, the use of deuterium labeling in mass spectrometric studies is now obvious.

One further point that must be mentioned concerns an extremely useful method for establishing the nature of the ion (or ions) of a given mass; this method is *high-resolution mass spectrometry*. With very high resolution, N_2^+, CO^+, and $C_2H_4^+$ ions at $m/e = 28$ can be separated and identified, as seen in Figure 3–12. Also, this same type of high-resolution mass spectrometric study can be employed with a large variety of organic compounds to establish the nature of (and the relative abundances of) two or more possible ions occurring at the same m/e value. Beynon (6) has reported such studies for a number of heterocyclic compounds containing oxygen, and Beynon and others have discussed and used this technique to advantage (6–9).

There have been many applications of mass spectrometry to qualitative identifications of various compounds. But one of the very obvious applications is to the study of the components eluted from the column in gas-liquid partition chromatography. One recalls that the use of a gas chromatograph (with, for example, a thermal conductivity cell as detector) has very broad applications in separations and "identifications" of multi-component mixtures. But a galvanometer deflection or a peak recorded on a strip chart due to the change in thermal conductivity between the reference and the sample cells does not constitute an identification of the component eluted. The retention volumes or retention times are useful guides, but do not establish the nature of the component eluted. The very small quantities commonly eluted from a gas chromatographic column make difficult the analysis of the component by infrared or even microchemical analysis. However, the mass spectrometer is nicely suited to such identifications, because the mass spectra obtained provide "fingerprints" of the compounds, and because only a very small sample is required. In fact, in-stream gas chromatographic analysis identifications can be accompished readily for many situations, providing that rapid scanning and recording of the mass spectrum is possible.

Now that we have seen a few of the qualitative techniques and uses of mass spectrometry, let us turn to a discussion of quantitative analyses with this instrumentation.

9.3 QUANTITATIVE ANALYSIS

One of the most numerous applications of mass spectrometry has been in the quantitative analysis of multi-component mixtures. We have noted already that much of the impetus for the early development of commercially manufactured mass spectrometers derived from the quantitative analytical applications of these instruments, particularly in the petroleum industry. In the following pages we shall describe the methods by which one can reduce the mass spectrum of a multi-component mixture to quantitative results indicating the actual percentage composition of the mixture.

Since the peak heights of the various ions in the mass spectrum of a given compound are proportional to the pressure of the sample in the ion source (which may usually be related to the pressure of the sample in a large external reservoir), and since Dalton's law of partial pressures applies, the *peak heights are quantitatively additive* at the usual operating pressures of the mass spectrometer. An example of this is shown in Figure 9–5, wherein the mass spectrum of a synthetic mixture of 10% methyl isothiocyanate, 20%

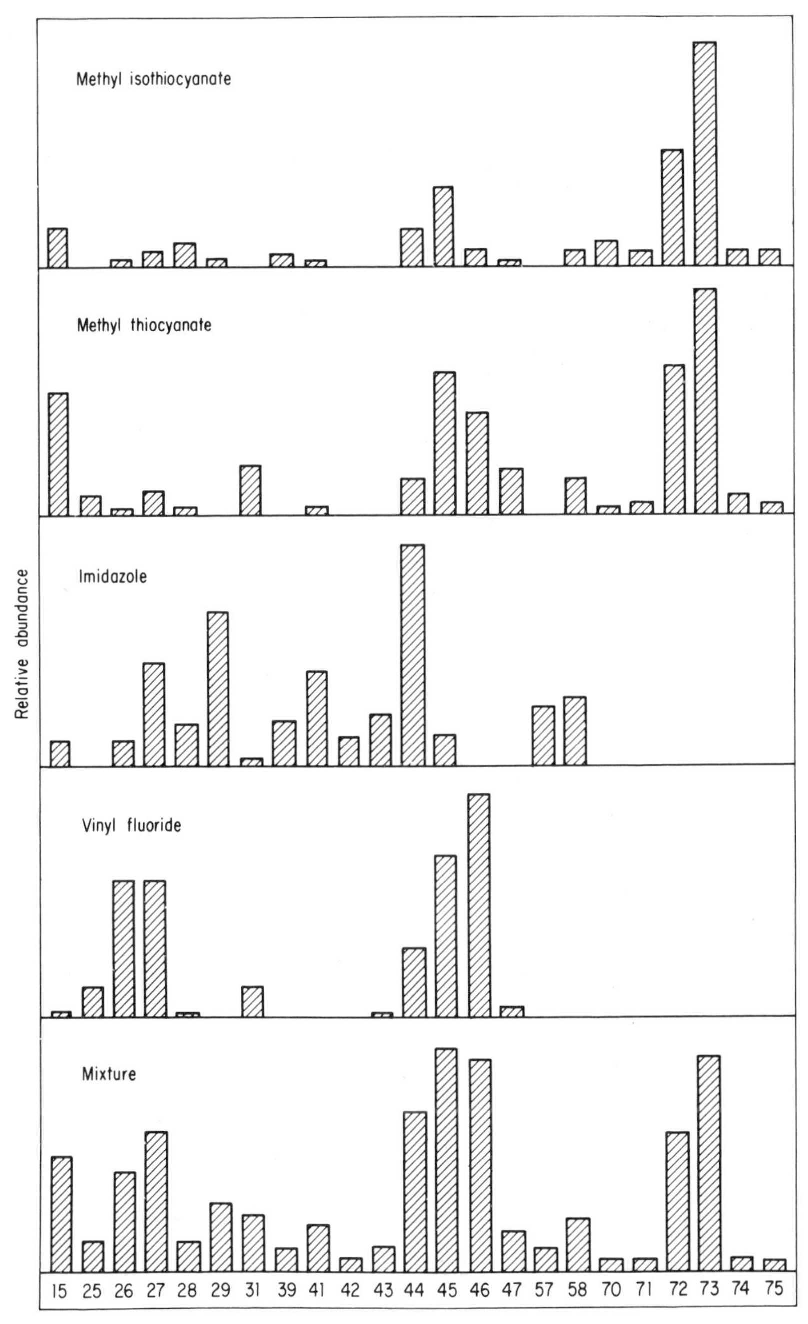

Fig. 9-5. An illustration of the addivity of the peak heights of the various components of a mixture.

imidazole, 30% vinyl fluoride, and 40% methyl thiocyanate is shown, along with the mass spectra of the four pure components of the mixture.

We have already seen, by means of examples, some of the ways in which the mass spectrometer is useful in qualitative analysis. In our discussion of the quantitative analysis of multi-component mixtures, we shall also make use of several examples to illustrate the methods for obtaining quantitative analytical information. Two very important methods commonly employed are (a) the solution of linear simultaneous equations, and (b) the subtraction technique. We shall take these up in turn.

THE LINEAR SIMULTANEOUS EQUATIONS METHOD

The experimental ion intensity data of a mixture of n components determined by means of the mass spectrometer may be analyzed to provide quantitative data concerning the composition of the mixture. The mass spectrometric data are represented by the following set of linear simultaneous equations:

$$\begin{aligned} p_1h_{11} + p_1h_{12} + \cdots + p_nh_{1n} &= H_1, \\ p_1h_{21} + p_2h_{22} + \cdots + p_nh_{2n} &= H_2, \\ \cdot \qquad \cdot \qquad\qquad \cdot \quad & \quad \cdot \\ \cdot \qquad \cdot \qquad\qquad \cdot \quad & \quad \cdot \\ \cdot \qquad \cdot \qquad\qquad \cdot \quad & \quad \cdot \\ p_1h_{m1} + p_2h_{m2} + \cdots + p_nh_{mn} &= H_m, \end{aligned} \tag{9–5}$$

where p_n is the partial pressure of the nth component of the mixture, and h_{mn} is the peak height (ion intensity) of the nth component for the mth peak (m/e value). Also, H_m is the peak height of the mth peak in the mixture analysis. For the m equations that can be written, we wish to determine the n quantities p_n. (Note here that usually $m > n$, although there may be exceptions.) We shall select $m = n$ to provide a square matrix. If $m > n$, permitting selection of n out of the m possible equations, the larger H_m values are commonly chosen to reduce the errors and thereby provide more satisfactory results. Again, there may be exceptions to this statement, and through familiarity with the mixtures and the determinations one is better able to decide which n of the m equations will provide the most satisfactory determinations of the n components.

Selecting $m = n$, we see that Equation (9–5) may be written as

$$\begin{aligned} p_1h_{11} + p_2h_{12} + \cdots + p_nh_{1n} &= H_1, \\ p_1h_{21} + p_2h_{22} + \cdots + p_nh_{2n} &= H_2, \\ \cdot \qquad \cdot \qquad\qquad \cdot \quad & \quad \cdot \\ \cdot \qquad \cdot \qquad\qquad \cdot \quad & \quad \cdot \\ \cdot \qquad \cdot \qquad\qquad \cdot \quad & \quad \cdot \\ p_1h_{n1} + p_2h_{n2} + \cdots + p_nh_{nn} &= H_n. \end{aligned} \tag{9–6}$$

The solution of the set of equations given by Equation (9–6) may be written as

$$\begin{aligned} p_1 &= a_{11}H_1 + a_{12}H_2 + \cdots + a_{1n}H_n, \\ p_2 &= a_{21}H_1 + a_{22}H_2 + \cdots + a_{2n}H_n, \\ &\;\;\cdot \qquad \cdot \qquad\qquad \cdot \qquad\qquad\quad \cdot \\ &\;\;\cdot \qquad \cdot \qquad\qquad \cdot \qquad\qquad\quad \cdot \\ &\;\;\cdot \qquad \cdot \qquad\qquad \cdot \qquad\qquad\quad \cdot \\ p_n &= a_{n1}H_1 + a_{n2}H_2 + \cdots + a_{nn}H_n, \end{aligned} \tag{9–7}$$

where the values of a_{rs} depend only upon the h_{rs} and are constant for a given mixture. If the a_{rs} are determined, they may then be written in columns alongside the H_r, as shown in Equation (9–8), and the desired solutions p_r may be calculated from a simple summation of the products.

$$\begin{matrix} a_{11} & a_{21} & \cdots & a_{n1} & H_1 \\ a_{12} & a_{22} & \cdots & a_{n2} & H_2 \\ \cdot & \cdot & & \cdot & \cdot \\ \cdot & \cdot & & \cdot & \cdot \\ \cdot & \cdot & & \cdot & \cdot \\ a_{1n} & a_{2n} & \cdots & a_{nn} & p_n \end{matrix} \tag{9–8}$$

Equation (9–6) may also be expressed as

$$Ap = H \tag{9–9}$$

and the solution as

$$p = A^{-1}H, \tag{9–10}$$

using the language and notation of matrix algebra. That is,

$$A^{-1}A = I_{nn}, \tag{9–11}$$

where I_{nn} is an *identity matrix*, i.e., a *scalar matrix* whose diagonal elements are unity, and A^{-1} is the *inverse matrix*. The elements of the matrix A are the coefficients h_{rs} of Equation (9–6); the elements of the inverse matrix A^{-1} are the coefficients a_{rs} of Equation (9–9).

The inverse matrix A^{-1} is determined from the square matrix A, whose determinant is $D = 0$, by means of the following steps: (a) replace each element of the matrix by its cofactor in the corresponding determinant; (b) transpose the resultant matrix; and (c) multiply the matrix (i.e., each element of the matrix) obtained by the quantity $(1/D)$. The cofactor of an element in row r and column s of a determinant is the minor obtained by striking out this row and column and multiplying by $(-1)^{r+s}$.

Consider the array

$$A = \begin{vmatrix} a_{11} & a_{12} & a_{13} & a_{14} \\ a_{21} & a_{22} & a_{23} & a_{24} \\ a_{31} & a_{32} & a_{33} & a_{34} \\ a_{41} & a_{42} & a_{43} & a_{44} \end{vmatrix}. \tag{9–12}$$

The minor element of a_{22}, A_{22}, is

$$A_{22} = \begin{vmatrix} a_{11} & a_{13} & a_{14} \\ a_{31} & a_{33} & a_{34} \\ a_{41} & a_{43} & a_{44} \end{vmatrix}, \tag{9–13}$$

and the minor element of a_{43}, A_{43}, is

$$A_{43} = - \begin{vmatrix} a_{11} & a_{12} & a_{14} \\ a_{21} & a_{22} & a_{24} \\ a_{31} & a_{32} & a_{34} \end{vmatrix}. \tag{9–14}$$

For the same array [Equation (9–12)], the transpose A' is

$$A' = \begin{vmatrix} a_{11} & a_{21} & a_{31} & a_{41} \\ a_{12} & a_{22} & a_{32} & a_{42} \\ a_{13} & a_{23} & a_{33} & a_{43} \\ a_{14} & a_{24} & a_{34} & a_{44} \end{vmatrix}. \tag{9–15}$$

Now, it is a property of matrices that

$$(A')^{-1} = (A^{-1})' \tag{9–16}$$

or, the inverse of the transpose matrix is the transpose of the inverse matrix. We shall see shortly that this is a very useful property.

The inverse matrix A^{-1} of A[Equation (9–12)] is, using the three steps outlined above,

$$A^{-1} = \frac{1}{D} \cdot \begin{vmatrix} A_{11} & A_{21} & A_{31} & A_{41} \\ A_{12} & A_{22} & A_{32} & A_{42} \\ A_{13} & A_{23} & A_{33} & A_{43} \\ A_{14} & A_{24} & A_{34} & A_{44} \end{vmatrix}, \tag{9–17}$$

and the transpose of the inverse matrix, $(A^{-1})'$, which, from Equation (9–16), is also the inverse of the transpose matrix, $(A')^{-1}$, is

$$(A')^{-1} = (A^{-1})' = \frac{1}{D} \cdot \begin{vmatrix} A_{11} & A_{12} & A_{13} & A_{14} \\ A_{21} & A_{22} & A_{23} & A_{24} \\ A_{31} & A_{32} & A_{33} & A_{34} \\ A_{41} & A_{42} & A_{43} & A_{44} \end{vmatrix}. \tag{9–18}$$

From the comments following Equation (9–7), we note that if the original matrix, A is inverted and transposed, the solution p_r can be calculated rapidly by recording the given H alongside the transpose, $(A^{-1})'$ of A^{-1}, and multiplying each column of (A^{-1}) in turn by the column H; we leave out step (b), outlined above, and arrive directly at Equation (9–18) as our solution.

EXAMPLE 9–3. An unknown sample may contain A, B, C, and D. The mass spectra of pure A, B, C, and D are given in the table below, along with the mass spectrum of the mixture. Determine the quantitative composition of the unknown sample.

m/e	Unknown	A	B	C	D
31	100.0	0.0	3.2	6.4	100.0
34	9.3	24.1	0.0	0.0	0.0
45	51.4	22.4	0.0	100.0	4.2
58	12.2	10.8	38.9	0.0	0.0

For this particular example we have already chosen just four peaks, so that $m = n$. The matrix has the coefficients of the following array for this set:

$$A = \begin{vmatrix} 0.0 & 3.2 & 6.4 & 100.0 \\ 24.1 & 0.0 & 0.0 & 0.0 \\ 22.4 & 0.0 & 100.0 & 4.2 \\ 10.8 & 38.9 & 0.0 & 0.0 \end{vmatrix}.$$

Then,

$$D = 9{,}374{,}900.$$

Now,

$$A_{11} = 0,$$

$$A_{12} = -\begin{vmatrix} 24.1 & 0 & 0 \\ 22.4 & 100.0 & 4.2 \\ 10.8 & 0 & 0 \end{vmatrix} = 0,$$

$$A_{13} = \begin{vmatrix} 24.1 & 0 & 0 \\ 22.4 & 0 & 4.2 \\ 10.8 & 38.9 & 0 \end{vmatrix} = -3937,$$

$$A_{14} = -\begin{vmatrix} 24.1 & 0 & 0 \\ 22.4 & 0 & 100.0 \\ 10.8 & 38.9 & 0 \end{vmatrix} = 93{,}749,$$

$$A_{21} = -\begin{vmatrix} 3.2 & 6.4 & 100.0 \\ 0 & 100.0 & 4.2 \\ 38.9 & 0 & 0 \end{vmatrix} = 387{,}954,$$

$$A_{22} = \begin{vmatrix} 0 & 6.4 & 100.0 \\ 22.4 & 100.0 & 4.2 \\ 10.8 & 0 & 0 \end{vmatrix} = -107{,}710,$$

$$A_{23} = -\begin{vmatrix} 0 & 3.2 & 100.0 \\ 22.4 & 0 & 4.2 \\ 10.8 & 38.9 & 0 \end{vmatrix} = -87{,}281,$$

etc. Therefore, we may write, using Equation (9–18),

$$(A')^{-1} = \frac{1}{9{,}374{,}900} \begin{vmatrix} 0 & 0 & -3{,}937 & 93{,}749 \\ 387{,}954 & -107{,}710 & -87{,}281 & 9{,}033 \\ 0 & 0 & 93{,}749 & -6{,}000 \\ 0 & 240{,}352 & 324 & -7{,}712 \end{vmatrix}$$

or

$$(A')^{-1} = \begin{vmatrix} 0 & 0 & -0.00042 & 0.01000 \\ 0.04138 & -0.01149 & -0.00931 & 0.00096 \\ 0 & 0 & 0.01000 & -0.00064 \\ 0 & 0.02564 & 0.00003 & -0.00082 \end{vmatrix}$$

and therefore,

A	B	C	D	H
0	0	−0.00042	0.01000	100.0
0.04138	−0.01149	−0.00931	0.00096	9.3
0	0	0.01000	−0.00064	51.4
0	0.02564	0.00003	−0.00082	12.2

From this,

$$p_A = (0.04138 \times 9.3) = 0.385,$$

$$p_B = -(0.01149 \times 9.3) + (0.02564 \times 12.2) = 0.206,$$

$$p_C = -(0.00931 \times 9.3) - (0.00042 \times 100.0) + (0.01000 \times 51.4) + (0.00003 \times 12.2) = 0.386,$$

$$p_D = (0.00096 \times 9.3) \times (0.01000 \times 100.0) - (0.00064 \times 51.4) - (0.00082 \times 12.2) = 0.966.$$

$$\sum_i (p_i) = 1.943.$$

Each partial pressure may be expressed, then, as a percentage of $\sum_i p_i$; i.e.,

$$\begin{aligned} A &= 19.8 \text{ mole \%} \\ B &= 10.6 \text{ mole \%} \\ C &= 19.9 \text{ mole \%} \\ D &= \underline{49.7} \text{ mole \%} \\ & \quad 100.0 \end{aligned}$$

is the composition of the sample.

THE SUBTRACTION TECHNIQUE

From Dalton's law, $p_A + p_B + p_C + p_D = p_t$, as employed in Example 9–2. We also know that the total pressure $\sum_i p_i$ is related to the total number of moles of gas. We may write this in terms of the mole fractions of the components:

$$x_A + x_B + x_C + x_D = x_t = 1. \tag{9–19}$$

Let b be the factor between p_t and x_t; i.e.,

$$bp_t = 1 \tag{9–20}$$

or

$$b = 1/p_t. \tag{9–21}$$

Then, $p_A^b = x_A$, $p_B^b = x_B$, etc.

EXAMPLE 9–4. To illustrate the subtraction technique, we shall use the data used in Example 9–3 for the simultaneous linear equations method. First, we choose a peak in the mass spectrum of the unknown that can arise from only one component of the mixture. For this purpose, we shall choose the $m/e = 34$ peak, due only to component A. Then $p_A = 9.3/24.1 = 0.386$. Let us calculate a new spectrum of A using the factor 0.386:

m/e	A
31	0.00
34	9.30
45	8.65
58	4.17

Now subtract this from the original unknown spectrum to give a new unknown spectrum without component A. Thus,

m/e	New Unknown
31	100.0
34	0.0
45	42.7_5
58	8.0_3

Now, of the remaining components, only B contributes to the $m/e = 58$ peak. Therefore, as before, $p_B = 8.0_3/38.9 = 0.206$. Now, a new spectrum of B can be obtained using the factor of 0.206. Thus,

m/e	R
31	0.66
34	0.0
45	0.0
58	8.0_1

Subtracting this from the previous spectrum eliminates component B, leaving only C and D in the new unknown spectrum:

m/e	New Unknown
31	99.34
34	0.0
45	42.75
58	0.02

Now both C and D contribute to both the $m/e = 31$ and the $m/e = 45$ peaks. So, the simple subtraction process must give way to the linear simultaneous equation method; however, in this case it is a simple matter of two equations in two unknowns. Thus,

$$6.4p_C + 100.0p_D = 99.34,$$

$$100.0p_C + 4.2p_D = 42.75.$$

Multiplying the first of the two equations by 100.0/6.4 gives

$$\begin{array}{rcl} 100.0p_C + 1562.5p_D &=& 1552.19 \\ 100.0p_C + \quad 4.2p_D &=& 42.75 \\ \hline 1558.3p_D &=& 1509.4 \\ p_D &=& 0.969. \end{array}$$

Then the new spectrum of D is

m/e	D
31	96.9
34	0.0
45	4.07
58	0.0

and subtracting this from the unknown to eliminate D, leaves us with, essentially, only the C component:

m/e	New Unknown
31	2.44
34	0.0
45	38.68
58	0.02

So, $p_C = 38.68/100 = 0.387$. And the new spectrum is

m/e	C
31	2.48
34	0.0
45	38.7
58	0.0

and subtraction of the C component should yield a spectrum where the ion intensities should now all be zero. We see that this is essentially the case.

m/e	Final Spectrum
31	−0.04
34	0.00
45	−0.02
58	0.02

Therefore,

Component	p_i	mole %
A	0.386	19.8
B	0.206	10.6
C	0.387	19.9
D	0.969	49.7
$\sum_i (p_i) =$	1.948	100.0

and we observe that these results are essentially the same as those obtained by the simultaneous linear equations method.

SENSITIVITIES

In the preceding section, a discussion of sensitivity was omitted for the sake of clarity. However, we must now consider the sensitivity factor s. The intensities I_i of the ion currents for the various ions in the mass spectrum of a given compound are actually recorded in units of current (or even in divisions of chart paper). For a given pressure p_j of the jth compound in the ionization chamber, there will be given intensities of ion currents; and for the primary species, the intensities I_{ij} are directly related to the pressure:

$$I_{ij} \propto p_j \tag{9–22}$$

or

$$I_{ij} = r_i s_j p_j, \tag{9–23}$$

where, again, the subscript i refers to an ion of given m/e value, and the subscript j refers to a given compound; r_i is the relative abundance of the ith ion in the mass spectrum. Note that s_j is used rather than simply s, for the sensitivity factor may be (and very often is) different for each compound considered. It is obvious, therefore, that the sensitivities s_j must be included in a proper data treatment.

Since, for a given mass spectrometer and for given filament conditions, the relative abundances of the various ions r_i is constant in the mass spectrum, we may write

$$I_j = S_j P_j \tag{9–24}$$

for the intensity of the most abundant ion ($r_i = 100.0$) in the mass spectrum of the jth compound. Because the absolute values of S_j may and frequently do change with time, relative S_j values are recorded by comparing S_j for a given compound to s_j for the $m/e = 43$ ion in the mass spectrum of n-butane.

In the examples above, it was simply assumed that the S_j of the various compounds were identical. If the S_j had been known, the final results would have been divided by the respective S_j values, and then the $\sum_i (p_i)$ would have been obtained. Let us consider another example to see this illustrated.

TABLE 9–2. MASS SPECTRA OF KNOWNS AND UNKNOWN FOR EXAMPLE 9–5

	Relative Abundances				
m/e	*Q*	*R*	*S*	*T*	Unknown
15	53.3	13.5	1.3	9.3	48.3
26	1.8	1.3	59.2	8.3	39.3
27	8.9	3.0	59.9	44.9	59.8
29	0.1	1.3	0.0	68.9	27.0
31	19.2	0.0	11.9	2.2	22.7
44	13.4	15.1	31.0	100.0	70.2
45	63.3	26.3	71.1	11.4	100.0
46	44.6	6.3	100.0	0.5	94.2
47	20.4	2.0	3.0	0.0	18.0
58	13.4	5.3	0.0	0.0	23.4
72	66.9	49.3	0.0	0.0	61.5
73	100.0	100.0	0.0	0.0	97.0
s	0.542	1.072	0.360	0.613	—

EXAMPLE 9–5. Consider the set of data presented in Table 9–2. We may use either the simultaneous linear equations method or the subtraction technique to solve for the composition. In either case, we must select $n = 4$ peaks with which to work from the $m = 12$ sets of data in Table 9–2. We shall select the data for ions of $m/e = 44$, 46, 72, and 73.

Using the data for the $(m/e) = 72$ and 73 ions, we can write

$$66.9x_Q + 49.3x_R = 61.5$$

and

$$100.0x_Q + 100.0x_R = 97.0.$$

Solving these two equations in two unknowns, we obtain

$$\begin{array}{r} 100.0x_Q + \;\; 73.7x_R = 91.9 \\ 100.0x_Q + 100.0x_R = 97.0 \\ \hline 26.3x_R = \;\; 5.1 \end{array}$$

so that

$$x_R = 0.194$$

and

$$100.0x_Q = 97.0 - 19.4,$$
$$100.0x_Q = 77.6,$$
$$x_Q = 0.776.$$

Now then, for the $m/e = 46$ ion, we see that

$$(44.6)(0.776) + (6.3)(0.194) + (100.0)x_S + (0.5)x_T = 94.2$$

or

$$100.0x_S + 0.5x_T = 58.4.$$

Note that this is one equation in two unknowns. However, we may proceed by making the assumption that $0.5x_T$ is small (maybe about 0.1 to 0.5) and we may neglect it in comparison to 58.4 (the error would probably be less than 1% in doing so). Thus,

$$100.0x_S \doteq 58.4$$

so that

$$x_S \doteq 0.584.$$

And now, from the data for the $(m/e) = 44$ ion,

$$(13.4)(0.776) + (15.1)(0.194) + (31.0)(0.584) + 100.0x_T \doteq 70.2$$

or

$$100.0x_T \doteq 38.8$$

so that

$$x_T \doteq 0.388,$$

and we see that our assumption concerning $0.5x_T$ is indeed satisfactory. Therefore, we have

$$x_Q = 0.776,$$
$$x_R = 0.194,$$
$$x_S = 0.584,$$
$$x_T = 0.388.$$

Including now the sensitivity factors given in Table 9–2, we have

$$P_Q = 0.776/0.542 = 1.430$$
$$P_R = 0.194/1.072 = 0.181$$
$$P_S = 0.584/0.360 = 1.620$$
$$P_T = 0.388/0.613 = \underline{0.633}$$
$$\sum_i (p_i) = 3.864,$$

and finally we obtain from $100p_i/[\sum_i (p_i)] =$ mole % composition,

$$\begin{aligned} Q &= (1.430/3.864)(100) = 37.0 \text{ mole } \% \\ R &= (0.181/3.864)(100) = 4.7 \text{ mole } \% \\ S &= (1.620/3.864)(100) = 41.9 \text{ mole } \% \\ T &= (0.633/3.864)(100) = \underline{16.4 \text{ mole } \%} \\ & \qquad\qquad\qquad\qquad\quad 100.0 \text{ mole } \% \end{aligned}$$

ISOTOPE DILUTION TECHNIQUE

Some analyses not conveniently carried out by the methods discussed in the preceding sections may be made by employing the isotope dilution method of analysis, a very powerful technique. This method may be applied through the use of either radioactive or nonradioactive isotopes. Nuclear radiation detectors are commonly used for the detection of the isotopic tracer in the former case, whereas mass spectrometric detection is commonly used in the latter case.

The isotopic dilution technique has a unique advantage: it is not necessary to recover all of the original material being analyzed to obtain the quantitative information desired. We shall see this more forcefully in the examples following the derivation of the equation for isotope dilution. Although the derivation for the case of radioactive tracers is similar, in the following derivation we shall be concerned only with nonradioactive tracers.

Let us examine this technique now in a more quantitative manner. Let W be the number of grams of the unknown substance present in a sample. This unknown substance originally contains only atoms of one isotope of a given element, so that the specific concentration of W, C, is zero. Now, we add W_0 grams of an isotopically labeled component, chemically identical to that being analyzed. The total number of atoms of the added isotope is A_0, and therefore the specific concentration of the added isotopic component is $C_0 = A_0/W_0$.

Upon completion of the addition and subsequent to thorough mixing through equilibration, the total component present is $(W + W_0)$ grams, and the total number of atoms of the added isotope remains as A_0.

We shall now separate out W_1 grams of the pure component. The total number of atoms of the added isotope present would be A_1, and therefore the specific concentration would be $C_1 = A_1/W_1$.

The fraction separated is $W_1/(W + W_0)$ of the total, and the number of isotopic atoms is A_1/A_0 of the total. Therefore,

$$\frac{W_1}{W + W_0} = \frac{A_1}{A_0} \tag{9–25}$$

or

$$\frac{W_1}{W + W_0} = \frac{W_1 C_1}{W_0 C_0} \tag{9–26}$$

and thus,

$$\frac{1}{W + W_0} = \frac{C_1}{W_0 C_0} \tag{9-27}$$

or

$$W_0 C_0 = WC_1 + W_0 C_1. \tag{9-28}$$

Rearranging, we obtain

$$WC_1 = W_0 C_0 - W_0 C_1 \tag{9-29}$$

or

$$WC_1 = W_0(C_0 - C_1) \tag{9-30}$$

and therefore,

$$W = W_0\left(\frac{C_0}{C_1} - 1\right). \tag{9-31}$$

EXAMPLE 9–6. A sample of 10.0 g of soluble sodium salts contained a certain unknown quantity of Na_2CO_3. A total of 15.0 mg of Na_2CO_3 containing 17.5 at. % C^{13} were added to the original 10.0-g sample and mixed. The entire sample was then treated with sulfuric acid to liberate carbon dioxide. Twenty milliliters (at STP) of the dried carbon dioxide gas released were collected and analyzed by means of a mass spectrometer. It was found from analyses of the $m/e = 44$ and 45 peaks that the CO_2 contained 1.96 at. % C^{13}. What was the percentage by weight of sodium carbonate in the original sample?

We are tempted to calculate this as follows:

$$C_1 = 1.96 \text{ at. } \% \text{ C}^{13}$$

and

$$C_0 = 17.5 \text{ at. } \% \text{ C}^{13};$$

therefore,

$$[(C_0/C_1) - 1] = [(17.5/1.96) - 1] = 7.94$$

and

$$W_0 = 15.0(7.94) = 119 \text{ mg}$$

so that,

$$\frac{0.119 \times 100}{10.0} = 1.19\% \text{ Na}_2\text{CO}_3 \text{ by weight in the original sample.}$$

However, we have assumed that the original sample contained no carbon-13. This is not so; carbon-13 comprises 1.11% of natural carbon. Therefore, this must be subtracted; then, the calculations give

$$C_1 = 1.96 - 1.11 = 0.85 \text{ at. } \% \text{ C}^{13}$$

and

$$C_0 = 17.5 - 1.11 = 16.4 \text{ at. } \% \text{ C}^{13}.$$

Therefore,

$$[(C_0/C_1) - 1] = [(16.4/0.85) - 1] = 18.3$$

or

$$15.0(18.3) = 290 \text{ mg}$$

so that

$$\frac{0.290 \times 100}{10.0} = 2.90\% \ Na_2CO_3 \text{ by weight in the original sample.}$$

Thus, the correct definitions of C_0 and C_1 in Equation (9–31) are

C_0 = specific concentration of the added isotopic component in excess over the normal isotopic concentration.

C_1 = specific concentration of the isotopic component of the mixture in excess over the normal isotopic concentration.

If $C = 0$, then the earlier definitions of C_0 and C_1 would be satisfactory.

Note that the volume of CO_2 collected, or that analyzed, is immaterial. One could just as well have analyzed only 1 ml of the CO_2 sample and obtained the same results. Note also that an analysis conducted by adding 1.50 mg of labeled Na_2CO_3 to a 1.00-g sample of the salts would have produced the same result. Furthermore, it was not at all necessary to treat the entire 10.015-g sample with H_2SO_4. Any conveniently smaller size sample producing enough CO_2 for an accurate analysis would have been sufficient.

Similar illustrations or examples could be given for other isotopes. Suffice it to say that isotopic dilution employing stable isotopes and mass spectrometric analysis has proved extremely useful for analyses involving nitrogen (nitrogen-15 tracer) and oxygen (oxygen-18 tracer), although there are other instances of utility for dilutions of other elements.

9.4 LOW-VOLTAGE MASS SPECTROMETRY

From the discussion in Chapter 8 and from Figure 8–7, one can see that as the voltage of the electron beam is decreased, the amount of fragmentation is also decreased, particularly below about 25 ev. The reduction in fragmentation often greatly simplifies the determination of the molecular weight of the compound (or compounds, when analyzing a mixture), as already mentioned. However, there is also an accompanying reduction in the sensitivity of detection of the ions. Thus, in practice, an intermediate value (of the order of 10 to 15 volts) of the ionizing voltage is usually selected in order to obtain the best sensitivities possible commensurate with holding the fragmentation to a minimum.

In addition to the simplified mass spectra obtained by using lower ionizing voltages, the peaks of a given *m/e* value are in many cases due only to a single compound, so that the quantitative analysis of a mixture may be readily accomplished at low voltages without the necessity of solving a large group of linear simultaneous equations. Stevenson and Wagner (10) made use of this low-voltage technique many years ago in analyzing low molecular weight monodeutero-paraffins.

As illustrations of low-voltage mass spectra, consider Figures 9–6 and 9–7.

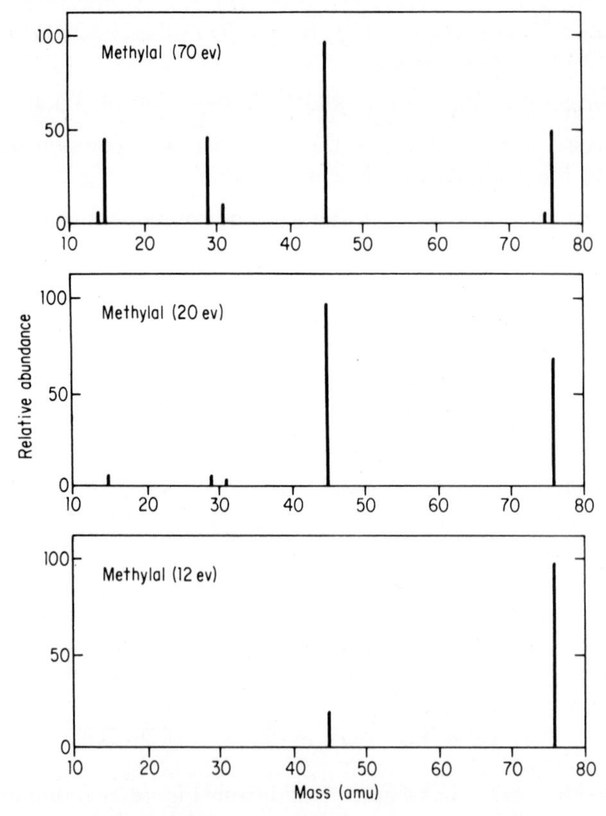

Fig. 9-6. Effect of electron energy on the mass spectrum of methylal (dimethoxy-methane, $CH_3OCH_2OCH_3$).

In the first of these, the mass spectrum of methylal ($CH_3OCH_2OCH_3$) is shown for ionizing voltages of 70, 20, and 12 ev. Note that the reduction of the electron energy reduces fragmentation. However, neither Figure 9–6 nor Figure 9–7 indicates the loss of sensitivity accompanying the reduction of the energy of the electron beam. In Figure 9–7 a somewhat more dramatic reduction in the fragmentation is observed for propylene upon going to lower ionizing voltages. Note that the $m/e = 43$ ion peak is due to carbon-13 (about 1.1% of all carbon in nature) in the propylene molecule.

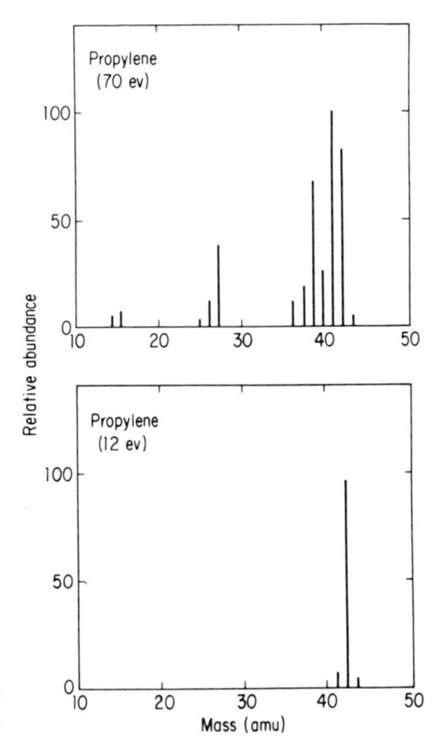

Fig. 9-7. The effect of electron energy on the mass spectrum of propylene ($CH_3CH = CH_2$).

The sensitivities are indeed low at the lower voltages. Reference to Table 9–3 will give some indication of the common sensitivities. Such sensitivities are about two to three orders of magnitude lower than for a 70-volt electron beam. This author has found that a 12-volt electron beam energy gives somewhat increased sensitivities without seriously increasing the fragmentation. Similar results have been reported by Lumpkin and Aczel (12). Crable, Kearns, and Norris (13) have found a correlation between the directing properties of substituent groups and the sensitivities of the substituted benzenes that is quite interesting (see Figure 9–4). Crable, *et al.*, (13) point out their preference for the use of "molar

TABLE 9–3. LOW-VOLTAGE SENSITIVITIES FOR SOME MERCAPTANS (11)

	At 9 volts, 20 μamp	
m/e	Mercaptan	Sensitivity (div./micron)
48	Methyl	7.73
62	Ethyl	8.13
76	Propyl	7.96
90	Butyl	6.79
104	Amyl	7.28
118	Hexyl	6.55
132	Heptyl	7.76

sensitivities" as the appropriate term, since divisions/micron can be related to divisions/mole. The values in Table 9–4 are standardized to a value of 1.0 divisions/micron for ethylbenzene. Lumpkin and Aczel (12) have corroborated and extended these findings, while placing greater emphasis on the use of ionization efficiency curves.

The high-voltage (70 ev) mass spectra of higher olefins show considerable fragmentation, particularly to form ions of the lower olefins. Kearns, Maranowski, and Crable (14) have shown that the use of low voltage (8.0 ev) produces little fragmentation, as indeed Figure 9–7 also shows. Kearns, *et al.*, also used a charge of 4.6 μliter into a 2-liter reservoir, about five times greater than the usual charge to a mass spectrometer for analytical purposes. They did this to partially offset the reduced sensitivity at 8.0 volts. The sensitivity in a given series of compounds is found to decrease as the molecular weight increases, as might be expected.

As has been noted by Varsel, Morrell, Resnik, and Powell (15), many appearance potentials for various ions exceed 11 ev, but in a great many compounds the ionization potential is less than 11 ev. Thus, low-voltage electron beams of about 8–12 ev are commonly employed. With an 11- or 12-volt electron beam, some fragmentation may be encountered, but it is usually balanced by the increased sensitivity (12). For some compounds, such as those containing nitrogen, the very low sensitivities demand somewhat higher voltages than 8 to 10 volts.

The low-voltage mass spectra of ferrocene and substituted ferrocenes have been studied by Clancy and Spilners (16). Using a high-temperature inlet system (about 350° C) and low ionizing voltages, these authors observed that the parent molecule-ions are quite intense [as they are also at higher voltages (17)] although a detailed study of the low-voltage sensitivities was not made. Very little fragmentation of the molecules was noted.

It should also be noted that differences in the mass spectra of isomers

TABLE 9–4. CORRELATION OF MOLAR SENSITIVITIES WITH DIRECTING PROPERTIES OF SUBSTITUENT GROUPS (13)

Substituent Group	Directing Property	Molar Sensitivity of Substituted Benzene
$-NH_2$	Strong ortho-para	3.42
$-OH$	Strong ortho-para	1.12
$-OCH_3$	Intermediate ortho-para	1.70
$-CH_3$	Weak ortho-para	0.83
$-Br$	Weak ortho-para	0.69
$-H$	—	0.35
$-CHO$	Weak meta	0.13
$-COOH$	Intermediate meta	0.21
$-CN$	Intermediate meta	0.07
$-NO_2$	Strong meta	0.03

may be enhanced in many cases by going to low-voltage techniques. For example, Momigny and Natalis (18) used this approach to analyze mixtures of *cis* and *trans* 1,2-dialkylcyclopentanes. By carefully choosing the ionizing voltage, additional advantage can be taken of the low-voltage techniques. Since the ionization potentials of the paraffin hydrocarbons are about 1 ev greater than the ionization potentials of the olefins, and still greater than for the aromatics, Field and Hastings (19) were able to choose the ionizing voltages such that analyses of these mixtures was greatly facilitated.

Certainly the determination of molecular weights and the greater ease of qualitative analysis make the low-voltage technique attractive, and generally these features off-set the disadvantage of reduced sensitivity.

9.5 CORRELATIONS OF MASS SPECTRA AND MOLECULAR STRUCTURE

We have observed that the analytical applications of the mass spectrometer are varied and many. Quantitative analyses may be performed on mixtures containing up to 20 or more components, and the analyses are generally good to about 1 mole %. Mass spectrometric isotope dilution techniques also may yield valuable quantitative information. The qualitative information yielded concerning a pure sample or mixture using both high- and low-voltage methods with nominal and high-resolution instruments can be extended to more than simple identification by means of comparisons to entries in catalogs of mass spectra. In this section we shall concern ourselves with the correlations between mass spectra and molecular structure and the use of mass spectrometry in structure determinations.

There are a large number of papers in the literature that relate the mass spectra of compounds to their molecular structure. Many workers (14, 15, 20–34) have discussed the correlations of mass spectra and molecular structure of aliphatic thiols and sulfides, aromatic oxygenated compounds, aliphatic esters, vinyl compounds, aromatic acids, esters and halides, petroleum products in the C_{12} range, aliphatic amines, amides, halides, and nitriles, high molecular-weight saturated hydrocarbons, fluorinated polyphenols, alcohols, thiophene and benzene homologs, and many others.

The use of various correlations in attempting to characterize samples and to determine their structure is quite important. Although it is beyond the scope of this volume to consider all of the correlations and applications in detail, an example of such use can be examined here.

EXAMPLE 9–7. Consider the following problem. A sample of a pure organic material (as received from a cut from a distillation column) containing carbon, oxygen, and hydrogen, was subjected to mass spectrometric analysis. By both high-voltage (70 ev) and low-voltage (13 ev) analyses, the molecular weight was found to be 58. This result was checked by observing that the fractional abundance of the $m/e = 58$ ion continually increased as the electron energy was decreased (to as low as 13 ev). At 70 ev, the mass spectrum of the unknown was found to contain only three ions of significant intensity: $m/e = 58$, 43, and 15. All other observed ions were present to less than 5% of the base peak ($m/e = 43$), except for the $m/e = 27$ ion, which was only about 8% of the base peak.

From the molecular weight of 58, we can see that the unknown could not contain more than three oxygen atoms. Furthermore, it could not contain three oxygen atoms, since $58 - 3(16) = 10$, and therefore it would not be possible to have even one carbon atom. However, it might contain two carbon atoms and two oxygen atoms, together with two hydrogen atoms. The unreasonable combination of two oxygen atoms, one carbon atom, and 14 hydrogen atoms is discarded. If the molecule contains only one oxygen atom, then there must also be present three carbon atoms and six hydrogen atoms. Any other possibilities would be ruled out. Therefore, we see that the molecular formula of the unknown could be either $C_2H_2O_2$ or C_3H_6O.

Because both the $m/e = 43$ peak (a parent ion minus 15 amu) and the $m/e = 15$ peak are present, the suggestion is strong that a CH_3 group is present in the unknown molecule. This causes us to neglect consideration of the $C_2H_2O_2$ which could not contain a CH_3 group. Furthermore, if the $C_2H_2O_2$ molecule were OCH—CHO, we would expect that this molecule would fragment upon ionization to give an abundance of $m/e = 29$ ions (CHO^+), and yet no intense $m/e = 29$ peak was observed. Therefore, we turn to the C_3H_6O possibilities. However, it should be noted that if one had the entire mass spectrum of the unknown before him, it would be possible to compare also the relative intensities of the $m/e = 58$ and 59 ions. If $m/e = 59$ (due to carbon-13 in nature) was found to be 3.3–3.4% of the intensity of the $m/e = 58$ peak, it would establish immediately that there are three carbon atoms in the parent molecule.

A number of possibilities exist with the molecular formula of C_3H_6O. Five such possibilities are propanal, CH_3CH_2CHO; acetone, CH_3COCH_3; allyl alcohol, $CH_2{=}CHCH_2OH$; propylene oxide, $CH_3\underline{CHCH_2O}$; and oxacyclobutane, $\underline{CH_2CH_2CH_2O}$. Let us see now if our experimental data will allow us to conclude that our unknown is one of these five.

For the propylene oxide, we might anticipate that the ions with $m/e = 15$ (corresponding to the cleavage of the methyl group), 43 (corresponding to the cleavage of the methyl group), 30 (corresponding to the elimination of C_2H_4 and leaving the CH_2O^+ ion), 29 (the CHO^+ ion), 28 (corresponding to the elimination of the $C_2H_4^+$ ion), 27 ($C_2H_3^+$) and 26 ($C_2H_2^+$) would all be large peaks. Certainly this does not fit our experimental data.

For the oxacyclobutane molecule, we would anticipate finding an intense $m/e = 28$ peak ($C_2H_4^+$) and strong $m/e = 29$ (CHO^+), 27 ($C_2H_3^+$), and 26 ($C_2H_2^+$) ions. Also, we would expect the parent ion (at $m/e = 58$) to be fairly strong. Since the three carbons are linked, possibly smaller amounts of $m/e = 41$ (due to $C_3H_5^+$) and 39 ($C_3H_3^+$) would be observed along with some $m/e = 30$ (CH_2O^+) ion. It is immediately obvious that our experimental findings do not correlate with these expectations, and we discard oxacyclobutane from consideration.

For allyl alcohol, we could anticipate that the ions of $m/e = 57$ (the parent with a hydrogen withdrawn from the α-carbon), 39 (the very stable $C_3H_3^+$ ion), 31 (the typical ion of many alcohols, CH_2OH^+), 29 (CHO^+), 28 (possibly both $C_2H_4^+$ and CO^+ or either), and 27 ($C_2H_3^+$) would be intense ions in the mass spectrum. Again, these anticipations do not fit our experimental data.

For acetone, we could anticipate that the ions of $m/e = 58$ (the parent ion), 43 (the parent minus a methyl group ion), and 15 (the CH_3^+ ion) would be the only really intense ions in the spectrum. We quickly see that this data does indeed fit the experimental data, and we begin to strongly suspect that our unknown is acetone. But to be certain, we check the molecule remaining in our original list of possibilities.

For propanal, we would anticipate only a small $m/e = 15$ ion, and a small $m/e = 43$ ion, since the carbon-carbon bond β to the aldehyde group is fairly strong here. However, it would be expected that the ions with $m/e = 29$, 28, 27, and 26 would all be rather intense. We again see that this does not agree with our experimental data, and we therefore may discard this as a possibility.

We conclude then, that the unknown, of formula C_3H_6O, is acetone, and actually has the structure of CH_3COCH_3.

This is, in fact, a very simple illustration of the determination of the molecular structure of a small molecule. But much more complicated structures can be determined in many cases. The arguments become somewhat more involved, and there is generally a much larger quantity of mass spectral data to consider in the determination, but the principles and approaches are quite similar to those outlined in Example 9–7.

If one brings all of the various techniques, such as molecular weight determinations, high- and low-voltage mass spectra, deuterium and other isotope-labeling, observations of the natural abundances of isotopes in the mass spectrum, studies of the metastable transitions, appearance potentials and high-resolution studies, to bear on the problem of structure determination much information can be obtained and utilized in making correct assignments of the structure. Using crucible techniques and heated inlets, high molecular weight compounds commonly of complex structure may be examined. Much has been done recently in these applications to the analysis of compounds of high molecular weight. Biemann (35–40), Djerassi (41–46), Reed (34, 47–49), Beynon (6–7, 50), Stenhagen (51–52), and others

(33, 53–58) have contributed significantly to the determination by mass spectrometric techniques of molecular structures of such complexity as peptides; amino acids and their esters; amino sugars; steroid ketones, alcohols, and steroidal estrogens; bile acids; triterpenoids; terpenes; indole, dihydroindole, and oxindole alkaloids; alpha- and beta-decalones; carbohydrates; and medicines.

F. W. McLafferty (59–60) has indicated the relationships of mass spectra to the whole of organic chemistry and has given a very concise and useful tabulation (61) of mass spectral correlations. Biemann's book (62), as well as Beynon's (7) and Budzikiewicz, Djerassi, and Williams' (63) books present in beautiful detail the approaches that can be made in the determination of molecular structures by means of mass spectrometry. Biemann (62) and Budzikiewicz, *et al.*, (63) cover many of the recent applications to organic materials, natural products, amino acids, carbohydrates, alkaloids, and steroids. For more details, the interested reader is referred to these works.

REFERENCES

1. E. H. Kennard, *Kinetic Theory of Gases*, McGraw-Hill Book Company, New York, 1938, pp. 292–308.
2. *Mass Spectral Data*, American Petroleum Institute Research Project 44, National Bureau of Standards, Washington, D.C.
3. *Mass Spectral Data*, Manufacturing Chemists Association Research Project, Agricultural and Mechanical College of Texas, College Station, Texas.
4. *File of Uncertified Mass Spectra*, American Society for Testing Materials, Committee E-14 on Mass Spectrometry.
5. J. L. Margrave and R. B. Polansky, *J. Chem. Ed.*, **39**, 335 (1962).
6. J. H. Beynon, "High Resolution Mass Spectrometry of Organic Materials," in *Advances in Mass Spectrometry*, J. D. Waldron (ed.), Pergamon Press, London, 1959, pp. 328–54; and J. H. Beynon, *Mikrochim. Acta*, **1956**, 437.
7. J. H. Beynon, *Mass Spectrometry and its Applications to Organic Chemistry*, Elsevier Publishing Company, Amsterdam, 1960, 640 pp.
8. J. H. Beynon, R. A. Saunders, and A. E. Williams, *J. Am. Chem. Soc.*, **82**, 288 (1960).
9. J. L. Occolowitz and G. L. White, *Anal. Chem.*, **35**, 1179 (1963).
10. D. P. Stevenson and C. D. Wagner, *J. Am. Chem. Soc.*, **72**, 5612 (1950).
11. W. P. Hoogendonk and F. W. Poersche, *Anal. Chem.*, **32**, 941 (1960).
12. H. E. Lumpkin and T. Aczel, *Anal. Chem.*, **36**, 181 (1964).
13. G. F. Crable, G. L. Kearns, and M. S. Norris, *Anal. Chem.*, **32**, 13 (1960).
14. G. L. Kearns, N. C. Maranowski, and G. F. Crable, *Anal. Chem.*, **31**, 1646 (1959).

15. C. J. Varsel, F. A. Morrell, F. E. Resnik, and W. A. Powell, *Anal. Chem.*, **32**, 182 (1960).
16. D. C. Clancy and I. J. Spilners, *Anal. Chem.*, **34**, 1839 (1962).
17. R. I. Reed and F. M. Tabrizi, *Appl. Spectroscopy*, **17**, 124 (1963); R. E. Winters and R. W. Kiser, unpublished results, 1964.
18. J. Momigny and P. Natalis, *Bull. soc. chim. Belges*, **66**, 26 (1957); L. D'Or, J. Momigny, and P. Natalis, "Mass Spectra and Geometric Isomerism," in *Advances in Mass Spectrometry*, Vol. 2, R.M. Elliott (ed.), Pergamon Press, London, 1963, pp. 370–76.
19. F. H. Field and S. H. Hastings, *Anal. Chem.*, **28**, 1248 (1956).
20. S. M. Rock, *Anal. Chem.*, **23**, 261 (1951).
21. E. J. Levy and W. A. Stahl, *Anal. Chem.*, **33**, 707 (1961).
22. T. Aczel and H. E. Lumpkin, *Anal. Chem.*, **33**, 386 (1961); **34**, 33 (1962).
23. R. A. Saunders and A. E. Williams, *Anal. Chem.*, **33**, 221 (1961).
24. E. M. Emery, *Anal. Chem.*, **32**, 1495 (1960).
25. F. W. McLafferty, *Anal. Chem.*, **31**, 2072 (1959); **34**, 2, 16 and 26 (1962).
24. F. W. McLafferty and R. S. Gohlke, *Anal. Chem.*, **31**, 2076 (1959).
27. J. A. Gilpin, *Anal. Chem.*, **31**, 935 (1959).
28. R. J. Clerc, A. Hood, and M. J. O'Neal, *Anal. Chem.*, **27**, 868 (1955).
29. P. Bradt and F. L. Mohler, *Anal. Chem.*, **27**, 875 (1955).
30. V. A. Yarborough, *Anal. Chem.*, **25**, 1914 (1953).
31. R. A. Friedel, A. G. Sharkey, J. L. Shultz, and C. R. Humbert, *Anal. Chem.*, **25**, 1314 (1953).
32. I. W. Kinney and G. L. Cook, *Anal. Chem.*, **24**, 1391 (1952).
33. L. Peterson, *Anal. Chem.*, **34**, 1781 (1962).
34. R. I. Reed, *J. Chem. Soc.*, **1958**, 3432.
35. K. Biemann and J. Seibl, *J. Am. Chem. Soc.*, **81**, 3149 (1959).
36. K. Biemann, *Tetrahedron Letters*, **15**, 9 (1960); *Chimia*, **14**, 393 (1960); *J. Am. Chem. Soc.*, **83**, 4801 (1961); and K. Biemann, J. Seibl, and F. Gapp, *Biochem. Biophys. Res. Comm.*, **1**, 307 (1959).
37. K. Biemann and M. Friedman-Spiteller, *Tetrahedron Letters*, 68, 299, and 485 (1961); and *J. Am. Chem. Soc.*, **83**, 4805 (1961).
38. K. Biemann, M. Spiteller-Friedman, and G. Spiteller, *J. Am. Chem. Soc.*, **85**, 631 (1963); and G. Spiteller and R. Kaschnitz, *Monatsh. Chem.*, **94**, 964 (1963).
39. K. Biemann and G. G. J. Deffner, *Biochem. Biophys. Res. Comm.*, **4**, 283 (1961).
40. K. Biemann, D. C. DeJongh, and H. K. Schnoes, *J. Am. Chem. Soc.*, **85**, 1763 (1963); D. C. DeJongh and K. Biemann, *J. Am. Chem. Soc.*, **85**, 2289 (1963); K. Biemann, H. K. Schnoes, and J. A. McCloskey, *Chem. Ind.* (*London*), **1963**, 448; and D. C. DeJongh and K. Biemann, *J. Am. Chem. Soc.*, **86**, 67 (1964).

41. H. Budzikiewicz and C. Djerassi, *J. Am. Chem., Soc.*, **84**, 1430 (1962).

42. L. D. Antonaccio, N. A. Pereira, B. Gilbert, H. Vorbrueggen, H. Budzikiewicz, J. M. Wilson, L. J. Durham, and C. Djerassi, *J. Am. Chem. Soc.*, **84**, 2161 (1962); C. Djerassi, S. E. Flores, H. Budzikiewicz, J. M. Wilson, L. J. Durham, J. LeMen, M. M. Janot, M. Plat, M. Gorman, and N. Neuss, *Proc. Natl. Acad. Sci.* (*U.S.*), **48**, 113 (1962).

43. C. Djerassi, J. M. Wilson, H. Budzikiewicz, and J. W. Chamberlain, *J. Am. Chem. Soc.*, **84**, 4544 (1962); C. Beard, J. M. Wilson, H. Budzikiewicz, and C. Djerassi, *J. Am. Chem. Soc.*, **86**, 269 (1964); D. H. Williams, H. Budzikiewicz, and C. Djerassi, *J. Am. Chem. Soc.*, **86**, 284 (1964).

44. B. Gilbert, J. A. Brissolese, N. Finch, W. I. Taylor, H. Budzikiewicz, J. M. Wilson, and C. Djerassi, *J. Am. Chem. Soc.*, **85**, 1923 (1963); and D. H. Williams, J. M. Wilson, H. Budzikiewicz, and C. Djerassi, *J. Am. Chem. Soc.*, **85**, 2091 (1963).

45. E. Lund, H. Budzikiewicz, J. M. Wilson, and C. Djerassi, *J. Am. Chem. Soc.*, **85**, 941 and 1528 (1963); Z. Pelah, M. A. Kielczewski, J. M. Wilson, M. Ohashi, H. Budzikiewicz, and C. Djerassi, *J. Am. Chem. Soc.*, **85**, 2470 (1963).

46. M. Ohashi, J. M. Wilson, H. Budzikiewicz, M. Shamma, W. A. Slusarchyk, and C. Djerassi, *J. Am. Chem. Soc.*, **85**, 2807 (1963); H. Budzikiewicz, J. M. Wilson, and C. Djerassi, *J. Am. Chem. Soc.*, **85**, 3688 (1963).

47. P. deMayo and R. I. Reed, *Chem. Ind.* (*London*), **1956**, 1481; R. I. Reed and W. K. Reid, *J. Chem. Soc.*, **1963**, 5933.

48. P. A. Finan and R. I. Reed, *Nature*, **184**, 1866 (1959); P. A. Finan, R. I. Reed, and W. Snedden, *Chem. Ind.* (*London*), **1958**, 1172; R. I. Reed, W. K. Reid, and J. M. Wilson, "The Mass Spectra of Some Flavones and Carbohydrates," in *Advances in Mass Spectrometry*, Vol. 2, R. M. Elliott (ed.), Pergamon Press, London, 1963, pp. 416–27; P. A. Finan, R. I. Reed, W. Snedden, and J. M. Wilson, *J. Chem. Soc.*, **1963**, 5945.

49. T. Gilchrist and R. I. Reed, *Experimentia*, **16**, 134 (1960); R. I. Reed and J. M. Wilson, *J. Chem. Soc.*, **1963**, 5949.

50. J. H. Beynon and A. E. Williams, *Appl. Spectry.*, **13**, 101 (1959); J. H. Beynon, R. A. Saunders, and A. E. Williams, *Appl. Spectry.*, **14**, 95 (1960).

51. R. Ryhage and E. Stenhagen, *J. Lipid Res.*, **1**, 361 (1960); *Arkiv Kemi*, **13**, 523 (1959) and **15**, 545 (1960); R. Ryhage, S. Ställberg-Stenhagen, and E. Stenhagen, *Arkiv Kemi*, **14**, 259 (1959); R. Ryhage and E. von Sydow, *Acta Chem. Scand.*, **17**, 2025 (1963); E. Stenhagen, *Z. anal. Chem.*, **181**, 462 (1961).

52. H. H. Brunn, S. Bergstrom, R. Ryhage, and E. Stenhagen, *Acta Chem. Scand.*, **12**, 789 and 1349 (1958).

53. C. O. Anderson, *Acta Chem. Scand.*, **12**, 1353 (1958).

54. H. J. M. Fitches, "The Mass Spectra of Some Steroids," in *Advances in Mass Spectrometry*, Vol. 2, R. M. Elliott (ed.), Pergamon Press, London, 1963, pp. 428–55.

55. S. S. Friedland, G. H. Lane, R. T. Longman, K. E. Train, and M. J. O'Neal, *Anal. Chem.*, **31**, 169 (1959).

56. G. Junk and H. Svec, *J. Am. Chem. Soc.*, **85**, 839 (1963).

57. W. Snedden, "The Mass Spectra of Some Borazoles," in *Advances in Mass Spectrometry*, Vol. 2, R. M. Elliott (ed.), Pergamon Press, London, 1963, pp. 456–74.

58. K. Heyns and H. J. Grützmacher, *Z. Naturforsch.*, **16B**, 293 (1960); K. Heyns and H. Scharmann, *Ann. d. Chem.*, **667**, 183 (1963); K. Heyns and H. F. Grützmacher, *ibid.*, **667**, 194 (1963) and **669**, 189 (1963).

59. F. W. McLafferty, "Mass Spectrometry," in *Determination of Organic Structures by Physical Methods*, Vol. 2, F. C. Nachod and W. D. Phillips (eds.), Academic Press, New York, 1962, pp. 93–179; F. W. McLafferty and R. S. Gohlke, *Chem. Eng. News*, May 18, 1964, pp. 96–108.

60. F. W. McLafferty (ed.), *Mass Spectrometry of Organic Ions*, Academic Press, New York, 1963, 730 pp.

61. F. W. McLafferty, *Mass Spectral Correlations*, Advances in Chemistry Series No. 40, American Chemical Society, Washington, D.C., 1963, 118 pp.

62. K. Biemann, *Mass Spectrometry: Applications to Organic Chemistry*, McGraw-Hill Book Company, New York, 1962, 370 pp.

63. H. Budzikiewicz, C. Djerassi, and D. H. Williams, *Interpretation of Mass Spectra of Organic Compounds*, Holden-Day, Inc., San Francisco, Calif., 1964, 271 pp.

CHAPTER 10

OTHER USES OF THE MASS SPECTROMETER

The rather lengthy list of present and possible applications of the mass spectrometer (or mass spectrograph) nearly precludes the discussion of them all. However, we should note a few of the more well-known applications that are of significance in chemical problems. Therefore, after examining briefly free radical studies via mass spectrometry, we shall describe a few applications in the rapidly growing field of high-temperature chemistry and in the determination of half-lives of radioisotopes. Although we previously mentioned precise mass determinations with mass spectrographs, we want to note this again and to show the excellent agreement between mass spectroscopic determinations and results of nuclear studies. Finally, a few examples of atomic weight determinations will be give along with a discussion of the unified carbon-12 = 12.00000 scale for atomic weights.

10.1 FREE RADICAL STUDIES

The experimental techniques for the study of free radicals differ somewhat from those discussed earlier. One essential difference is in the method of introducing the sample to the ion source. Different methods of sampling are used in various studies.

One method of sampling free radicals is shown in Figure 10–1. Gases from the flame or the explosion occurring in the reaction chamber *RC* are sampled near the center of the chamber by an essentially collision-free flow

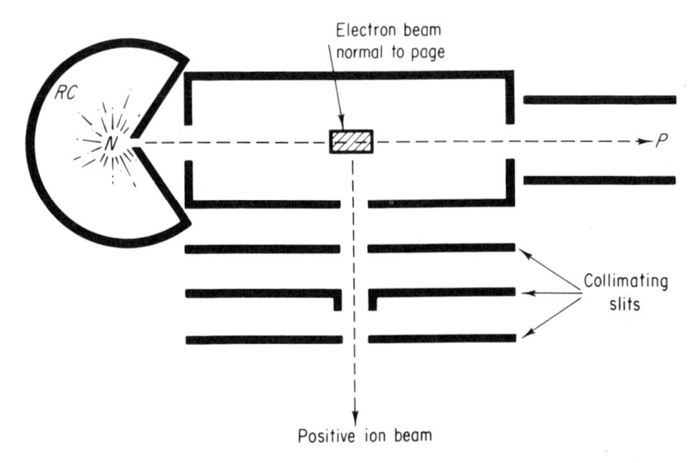

Fig. 10-1. Schematic diagram of a Leger-type ion source for reaction analysis.

through a fine opening in a quartz nipple *N*. The sample flows through the ionization chamber *C* to the high-speed vacuum pump *P*. In this way, the sample is introduced almost directly into the electron beam, keeping the possibility of contact with cool surfaces to a minimum.

Phillips and Schiff (1, 2) used a microwave discharge to produce hydrogen atoms and nitrogen atoms. Using mass spectrometric techniques, they then studied the reactions of these atoms with NO_2 and O_3 and also with NO. Their experimental sampling method was somewhat different from that shown in Figure 10–1 (1).

Foner and Hudson (3) used a collision-free molecular-beam sampling system modulated at 170 cps by means of a vibrating reed beam chopper to study free radicals. These workers used a 12-mm OD quartz tube and a microwave discharge. The sample gas flowed through the tube at a linear velocity of about 1 liter/sec. The distance from the exit slit of the discharge tube to the ion source was about 10 cm, so that the time required to reach the source was of the order of a few hundred microseconds. This limited their range of study to excited states whose radiative transitions to lower energy states were highly forbidden. The sampling times were varied by positioning the microwave cavity at various distances from the mass spectrometer inlet. The results of their study of the discharge in nitrogen and helium-nitrogen mixtures demonstrated the presence of $N(^2D)$ and $N(^2P)$ atoms as well as $N(^4S)$ atoms. They also obtained evidence for the $X(^1\Sigma_g^+)$ vibrationally excited ground state and the $A(^3\Sigma_u^+)$ state of N_2.

Foner and Hudson have noted that metastable species are generally more reactive than free radicals and that one must therefore use mass spectrometric analysis to eliminate or at least minimize wall collisions in the sampling system. These same authors have recently reported a study of the HO_2 free radical produced by photolysis of H_2O_2 with a General Electric resonance lamp. However, they note that the use of a low-power electrodeless glow discharge in a stream of hydrogen peroxide vapor was a very good source of HO_2 radicals, and that they produced almost no O_2 by this latter method (4, 5). In addition to reporting details of their sampling system, they also give their results obtained for D(H—OOH), D(H—O_2), I(HO_2), A.P.(HO_2^+), and ΔH_f(HO_2).

A number of other workers have also made studies of free radicals. Two of these are G. C. Eltenton (6), who was the first to make such investigations, and E. G. Leger (7). Although not directly a free radical study, Calcote and Reuter (8) have reported means of sampling a large-diameter flat flame at low pressures [about 1–6 mm (Hg)] into a Bennett-type rf mass spectrometer manufactured by Beckman Instruments, Inc. To obtain molecular flow through the orifice of their sampling probe, the probe was constructed from a plate 0.02 cm thick containing a 0.025-cm diameter hole. They found that this conical probe, together with the flat flame, was satisfactory so that the probe would not itself cause a distortion of the flame.

Another study, made by Knewstubb and Tickner (9), was concerned with investigating the reactions in electric discharges. These authors used a dc glow discharge in argon and krypton to study the positive and negative ions formed in these noble gases. Recently they also studied water vapor, and have found such species as $H_7O_3^+$ and $H_9O_4^+$ present in the discharge. Their sample probe was made of Pyrex glass, and the stainless steel end wall was about 30 microns thick with a centered hole of about 45 microns diameter. The discharge was run at ~0.4 ma in systems of about 0.4 mm pressure. A double-focusing mass spectrometer of the Johnson and Nier type (10) was used to achieve high resolution (about 1200), allowing them to differentiate between NH_4^+ and H_2O^+.

Related to the free radical studies are investigations of fast reactions. These too may be conveniently studied by mass spectrometry. We shall cite here just two examples. The first is the study of thermal decompositions in shock waves, made by Bradley and Kistiakowsky (11). They used a time-of-flight mass spectrometer to analyze their system of N_2O by photographing the cathode-ray tube face of the oscilloscope with a rotating-drum camera. The sample leak was a 0.001-in.-thick plate with a 0.005-in.-diameter hole in its center. The time-of-flight mass spectrometer was chosen because of short resolution time (about 50 μsec) and its ability to follow concentrations of several species simultaneously. Bradley and Kistiakowsky identified reaction intermediates and measured rate constants of the elementary steps at the high temperatures provided by the rapid homogeneous temperature rise through the shock front. Recently, Diesen and Felmlee have performed similar studies (see Chapter 11).

A second study is one made by Goldfinger, Huybrechts, and Verbeke (12) of the photochlorination of trichloroethylene (13). A conventional, high-sensitivity, 60°-sector, single-focusing mass spectrometer was used. A molecular beam entered the ion source from a 5-micron-diameter leak in the Pyrex reactor. Differential pumping and a shutter were employed in combination with rapid electrostatic scanning of the mass spectrum.

Numerous other reports of the use of mass spectrometers in studies of free radicals and fast reactions have been published. A few additional studies of this type are noted in Chapter 11. But the examples given here illustrate some of the investigations conducted with this instrumentation.

One further point is to be made. Direct electron impact studies of free radicals are also possible, and a great many have been carried out, particularly by Lossing and co-workers (14). In fact, a very large fraction of the ionization potentials listed in Appendix IV-C were determined by Lossing, *et al.*

10.2 HIGH-TEMPERATURE STUDIES

The basic objects of the application of mass spectrometry to high-temperature studies are twofold: to identify the gaseous molecules, and to determine the heats of formation, dissociation energies, heats of dimerization, and other thermodynamic properties of the gaseous molecules. In just a few short years there has evolved a large literature involving these techniques. It will be impossible to discuss here all of the systems that have been studied and for which data has been obtained; a brief examination with a number of literature references must suffice.

A Knudsen cell (see Section 9.1) with a tantalum, molybdenum, tungsten, or graphite crucible is heated and the gaseous molecules effuse from the crucible through a small hole in the crucible lid to form a molecular beam. The diameter of this hole is of the order of 0.001 cm. The temperature of the sample in the crucible may be determined by sighting into the black-body well drilled into the crucible and by using an optical pyrometer, or by measurement with a thermocouple [such as a Pt-PtRh (10%) thermocouple]. The molecular beam intersects the electron beam of the mass spectrometer in the ionization chamber, and the ions formed are analyzed and detected. Appearance potential determinations can aid in deciding the origin of a given species, and ion intensity measurements as a function of the crucible temperature provide thermodynamic data. Many mass spectrometric high-temperature studies have been performed in this manner (15–26).

As an illustration of the first object in the application of mass spectrometry to high-temperature chemistry, as mentioned above, Greene and Gilles recently observed (27) a large number of new and different boron-sulfur species in the vapors effusing from a Knudsen cell containing a slightly sulfur-rich, glassy B_2S_3 sample. The species were identified by their mass and by the isotopic abundances of both the boron and sulfur isotopes. Low-voltage mass spectrometry together with the variation in the relative intensities with time indicated many of the species were parent-molecule ions. The intensity of the species in the $m/e = 400$–500 range was observed to go through a maximum. With higher resolution and higher sensitivity instrumentation, it is likely that additional observations of this sort will be reported.

Let us now consider some data to illustrate the second object of the mass spectrometer application to high-temperature investigations.

Using the Second Law of thermodynamics, one may calculate $\Delta H_{\text{vap.}}$ or $\Delta H_{\text{subl.}}$ for inorganic materials if their change in vapor pressure with temperature can be determined. This is conveniently done with a mass spectrometer, which also allows identification of the species and a determination of the relative vapor pressure. Then from

$$\ln\left(\frac{P_1}{P_2}\right) = \frac{\Delta H}{R}\left(\frac{1}{T_2} - \frac{1}{T_1}\right) \tag{10–1}$$

one can obtain ΔH.

For example, from Figure 10–2 take $P_2 = 8.1 \times 10^4$ and $P_1 = 1. \times 10^2$; and $1/T_1 = 1.20 \times 10^{-3}$ and $1/T_2 = 1.00 \times 10^{-3}$, for K_2Cl^+. Then, $\Delta H = 61.4$ kcal/mole. Similarly, for the K^+ data, $P_2 = 1.0 \times 10^5$, $P_1 = 1.2 \times 10^3$, $1/T_2 = 1.025 \times 10^{-3}$ and $1/T_1 = 1.20 \times 10^{-3}$, giving $\Delta H = 50.0$ kcal/mole.

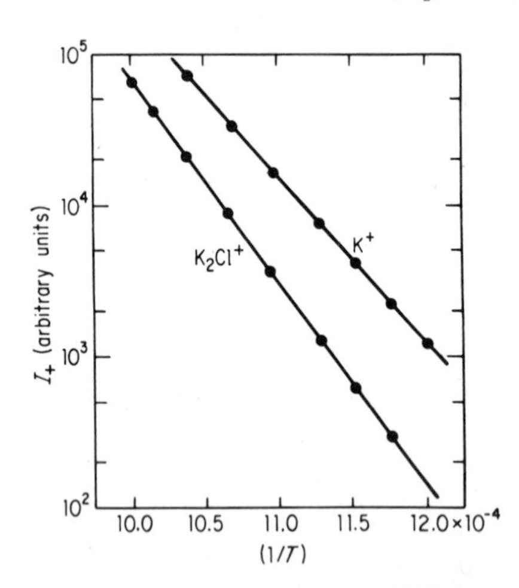

Fig. 10-2. Relative vapor pressures of KCl and K_2Cl_2 at various temperatures, as determined with a mass spectrometer. [After Milne and Cubiciotti (18).]

In Table 10–1 are given the relative abundances of various ions observed (18) in the mass spectra of a series of alkali metal chlorides. Table 10–2 presents the heats of sublimation of a number of alkali metal chlorides, their dimers, and a trimer of one, as calculated from relative vapor pressure curves (18), using the method outlined above. From the data of Table 10–2, one can calculate the heats of dimerization of the alkali metal chlorides (Table 10–3).

TABLE 10–1. IONS OBSERVED IN THE MASS SPECTRA OF THE ALKALI CHLORIDES AT PRESSURES OF ABOUT 10^{-5} atm AND THEIR RELATIVE INTENSITIES USING 20-ev BOMBARDING ELECTRONS (18)

Salt	M^+	MX^+	M_2X^+	$M_3X_2^+$
LiCl	—	27	100	4
NaCl	110	80	100	—
KCl	570	—	100	—
RbCl	600	37	100	—
CsCl	980	—	100	—

TABLE 10–2. HEATS OF SUBLIMATION (in kcal/mole) DETERMINED FROM THE SECOND LAW OF THERMODYNAMICS (18)

	M^+	M_2Cl^+	$M_3Cl_2^+$
LiCl	53.3	50.5	57.6
NaCl	51.9	59.3	—
KCl	50.0	61.4	—
RbCl	46.8	56.5	—
CsCl	41.8	48.7	—

TABLE 10–3. HEATS OF DIMERIZATION (18)
$2MX(g) \longrightarrow M_2X_2(g)$

LiCl :	$50.5 - 2(53.3) = 50.5 - 106.6 = -56.1$ kcal/mole
NaCl:	$59.3 - 2(51.9) = 59.3 - 103.8 = -44.5$ kcal/mole
KCl :	$61.4 - 2(50.0) = 61.4 - 100.0 = -38.6$ kcal/mole
RbCl:	$56.5 - 2(46.8) = 56.5 - 93.6 = -37.1$ kcal/mole
CsCl :	$48.7 - 2(41.8) = 48.7 - 83.6 = -34.9$ kcal/mole

10.3 RADIOISOTOPE HALF-LIFE DETERMINATIONS

The common methods of determining the half-lives of radioactive species employ nuclear radiation detectors in measurements of the specific activity of the species as a function of time. Use is made of the first-order decay of a radioisotope:

$$-(dN/dt) = \lambda N \tag{10–2}$$

or, in the integrated form,

$$\ln (N_0/N) = \lambda t, \tag{10–3}$$

where N_0 is the number of radioactive atoms at time $t = 0$, N is the number of radioactive atoms remaining at time t, and λ is the decay constant, equal to $\ln 2/t_{1/2}$, and $t_{1/2}$ is the half-life of the radioisotope.

Another very fruitful approach to the determination of the half-life of a radioisotope is the measurement of either the rate of disappearance of the radioisotope or the rate of appearance of the product of the radioisotope decay.

H. G. Thode and R. L. Graham (28) first studied the rate of disappearance of a radioactive species. They discovered krypton-85 as a fission product and periodically measured the abundance of this radioisotope relative to the stable isotopes of krypton. Using Equation (10–3), R. K. Wanless and H. G. Thode (29) found after a seven-year study of krypton-85 that the half-life was 10.27 ± 0.18 yr. Generally speaking, the study of the disappearance of a radioactive species is the more accurate method for radioisotopes with short half-lives.

When the half-lives are long, measurement of the rate of growth of the product (the daughter) is usually more accurate, since even a small number of disintegrations of the parent may cause an appreciable fractional change in the daughter abundance. From observations of the quantities of Pb^{207} in uranium minerals of different ages, A. O. Nier (30) determined the half-life of uranium-235 to be 7.13×10^8 yr. Lead-207 is the final product in the natural disintegration series beginning with uranium-235, as shown in Figure 10–3.

Inghram, Hess, Fields, and Pyle (31) determined the half-life of plutonium-240 by means of mass spectrometric analysis of a mixture of plutonium-239 and plutonium-240.

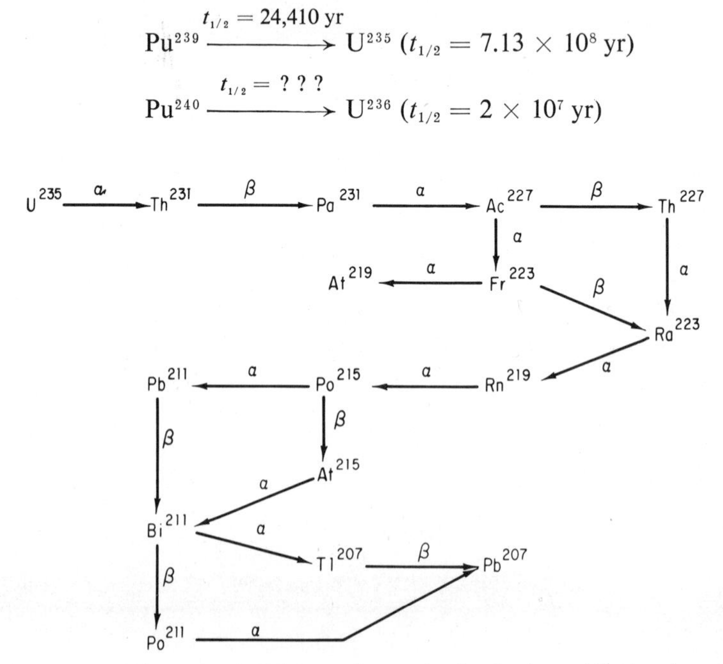

Fig. 10-3. The natural disintegration series beginning with Uranium-235.

Equation (10–3) may be written as

$$N = N_0 e^{-0.693t/t_{1/2}}. \tag{10–4}$$

However, the number of daughter atoms produced is the number of parent radioactive atoms minus those which remain: $(N_0 - N)$. Then,

$$(N_0 - N) = N_0 - N_0 e^{-0.693t/t_{1/2}} \tag{10–5}$$

or

$$(N_0 - N) = N_0(1 - e^{-0.693t/t_{1/2}}). \tag{10–6}$$

but if $t_{1/2} \gg t$,

$$1 - e^{-0.693t/t_{1/2}} \doteq 0.693t/t_{1/2} \tag{10–7}$$

and therefore

$$t_{1/2}/t = [0.693N_0/(N_0 - N)] \tag{10–8}$$

or

$$t_{1/2}^{239} = [0.693N_0/(N_0 - N)]\cdot t = 0.693t\left(\frac{N_{\mathrm{Pu}^{239}}}{N_{\mathrm{U}^{235}}}\right).$$

Since $(N_0 - N) \doteq N_0$,

$$t_{1/2}^{240} = 0.693t\left(\frac{N_{\mathrm{Pu}^{240}}}{N_{\mathrm{U}^{236}}}\right),$$

and therefore

$$t_{1/2}^{240} = \left(\frac{N_{\mathrm{Pu}^{240}}}{N_{\mathrm{U}^{235}}}\right)\left(\frac{N_{\mathrm{U}^{235}}}{N_{\mathrm{Pu}^{239}}}\right)t_{1/2}^{239},$$

so that by determining the uranium and the plutonium isotope abundance ratios with a mass spectrometer, and by making use of $t_{1/2}(\mathrm{Pu}^{239})$, the half-life of Pu^{240} could be determined. In this way, Inghram, Hess, Fields and Pyle, found the half-life of plutonium-240 to be 6580 ± 40 yr, a value three to four times more precise than values obtained by radioactivity counting techniques.

Recently, Dietz, Pachucki, and Land (32) reported very precise determinations of the half-lives of cesium-134 and cesium-137. They employed a mass spectrometer with a thermal ionization source, together with their internal standard technique, to achieve greater precision in their results. Although their studies are not yet complete, one notes that already the values they report appear to be superior to any previously determined.

10.4 PRECISE MASS DETERMINATIONS

We have already indicated in several places earlier in this volume the determinations of precise masses. However, we might examine the actual calculation of precise masses and then compare them to the results obtained from nuclear studies.

In Figure 3–12, the separation in mass of the $C_2H_4^+$ and the $C_2H_3^+$ lines is (28.0312984 – 27.0234738) = 1.0078246. In terms of arbitrary units, the linear separation of these two lines is 1155 units. The $m/e = 28$ line due to N_2^+ is 28.8 arbitrary units from the $C_2H_4^+$ line, and the line due to CO^+ is 41.7 units removed from the $C_2H_4^+$ line. Therefore, since the scale is essentially linear,

$$\Delta M_{N_2} = 1.0078246 \times (28.8/1155) = 0.02513$$

and

$$\Delta M_{CO} = 1.0078246 \times (41.7/1155) = 0.03639.$$

Note that actually one digit beyond the correct number of significant figures has been retained for the time being. These values, then, are the mass differences between the mass of the $C_2H_4^+$ ion and the N_2^+ and CO^+ ions, respectively. Thus, the masses of the N_2^+ and the CO^+ are

$$\begin{array}{r} 28.031298 \\ -0.02513 \\ \hline 28.00617 \end{array} \quad \text{and} \quad \begin{array}{r} 28.031298 \\ -0.03639 \\ \hline 27.99491 \end{array}$$

These values are seen to compare favorably to the values of 28.0061464 and 27.9949141 shown in Figure 3–12.

Actually, under better circumstances, the distances between the lines can be read more precisely than given in the preceding illustration; consequently, the masses determined are known to better than one part in a million. In the studies made by Ries, Damerow, and Johnson (33), errors of the order of 5×10^{-8} are given. It might be noted that these authors obtained a resolution of about 300,000 with their 16-in. instrument.

Many determinations of atomic masses have been made, and a fairly recent publication (34) summarizes much of this work. The nuclidic masses listed in Appendix I have been taken from several sources, but basically follow from the report of Cameron and Wichers (35). From these values and knowledge of the isotopic abundances, atomic weights may be determined, as we shall see in Section 10.5.

Let us pick as an example the negatron emission of carbon-14

$$C^{14} \longrightarrow N^{14} + \beta^- + \bar{\nu} \tag{10–9}$$

to compare the nuclidic masses determined by mass spectroscopy and those derived from the energetics of nuclear processes. The maximum energy of the β^- particle gives the mass difference of carbon-14 and nitrogen-14, since no γ-ray is involved and since the loss of rest mass of the β^- particle from the neutral carbon-14 atom is balanced by the incorporation of an extra valence electron into the nitrogen-14 atom.

The mass of carbon-14 is 14.003242 amu and that of nitrogen-14 is 14.003074 amu on the $C^{12} = 12.000000$ scale. Thus, Δm for the reaction is 0.000168 amu. The maximum energy of the β^- particle is 155 kev. Now, we know the relation

$$E = \Delta mc^2 \tag{10–10}$$

Also, the energy equivalent of 1 amu is 931.478 Mev. Therefore, for $\Delta m =$ 0.000168 amu, the carbon-14 decay reaction is seen to be 931.478 = 0.000-168 = 156 kev, in good agreement with the determination of the maximum energy of the β^- particles (0.155 Mev).

THE CHOICE OF CARBON-12 AS THE REFERENCE FOR NUCLIDIC MASSES

Of course, all measurements of nuclidic masses must be relative to some given standard. We might well stop and inquire here as to the nature of the standard, and how we came to use this particular one.

Since the early 1900's, the atomic weights of the elements have been referenced to oxygen = 16.00000. But then in 1929 Giauque and Johnston (36) found that naturally occurring oxygen was not monoisotopic, and that it contained small amounts of oxygen-17 and oxygen-18. Since the amounts of O^{17} and O^{18} vary slightly, the element oxygen was somewhat unsatisfactory as a reference for chemical atomic weights, and it was quite unacceptable for the reference on the scale of nuclidic masses. Therefore, a new scale based on oxygen-16 = 16.00000 became established to refer physical measurements of nuclidic masses. By 1940 the amounts of O^{17} and O^{18} in naturally occurring oxygen were pretty well established, sufficiently so that the values permitted the use of the conversion factor 1.000275 between the chemical and physical scales. But the two scales were very nearly alike, and this led to discussions of a new unified scale. To use only the old chemical scale would cause physicists difficulty in not having any integral mass value. To change the chemical scale in favor of the physical scale would force chemists to change all values by nearly three parts in 10,000, and would be unsatisfactory.

In 1957, A. Ölander and A. O. Nier independently proposed (35) a new and unified scale based on carbon-12 = 12.00000. The adoption of this scale required that chemists change values no more than if $F^{19} = 19.00000$ had been chosen as the scale (which was unacceptable to the physicists). In 1959 the International Union of Pure and Applied Chemistry recommended adoption of the carbon-12 scale, providing the International Union of Pure and Applied Physics would adopt the same scale. The IUPAP adopted the carbon-12 scale in Ottawa, Canada in 1960, and the following year, the IUPAC approved this adoption at its meeting in Montreal. To attain a unified scale based on carbon-12, values on the old chemical scale would have to be reduced by 43 ppm, and the old physical scale values would be reduced even more, by a factor of 318 ppm. Therefore, in preparation for the 1961 IUPAC meeting, Cameron and Wichers (35) prepared with the aid of advisors and consultants a revised table of atomic weights. The last extensive revision prior to 1961 had been made many years earlier, in 1925. As a result, much more recent data could be critically examined with the older data, and judgments could be made concerning the best values of the atomic weights. The end product of all this great work was the revised atomic weights, nuclidic masses, and in some cases, isotopic abundances. These values are given in Appendix I, based on the recommendations made to the IUPAC and the IUPAP.

In order to gain a little perspective concerning the values of the atomic weights (and nuclidic masses), examine Table 10–4. As mentioned above, we see that the values were reduced on both scales, and that the physical scale values were reduced by a greater amount than were the chemical scale values. Yet the change to these values was not very large for the chemists. And the physicists were satisfied, since the measurements of nuclidic mass are made against standards commonly containing carbon atoms (as the case is in Figure 3–12).

TABLE 10–4. A COMPARISON OF SOME ATOMIC WEIGHTS BASED ON THE OXYGEN = 16, THE OXYGEN-16 = 16, AND THE CARBON-12 = 12 SCALES

	Old Chemical Scale (Oxygen = 16)	Old Physical Scale (Oxygen-16 = 16)	1961 Unified Scale (Carbon-12 = 12)
Carbon-12		12.0038	12.00000
Carbon in nature	12.011		12.01115
Oxygen-16		16.00000	15.99491
Oxygen in nature	16.00000		15.9994
Chlorine in nature	35.457		35.453
Bromine in nature	79.916		79.909
Silver in nature	107.880		107.870

THE RELATION OF NUCLIDIC MASSES TO THE PACKING FRACTION

From tables of nuclidic masses, a packing fraction curve may be constructed. Using the data from Appendix I, the packing fraction curve shown in Figure 10–4 was prepared. The mass defect, $(M - A)$, is the difference between the nuclidic mass and the mass number (the mass number is the whole number nearest to the nuclidic mass). The packing fraction f is

$$f = (M - A)/A. \tag{10–11}$$

Aston (37) chose to employ the packing fraction, rather than the mass defect in his early determinations of atomic weights by mass spectrometry. Note that the nuclei with mass numbers which are multiples of four have

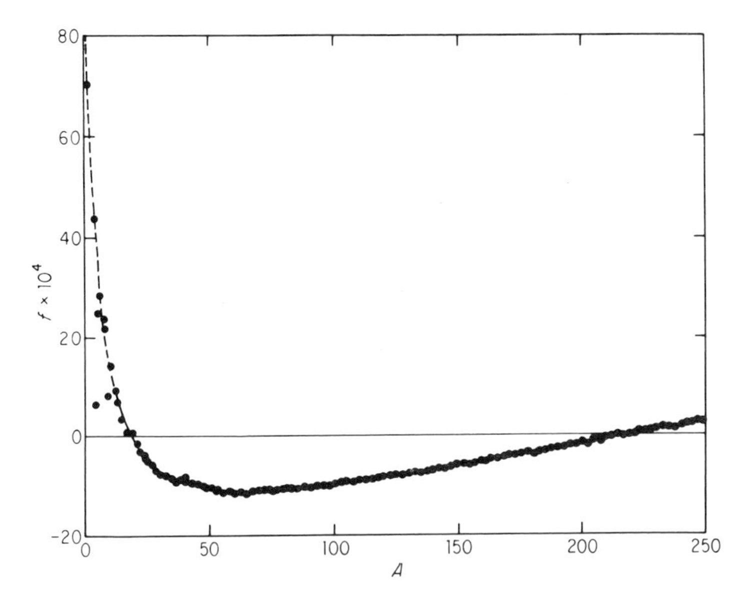

Fig. 10-4. Packing fraction curve. $f = (M - A)/A$, where M = nuclidic mass and A = mass number. (Based on carbon-12 = 12.00000.)

significantly smaller packing fractions than those of neighboring mass numbers in the low mass region.

The packing fraction is also related to the binding energy per nucleon, and the lower the packing fraction, the greater the binding energy. Because of the relationship between mass and energy, nuclei with positive packing fractions may be considered to possess excess energy, and therefore tend to be unstable. Elements that fission occur in the large mass range and elements that may enter into fusion are to be found in the very low mass range. Hence, the determination of precise mass values for the nuclides is important to nuclear chemistry and nuclear physics.

10.5 ISOTOPIC ABUNDANCES AND ATOMIC WEIGHT DETERMINATIONS

Earlier we remarked on the large number of isotopes known to exist in nature, and we pointed out that Aston was responsible for a large amount of our very early knowledge in this area. In recent times, only a very few new stable isotopes have been discovered, and the existing measurements of isotopic abundances appear to be reasonably satisfactory for most of the elements. Coupling this isotopic abundance information with the precise masses determined by mass spectroscopic methods, one may determine with very good precision the atomic weights of the elements (except in those cases where certain variations in isotopic abundances with sample origin have been noted). Just to make a few comparisons of the results from the time-of-flight mass spectrometer in our laboratories with the more carefully determined (and more precise) values reported by others, see Tables 10–5 to 10–8.

TABLE 10–5. MERCURY ISOTOPES

		Isotopic Abundances (%)			
m/e	Nuclidic Mass (amu) (Carbon-12 = 12)	Time-of-Flight	Aston, 1930 (37)	Nier, 1937 (38)	Nier, 1950 (39)
196	195.965829	0.15	0.10	0.15	0.146
198	197.966769	10.29	9.89	10.11	10.02
199	198.968256	16.84	16.45	17.03	16.84
200	199.968344	23.23	23.77	23.26	23.13
201	200.970315	12.96	13.67	13.17	13.22
202	201.970630	29.80	29.27	29.56	29.80
204	203.973482	6.73	6.85	6.72	6.85

From this, the atomic weight of mercury is 200.6; the accepted (1961) atomic weight of mercury is 200.59.

TABLE 10–6. XENON ISOTOPES

		Isotopic Abundance (%)	
m/e	Nuclidic Mass (amu) (Carbon-12 = 12)	Time-of-Flight	Beynon (40)
124	123.906120	0.09	0.096
126	125.904169	0.08	0.090
128	127.903538	1.60	1.919
129	128.904784	26.65	26.44
130	129.903510	4.01	4.08
131	130.905087	21.47	21.18
132	131.904162	27.29	26.89
134	133.905398	10.33	10.44
136	135.907221	8.47	8.87

From this, the atomic weight of xenon is 131.3; the accepted (1961) atomic weight of xenon is 131.30.

TABLE 10–7. CHLORINE ISOTOPES

		Isotopic Abundance (%)			
m/e	Nuclidic Mass (amu) (Carbon-12 = 12)	Time-of-Flight	Boyd, 1955 (41)	Meyerson, 1961 (42)	Shields, 1962 (43)
35	34.968854	75.36	75.529	75.80	75.7705
37	36.965896	24.64	24.471	24.20	24.2295

From this, the atomic weight of chlorine is 35.46; the accepted (1961) atomic weight of chlorine is 35.453.

TABLE 10–8. ATOMIC WEIGHT DETERMINATIONS

Element	m/e	Obs. % Abund.	Mass (amu) (Carbon-12 = 12)	Abundance × mass	Calculated At. Wt.	1961 Int. At. Wt. (Carbon -12 = 12)
Neon	20	90.5	19.992440	18.09		
	21	0.3	20.993849	0.063	20.17	20.183
	22	9.2	21.991384	2.02		
Argon	36	0.35	35.967548	0.126		
	38	—	37.962724	0.0	39.95	39.948
	40	99.65	39.962384	39.823		

From Tables 10–5 to 10–7 it is observed that the time-of-flight mass spectrometer performs satisfactorily in routine measurements of isotopic abundances, but that it is not suitable for precise measurements in this area. Table 10–8 indicates similar information, also calculated from isotopic abundances determined with the time-of-flight mass spectrometer in our laboratories. Table 10–8 further illustrates how the atomic weights are calculated from nuclidic mass data and isotopic abundances. The same calculational procedures were employed in determining the atomic weights from the time-of-flight data given in Tables 10–5 to 10–7. It should be noted that, although these comparisons of relative measurements of isotopic abundances are instructive, the calculation of meaningful atomic weights from mass spectrometric data requires that the mass spectrometer be calibrated with known mixtures of nearly pure, separated isotopes.

Reference to the recent article by Cameron and Wichers (35) and Beynon's book (40) will open up the previous literature on the results of isotopic abundance determinations and atomic weights. It is of interest to note that for the great majority of the elements, the 1961 atomic weight values are based on mass spectroscopic determinations of isotopic abundances and nuclidic masses. Only values for a few elements remain based on chemical determinations.

One very interesting investigation is that reported recently by Leipziger (44). Using an AEI MS-7 spark source mass spectrograph, with its high sensitivity, a search was made for undiscovered, naturally occurring isotopes of low abundance. Although upper limits of isotopic abundances were reported for many isotopes of the 21 different elements studied, no new isotopes were found in this investigation.

REFERENCES

1. L. F. Phillips and H. I. Schiff, *J. Chem. Phys.*, **36**, 1509 (1962).
2. L. F. Phillips and H. I. Schiff, *J. Chem. Phys.*, **36**, 3283 (1962); **37**, 1233 (1962).

3. S. N. Foner and R. L. Hudson, *J. Chem. Phys.*, **37**, 1662 (1962).

4. S. N. Foner and R. L. Hudson, *J. Chem. Phys.*, **36**, 2681 (1962).

5. S. N. Foner and R. L. Hudson, *J. Chem. Phys.*, **21**, 1374 and 1608 (1953); **23**, 1364 and 1974 (1955).

6. G. C. Eltenton, *J. Chem. Phys.*, **10**, 403 (1942); **15**, 455 (1947); *J. Phys. and Coll. Chem.*, **52**, 463 (1948).

7. E. G. Leger, *Can. J. Phys.*, **33**, 74 (1955).

8. H. F. Calcote and J. L. Reuter, *J. Chem. Phys.*, **38**, 310 (1963).

9. P. F. Knewstubb and A. W. Tickner, *J. Chem. Phys.*, **36**, 674 and 684 (1962); **37**, 2941 (1962); **38**, 464 (1963); P. F. Knewstubb, P. H. Dawson, and A. W. Tickner, *J. Chem. Phys.*, **38**, 1031 (1963).

10. E. G. Johnson and A. O. Nier, *Phys. Rev.*, **91**, 10 (1953).

11. J. N. Bradley and G. B. Kistiakowsky, *J. Chem. Phys.*, **35**, 256 (1961).

12. P. Goldfinger, G. Huybrechts, and G. Verbeke, "Mass Spectrometric Study of Fast Reactions at Atmospheric Pressure," in *Advances in Spectrometry*, Vol. 2, R. M. Elliott (ed.), Pergamon Press, London, 1963, pp. 360–69.

13. P. Goldfinger, G. Huybrechts, and G. Verbeke, *Trans. Faraday Soc.*, **58**, 1128 (1962).

14. F. P. Lossing, *et al.*, *J. Chem. Phys.*, **27**, 621 and 1489 (1954); *Can J. Chem.*, **34**, 701 (1956); **35**, 305 (1957).

15. W. A. Chupka and M. G. Inghram, *J. Phys. Chem.*, **59**, 100 (1955); R. F. Porter, P. Schissel, and M. G. Inghram, *J. Chem. Phys.*, **23**, 339 (1955); M. G. Inghram, W. A. Chupka, and J. Berkowitz, *Mem. Soc. Roy. Sci. Liege*, **18**, 513 (1957).

16. R. C. Miller and P. Kusch, *J. Chem. Phys.*, **25**, 860 (1956); **27**, 981 (1957); J. Drowart and R. E. Honig, *J. Phys. Chem.*, **61**, 980 (1957).

17. J. Drowart and P. Goldfinger, *J. chim. Phys.*, **55**, 721 (1958); G. Verhaegen, S. Smoes, and J. Drowart, *J. Chem. Phys.*, **40**, 239 (1964).

18. T. A. Milne and D. Cubiciotti, *J. Chem. Phys.*, **29**, 846 (1958); T. A. Milne and H. M. Klein, *J. Chem. Phys.*, **33**, 1628 (1960); F. J. Keneshea and D. Cubicciotti, *J. Chem. Phys.*, **40**, 191 (1964).

19. M. Ackerman, F. E. Stafford, and J. Drowart, *J. Chem. Phys.*, **33**, 1784 (1960); R. Colin and J. Drowart, *ibid*, **37**, 1120 (1962); G. Verhaegen and J. Drowart, *ibid*, **37**, 1367 (1962); R. P. Burns, G. DeMaria, J. Drowart, and M. G. Inghram, *ibid*, **38**, 1035 (1963); and J. Drowart, "High Temperature Vaporization Studies," 10th annual meeting of the ASTM Committee E-14 on Mass Spectrometry, New Orleans, La., June 3–8, 1962.

20. M. G. Inghram and J. Drowart, "Mass Spectroscopy Applied to High Temperature Chemistry," in *International Symposium on High Temperature Chemistry*, Asilomar, Calif., McGraw-Hill Book Company, New York, 1960, pp. 219–40.

21. J. Berkowitz and W. A. Chupka, *Ann. N. Y. Acad. Sci.*, **79**, 1073 (1960); J. Berkowitz and J. R. Marquart, *J. Chem. Phys.*, **37**, 1853 (1962); **39**, 275 (1963); J. R. Marquart and J. Berkowitz, *J. Chem. Phys.*, **39**, 283 (1963).

22. T. Babeliowsky and A. J. H. Boerboom, "Thermodynamic Study of CaO and Ta," 9th annual meeting of the ASTM Committee E-14 on Mass Spectrometry, Chicago, III., June 4–9, 1961; "Mass Spectrometric Study of CaO and Ta," in *Advances in Mass Spectrometry*, Vol. 2, R. M. Elliott (ed.), Pergamon Press, London, 1963, pp. 134–40; T. P. J. H. Babeliowsky, *Physica*, **28**, 1160 (1962).

23. A. Büchler and J. B. Berkowitz-Mattuck, *J. Chem. Phys.*, **39**, 286 (1963).

24. M. B. Panish and L. Reif, *J. Chem. Phys.*, **38**, 253 (1963); J. D. McKinley, *J. Chem. Phys.*, **40**, 120 (1964).

25. W. A. Chupka, J. Berkowitz, D. J. Meschi, and H. A. Tasman, "Mass Spectrometric Studies of High Temperature Systems," in *Advances in Mass Spectometry*, Vol. 2, R. M. Elliott (ed.), Pergamon Press, London, 1963, pp. 99–109.

26. D. White, A. Sommer, P. N. Walsh, and H. W. Goldstein, "The Application of the Time-of-Flight Mass Spectrometer to the Study of Inorganic Materials at Elevated Temperatures," in *Advances in Mass Spectrometry*, Vol. 2, R. M. Elliott (ed.), Pergamon Press, London, 1963, pp. 110–27.

27. F. T. Greene and P. W. Gilles, *J. Am. Chem. Soc.*, **84**, 3599 (1962).

28. H. G. Thode and R. L. Graham, *Can. J. Res.*, **25A**, 1 (1947).

29. R. K. Wanless and H. G. Thode, *Can. J. Phys.*, **31**, 517 (1953).

30. A. O. Nier, *Phys. Rev.*, **55**, 153 (1939).

31. M. G. Inghram, D. C. Hess, P. R. Fields, and G. L. Pyle, *Phys. Rev.*, **83**, 1250 (1951).

32. L. A. Dietz, C. F. Pachucki, and G. A. Land, *Anal. Chem.*, **35**, 797 (1963).

33. R. R. Ries, R. A. Damerow, and W. H. Johnson, Jr., *Phys. Rev.*, **132**, 1662 and 1673 (1963).

34. H. E. Duckworth (ed.), *Proceedings of the International Conference on Nuclidic Masses*, Sept. 12–16, 1960, University of Toronto Press, Toronto, Canada, 1960, 540 pp.

35. A. E. Cameron and E. Wichers, *J. Am. Chem. Soc.*, **84**, 4175 (1962); A. E. Cameron, *Anal. Chem.*, **35**, (2), 23A (1963); E. Wichers, *Anal. Chem.*, **35**, (3), 23A (1963).

36. W. F. Giaque and H. L. Johnston, *J. Am. Chem. Soc.*, **51**, 1436 and 3528 (1929).

37. F. W. Aston, *Mass Spectra and Isotopes*, second ed., Edward Arnold and Co., London, 1942, 276 pp; and F. W. Aston, *Proc. Roy. Soc.* (*London*), **A126**, 511 (1930).

38. A. O. Nier, *Phys. Rev.*, **51**, 1007 (1937); *Phys. Rev.*, **52**, 933 (1937).

39. A. O. Nier, *Phys. Rev.*, **79**, 450 (1950).

40. J. H. Beynon, *Mass Spectrometry and Its Applications to Organic Chemistry*, Elsevier Publishing Company, Amsterdam, 1960, pp. 560–61.

41. A. W. Boyd, F. Brown, and M. Lounsbury, *Can. J. Phys.*, **33**, 35 (1955).

42. S. Meyerson, *Anal. Chem.*, **33**, 964 (1961).

43. W. R. Shields, E. L. Garner, T. J. Murphy, and V. H. Dibeler, *J. Am. Chem. Soc.*, **84**, 1519 (1962).

44. F. D. Leipziger, *Appl. Spectroscopy*, **17**, 158 (1963).

CHAPTER 11

SOME FRONTIERS

D. M. Yost has noted (1), concerning a symposium on the noble gas compounds, that George Santayana supposedly said that those who do not study history may have to repeat it. The circumstances for this observation are not foreign to our introduction to mass spectrometry, for the existence of XeF_4 was confirmed by mass spectrometry, and the mass spectral studies gave the first indication of the possible existence of XeF_2 and xenon oxyfluorides (2–5). Aside from the circumstances, the observation itself is most pertinent to those entering into any new field, including mass spectroscopy.

In Chapter 2 it was indicated that a discussion of the history of mass spectroscopy would serve to show the growth and development of the science, as based on past ideas and efforts, and that it would then prove useful to apply these various features to our subsequent discussions. It is now proper to use this entire field of mass spectroscopy as the historical background, and to apply the numerous recent advances together with our own ideas and newer technology to solve other problems with one of the most versatile of all modern pieces of instrumentation, the mass spectrometer.

In various places in the preceding chapters, we have discussed some of the recent advances in mass spectrometry. Many of these advances are active areas of study which demand still more investigation. But only in a few instances have attempts been made to point out new fields of study recently undertaken and that can be expected to be fruitful in the next several years. It is these two categories which we shall consider briefly in this final chapter. Possibly some of these studies described* will stimulate readers of this volume to turn their talents to these research activities and, even better, to problems and studies that this author and others have not even considered.

11.1 NEUTRAL FRAGMENTS FROM ELECTRON IMPACT

Relatively little is known of the neutral fragments formed during the processes of ionization and dissociation. One reason for our very scanty knowledge of neutrals is that they are uncharged and therefore are not measured with the usual mass spectrometers. However, information about their nature is frequently inferred from studies involving appearance potential measurements and from deuterium (or other isotope) labeling studies. There are at least two other ways in which information about neutrals may be derived: through the use of a double ionization chamber and from a study of metastable transitions. In the following brief paragraph a method involving the use of a double ionization chamber is discussed; the remainder of this section shall be devoted to time-of-flight studies of neutrals from metastable transitions.

Upon ionization and fragmentation, the neutrals formed in the ion source are unaffected by the various repeller or draw-out potentials, and therefore essentially remain in the ion source until they either react or collide with the walls of the ionization chamber, or are pumped away by the vacuum pumps. If a second ionization chamber were employed to cause ionization (and dissociation, if desired) of these neutrals, their nature and abundance could be studied. However, the number of neutrals produced is small compared to the total number of molecules present in the ionization chamber at the common pressures of 10^{-6} mm (Hg); it is therefore difficult to study the low abundance neutrals in the presence of the parent molecules. It is conceivable, however, that by working at much lower pressures in the ion source, and by using much greater ionizing electron beam currents, the ratio of neutrals-to-molecules could be substantially improved. By employing pulsed ionizing beams with variable repetition rates it might be possible to do this within one ionization chamber if time-of-flight techniques were used. Other designs might be suggested, but this suffices to indicate some of the problems to be encountered and surmounted.

For an ion dissociation process that produces a neutral fragment

$$AB^+ \longrightarrow A^+ + B$$

after it has left the ion source, both A^+ and the neutral fragment B will have

*Several of the topics chosen for discussion in this chapter were those which Professor J. L. Franklin suggested to the author. The title of this chapter is drawn from words used by Dr. Franklin in comments to the author.

about the same velocity as the original AB^+ ion, providing the momentum imparted to A^+ and B in the dissociation process itself is negligible. However, their kinetic energies will be less than that of AB^+. Since their velocities are the same, both the fragment ion and the neutral will continue to travel with the undissociated parent ion and they will all arrive at the detector at the same time.

However, because they have different kinetic energies, and because the neutral ion has no charge, the three components of the bunch—AB^+, A^+, and B—can be separated and studied by introducing at some point in the flight tube a potential barrier. Although this was discussed briefly in Section 6.4, we now will examine it in somewhat greater detail.

We shall follow the discussion of Hunt, *et al.*, (6) and describe what occurs when a symmetrical potential barrier with a flat top, such as that shown in Figure 11-1, is introduced into the drift tube. The parent ions, fragment ions, and neutrals, constituting a single bunch of particles, all are traveling together at the same velocity as they arrive at the potential barrier. Upon emerging from this potential barrier, there will be three discrete bunches of particles, each again moving at the same velocity as the bunch which entered the barrier. However, all three bunches will be separated in space and time.

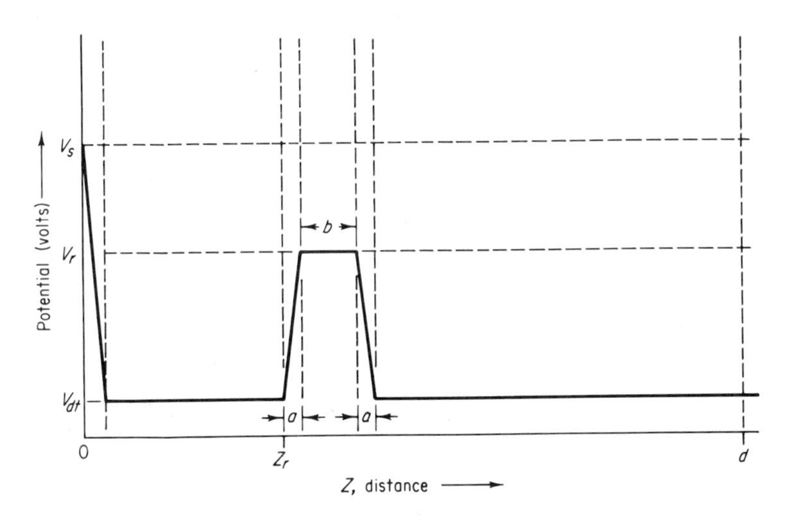

Fig. 11-1. Symmetrical flat-top potential barrier.

First to exit from the barrier will be the neutral fragments, for they will be unaffected by the barrier. Next, the undissociated parent ions will emerge, for they will travel through the barrier at a reduced velocity. Finally, the fragment ions will emerge, for they will be decelerated most because of their decreased kinetic energy. The three new ion bunches will arrive at the electron multiplier detector at different times, as shown schematically in

Figure 11–2. Their arrival times correspond to different flight times through the potential barrier.

If the potential barrier shown in Figure 11–1 were absent, the parent ion in the drift tube would have a kinetic energy of

$$E = \tfrac{1}{2}mu^2 = e(V_s - V_{dt}), \tag{11–1}$$

where $(V_s - V_{dt})$ is the accelerating potential and u is the velocity of the ion of mass m and charge e in the z-direction. The flight time of the ion through the drift tube of length d is just

$$t(d) - t(0) = (d/u) = d\left[\frac{(m/e)}{2(V_s - V_{dt})}\right]^{1/2}. \tag{11–2}$$

The drift time of the parent ion will be longer if the potential barrier is imposed. From Z_r to $Z_r + a$, the ion is retarded, and from $Z_r + a + b$ to $Z_r + 2a + b$, the ion is again accelerated. The force acting on the ion in both of these regions is identical in magnitude, but opposite in direction. This force, $\mathscr{F}$, is the product of the charge on the ion and the constant electric field strength,

$$\mathscr{F} = e(V_r - V_{dt})/a = m\left[\frac{du(z)}{dt}\right]. \tag{11–3}$$

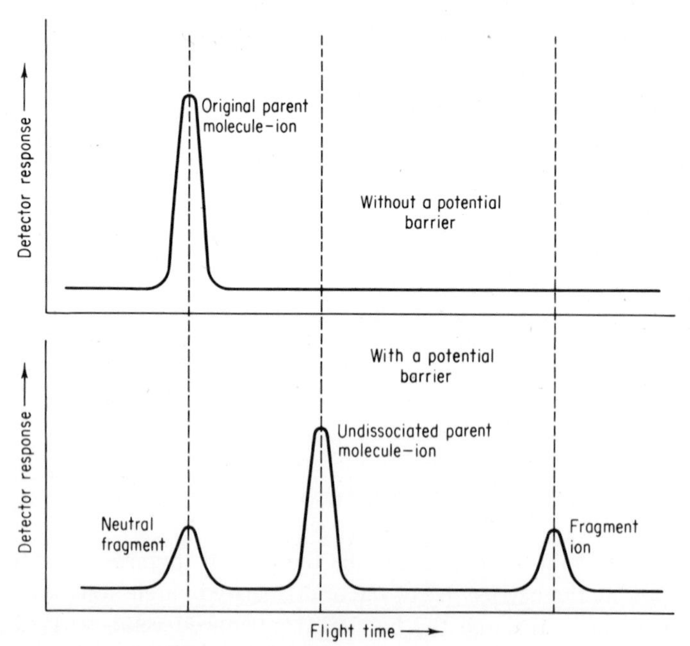

Fig. 11-2. Schematic drawing of a mass spectrum, with, and without, a potential barrier.

Integration of Equation (11–3) yields

$$t(Z_r + a, V_r) - t(Z_r, V_{dt}) = \frac{ma}{q(V_r - V_{dt})}\left\{\left[\frac{2(V_s - V_{dt})}{m/e}\right]^{1/2} - \left[\frac{2(V_s - V_r)}{m/e}\right]^{1/2}\right\}, \tag{11–4}$$

which is the time it takes the ion to traverse the region V_r to $V_r + a$, and the time it takes the ion to traverse the region $V_r + a + b$ to $V_r + 2a + b$. The time spent by the ion in the constant retarding potential region, of length b, is

$$t(Z_r + a + b, V_r) - t(Z_r + a, V_r) = b\left[\frac{m/e}{2(V_s - V_r)}\right]^{1/2}. \tag{11–5}$$

The total time an ion would spend in the region of V_r to $V_r + 2a + b$ if no potential barrier were present would be

$$t(Z_r + 2a + b, V_{dt}) - t(Z_r, V_{dt}) = (2a + b)\left[\frac{m/e}{2(V_s - V_{dt})}\right]^{1/2}. \tag{11–6}$$

The time required for the ion to pass through this same region if the retarding potential is present, is the appropriate sum of Equations (11–4) and (11–5):

$$t(Z_r + 2a + b, V_r) - t(Z_r, V_r) = \left[\frac{m/e}{2(V_s - V_{dt})}\right]^{1/2}\left\{\frac{4a}{F}[1 - (1 - F)^{1/2}] + \frac{b}{(1 - F)^{1/2}}\right\}, \tag{11–7}$$

where $F = (V_r - V_{dt})/(V_s - V_{dt})$. The flight time shift is the difference between the times given by Equations (11–6) and (11–7):

$$\Delta t = \left[\frac{m/e}{2(V_s - V_{dt})}\right]^{1/2}\left\{\frac{4a}{F}\left[1 - (1 - F)^{1/2} - \frac{F}{2}\right] + b\left[\frac{1}{(1 - F)^{1/2}} - 1\right]\right\}. \tag{11–8}$$

As an illustration, for $V_r = 1500$ volts and $V_{dt} = 3000$ volts below the ion source potential, and for $b = 2a = 1.00$ cm, the Δt for the 58^+ ion in n-butane is 0.059 μsec. If V_r were only 1000 volts below the ion source potential, Δt would be greater (0.10 μsec). Since time measurements can be made from the oscilloscope attachment to within ± 10 nsec, much information can be determined from these retardation studies.

For fragment ions, if one assumes that there is no momentum transfer and that no kinetic energy of dissociation contributes to the total velocities of the products, the equation for the time shift is nearly the same, except that the values of F are everywhere replaced by RF, where

$$R = (m_p/e_p)/(m_f/e_f) \tag{11–9}$$

in which the p and f subscripts refer to parent ion and fragment ion, respectively; then the expression for the shift is

$$\Delta t = \left[\frac{m_p/e_p}{2(V_s - V_{dt})}\right]^{1/2} \left\{\frac{4a}{RF}\left[1 - (1 - RF)^{1/2} - \frac{RF}{2}\right] + b\left[\frac{1}{(1 - RF)^{1/2}} - 1\right]\right\}. \tag{11–10}$$

Equation (11–10) is the more general expression; when $f^+ = p^+$, $R = 1$, and Equation (11–10) reduces to Equation (11–8).

By measuring Δt for various components of the parent ion peak as they separate with an increasing retarding potential, and then graphically comparing these results to values calculated from Equation (11–10), the m/e values of the various fragment ions can be determined and the metastable processes can be established. However, it actually is more convenient to determine the differential flight time shift between the fragment and its undissociated parent ion.

In the studies reported by Ferguson, McCulloh, and Rosenstock (7), and in those presented by McLafferty (8), only the region of V_r to $V_r + a$ was employed, and it was situated at the end of the drift tube, just ahead of the detector stack. McLafferty (8) has given a simplified equation [a less general one than Equation (11–10)] for peak shifts for this case which allows rapid calculation of fragment ion and neutral fragment masses. He has also illustrated some of the applications of the information obtained. Hunt, *et al.*, (6) have also described a modification in which 15 retarder grid assemblies are positioned at intervals in the flight tube, permitting studies of the lifetimes of metastables in the drift tube, as well as in the ion source. A minor modification might be made to permit a single retarder grid assembly to be adjustable to any position in the flight tube by means of a travel arrangement using micrometer threadings.

With the development of this means of studying neutral fragment production in the drift tube, plus the development of methods for the variation of the residence time of metastable ions in the ion source, we can look forward to learning much more about the formation of neutral fragments.

Two other related problems might be indicated here briefly. Since there are many and various neutral fragments produced in the ion source of the mass spectrometer, is it not possible that some ions, after formation but prior to mass analysis, undergo ion-molecule reactions with these neutral fragments? Certainly, the concentration effect is significant in causing such reactions to be few in number, but possibly these reactions of neutral fragments are more important than we have thought. Also, could not ion-ion reactions in the ion source, particularly in cases where the positive ions are held for a length of time in a potential well in the ion source, be important for polyatomic ions? Although the occurrences might be few, the reactions are not likely to be insignificant in our understanding of fundamental processes.

11.2 STUDIES OF REACTION INTERMEDIATES AND MECHANISMS

Probably the most important aid the chemist can receive in his study of the mechanisms of chemical reactions is the determination of unstable intermediates of the chemical reactions. These intermediates may be missed completely if the analyses must be postponed; therefore, the sample must be obtained from the reaction mixture and analyzed in a short time, i.e., short in comparison to the reaction time. One additional limitation is imposed on mass spectrometric studies of chemical reactions: the sample must be taken when the reaction is proceeding very rapidly, for the steady-state concentrations of intermediates are much too low to be detected.

Two basic methods of study of the reactions are then possible: (a) use of fast-flow reactors in which samples are continuously taken into the ion source of the mass spectrometer at variable points downstream from the reaction zone, and (b) use of extremely rapid analysis in static analysis. Studies with the former method have been more numerous, but with the development of the time-of-flight mass spectrometer and oscillographic display of the output from the secondary electron multiplier, the latter method will see more frequent use in future studies of chemical reactions.

Jackson and Schiff (9, 10) showed that the active nitrogen produced in a discharge tube contained nitrogen atoms in the ^4S ground state. Berkowitz, Chupka, and Kistiakowsky (11) have confirmed the result of Jackson and Schiff, and have shown that the intensity of the afterglow is proportional to the square of the $N(^4S)$ concentration. Although the presence of oxygen lowered the rate of combination of nitrogen atoms at the wall, it was found that oxygen was not essential to the formation of the afterglow. In a study of the pink afterglow in nitrogen with a quadrupole mass spectrometer, Spokes and Evans (12) have found N_x^+ ions (where $x = 1$ to 4) when the pink afterglow is present. The recent studies of Foner and Hudson (13) of species produced by a microwave discharge in nitrogen were discussed in Section 10.1.

Reactions of nitrogen atoms with acetylene, ethylene, and propylene have been studied by Herron, Franklin, and Bradt (14) who found that their flow rate was not sufficiently fast for the radical intermediates to be detected directly. However, they did note that cyanoacetylene was formed from both acetylene and ethylene. This indicates that the CN radical undergoes replacement reactions involving a hydrogen atom in these compounds. Further studies of nitrogen atoms with organic molecules should prove to be very interesting.

Foner and Hudson (15, 16) have examined the products of electrodeless discharges in hydrazoic acid and hydrazine and have identified N_2H_2, N_3H_3, and N_4H_4, in addition to NH_2 and N_2H_3. Direct photolysis of N_2H_4 by Terenin, Kurbatov, and Vilesov (17) and recent mass spectral studies of the kinetics behind shock waves in hydrazine (18) have confirmed this. N_2H_3 is one of the radicals commonly employed in mechanisms for the thermal decomposition of hydrazine.

Recently, Foner (19) has indicated that no searching studies for highly unstable noble gas compounds have been made in fluorine-noble gas systems with the mass spectrometer. As Foner points out (19), this is an area of research that clearly should be explored.

Herron and Schiff (20, 21) found that the $O^+ : O_2^+$ ratio increased by about 50% (corresponding to approximately a 3% change in the gas stream composition) when they passed a discharge through molecular oxygen. It is very probable that the increased amount of O^+ was caused by oxygen atoms formed in the discharge. They also found that less than 0.02% ozone was present in the gas stream.

Herron and Schiff (21) could detect no NO_3 formation in reactions of oxygen atoms with NO and with NO_2, although the NO_3 intermediate has been proposed. Kistiakowsky and Kydd (22) in their flash photolysis studies (see below) were unable to see any NO_3 formation from NO_2. In fact, Benson (23) recently commented on the structure of the NO_3 radical and upon the use of an ONOO complex rather than a symmetrical NO_3 intermediate (24) in the reaction

$$O + NO_2 \longrightarrow O_2 + NO. \qquad (11\text{–}11)$$

Klein and Herron (21) also have recently studied the reactions of oxygen atoms with NO and NO_2. Quite possibly future mass spectrometric studies will shed additional light on this proposed intermediate.

Robertson (25) detected the HO_2 radical in reactions of hydrogen atoms with molecular oxygen in a Wood's discharge tube at pressures of the order of 0.1 to 0.5 mm, and Foner and Hudson (26, 27) have detected the HO_2 radical to pressures of the order of 30 mm. More recent studies by Foner and Hudson (28) of HO_2 radicals produced by a low-power electrodeless discharge in hydrogen peroxide vapor have been described in Section 10.1.

A mass spectrometric study by Lossing, *et al.*, (29) of the thermal decomposition of ethylene oxide showed that 0.6 CH_3 radicals resulted from each molecule of ethylene oxide. However, no acetaldehyde intermediate was detected, and it was therefore concluded that the ethylene oxide did not isomerize to give an CH_3CHO intermediate, since acetaldehyde itself does not decompose at the temperatures employed. But the mass spectra of ethylene oxide and acetaldehyde are rather similar, and Gallegos (30) has suggested that the parent-molecule ion formed from both molecules is the same: the CH_3CHO^+ isomer.

The fast-flow reactor is advantageous for thermal reactions, and with it Lossing and his co-workers (29, 31–33) have examined the presence and nature of various free radicals produced by the thermal decomposition of many compounds. All of the interior surfaces of Lossing's reactor were constructed of quartz in order to reduce any catalytic disturbances or reactions of the intermediates formed. Lossing and Ingold (34, 35) measured the rate of dimerization of CH_3 radicals from the thermal decomposition of mercury dimethyl, and they found that the results agreed with those obtained from sector photolysis experiments.

Detection and identification of intermediates and products formed in photochemical reactions also can be made by mass spectrometry. Because relatively low concentrations of intermediates are produced upon photolysis, these studies can be quite difficult. However, by using mercury photosensitization, as indicated in the processes

$$Hg(^1S_0) \xrightarrow{2537\,\text{Å}} Hg(^3P_1) \tag{11–12}$$

$$Hg(^3P_1) + M \longrightarrow R_1 + R_2 + Hg(^1S_0), \tag{11–13}$$

where M is the molecule under study and R_1 and R_2 are intermediates formed in the photosensitization process, significant quantities of intermediates may be formed and then studied by mass spectrometry (36, 37). Lossing and his co-workers (36–40) have made good use of the mercury photosensitization technique to study many interesting intermediates of chemical reactions.

The use of flash photolysis can overcome some of the drawbacks of the photosensitization method, but extremely rapid mass spectra scanning must be employed. Kistiakowsky and Kydd (22) have used flash photolysis together with a time-of-flight mass spectrometer to study the intermediates of the photochemical decomposition of ketene in a neon diluent. They also studied the flash photolysis of NO_2, as mentioned earlier in this Section. The methods of Kistiakowsky and Kydd look very promising in studies of chemical reactions and intermediates and should receive more attention in future experimental studies.

A different and potentially powerful method employed by Terenin, Kurbatov, and Vilesov (17, 41) involves an ionization chamber through which passes both the usual electron beam and a photon beam (from a hydrogen lamp). The electron energy was set sufficiently low so as to form only parent-molecule ions (with the lamp off), and then the lamp was turned on. Ions formed by ionization of the photolytically produced intermediates were studied in this way. NH_2, N_2H_3, and N_2H_2 were observed from the photolysis of hydrazine, and NH_2 radicals, leading to methylamine formation, were observed from a mixture of methane and ammonia. This rather simple and yet powerful method should be of significant interest in many future studies.

The use of mass spectrometry by Bradley and Kistiakowsky (42) for studying the kinetics behind shock waves was noted in Chapter 10. More recently, Diesen and Felmlee (18, 43) have continued studies of this nature and have used a time-of-flight mass spectrometer in their investigations of the thermal decompositions of chlorine and of hydrazine. It is anticipated that these important studies also will become more prominent in the next few years.

A technique that promises to be of significant aid in the production and study of free radicals and in the study of surface catalysis was reported recently by Martin and Rummel (44). A palladium catalyst is used to obtain thermal radicals at temperatures as low as 40° C. These workers prepared methyl radicals from CH_4 at low temperatures, and in the process of studying the mechanism of heterogeneous hydrogenations observed a very large $m/e = 44$ peak being formed from methyl cyanide ($m/e = 41$). The $m/e = 44$ ion is from the C_2H_6N radical and becomes quite abundant as it is being desorbed from the palladium catalyst, but the intervening masses (at $m/e = 42$ and 43) do not increase nearly as fast as does the $m/e = 44$ peak. Martin and Rummel suggest as an explanation, the possible existence of the H_3 molecule. It would appear that this new technique will find many applications and open new areas of investigation in the mass spectrometry of free radicals, mechanisms, and catalyst studies.

Recently, Lampe *et al.*, (146) have made a careful study of the reaction of methyl-d_3 radicals with nitric oxide, sampling the reactants and products of the photolyses through a 0.002 in. diameter pin-hole in a gold foil into the ionization chamber of a time-of-flight mass spectrometer. This study very clearly indicates the advantages of using a mass spectrometer in studying reaction mechanisms. The formation of $(CD_3)_2NO$ and $(CD_3)_2NOCD_3$ was observed after the nitric oxide consumption was complete (prior to this, CD_3NO was the sole product), and it was found that the rate of the reaction between CD_3 and CD_3NO to give $(CD_3)_2NO$ was greater than 6.5×10^{-14} cm^3/molecule. The specific rate of this reaction and the reaction between CD_3 and $(CD_3)_2NO$ to give $(CD_3)_2NOCD_3$ are sufficiently high that these reactions have to be considered in the analysis of free radical reactions which are inhibited by nitric oxide, particularly in those studies over the temperature range in which the $(CD_3)_2NO$ and $(CD_3)_2NOCD_3$ are thermally stable.

Also recently, Greene and Milne (45) and Greene, Brewer, and Milne (46) have reported studies that they suggest may provide a unique means of studying kinetics and mechanisms of nucleation phenomena. They reported the observation of polymeric ionic species from the ionization of polymeric molecular species produced when gases were expanded as a molecular beam from pressures of near 1 atm into a mass spectrometer. The expansion of the gas forms a supersonic molecular beam with high Mach number (ten or greater), at the expense of its own internal energy and random translational energy. As a result, an extreme cooling occurs (to temperatures of the order of 10° K) and the gas becomes supersaturated. Polymerization (condensation) occurs and the polymers (bonded by van der Waals' forces) are preserved even when the gas expands into the molecular flow region.

11.3 REACTION MECHANISMS OF IONS IN THE ION SOURCE

Correlations of mass spectra and structural features permit both qualitative analysis and structure determinations of molecules, as has already been indicated. But such correlations also suggest fragmentation processes that occur in the ion source. If these suggested decomposition mechanisms serve no purpose other than simplifying and summarizing the correlations, they are justified. But they do serve at least one additional purpose: they require additional studies to test the particular suggested mechanistic route for decomposition. Since mechanisms are never proven, only by additional searching studies can it be determined how closely the proposed mechanism explains the experimental facts. In such additional investigations, some mechanisms may be disproved, but those which survive have an enhanced probability for being considered satisfactory.

There are several types of experiments that can be performed in proposing and testing mechanistic pathways. These include (a) use of mass spectral cracking patterns; (b) use of information about metastable transitions; (c) use of isotope-labeling and the resultant effect upon mass spectral cracking patterns and metastable transitions; (d) use of energetic information from appearance potential measurements; and (e) theoretical calculations of mass spectra. Of course, where more than one type of ion may contribute to the same nominal mass peak, high-resolution studies aid in distinguishing the various possibilities. Attempts to study and elucidate proposed mechanisms with these methods lead to new information concerning gaseous ion chemistry. In the following paragraphs we shall examine briefly some of the uses of these data in proposing mechanisms by which the various ions arise subsequent to the electron impact process.

Structural features of the molecule control the decomposition reactions leading to the production of the mass spectrum of that molecule. A preliminary study of the mass spectrum will establish the base peak and, quite frequently, will indicate the parent-molecule ion. In addition, other ions of significant intensity in the mass spectrum will be noted. This information, taken together with that of a similar kind for many other molecules of like structural features, suggests which ions fragment to form which other ions.

From the partial mass spectrum of unlabeled benzaldehyde given by McCollum and Meyerson (47), and shown in Table 11–1, a general fragmentation scheme could be written as

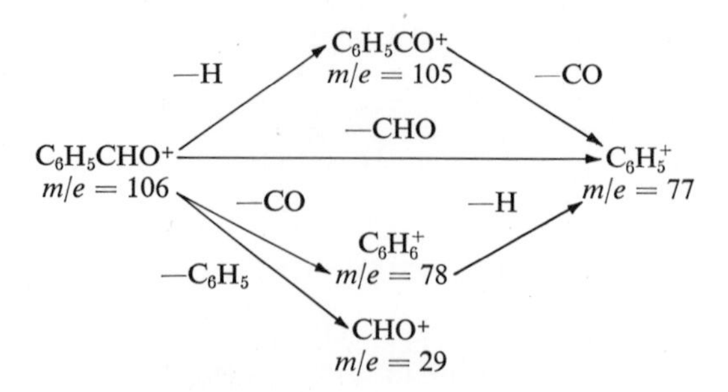

Because of the observed relative abundances, the following less general scheme also might be suggested:

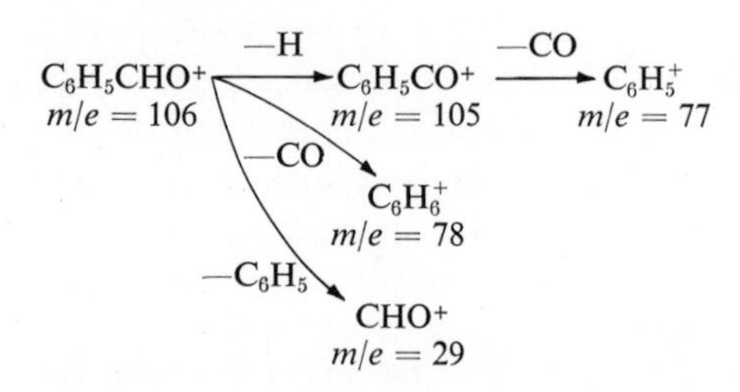

The metastable transitions of 104.0 ($C_6H_5CHO^+ \longrightarrow C_6H_5CO^+ + H$) and 56.5 ($C_6H_5CO^+ \longrightarrow C_6H_5^+ + CO$) agree with this suggestion (although they do not rule out the path of $C_6H_6^+ \longrightarrow C_6H_5^+ + H$; see below).

Also shown in Table 11–1 are the partial mass spectra of three deuterium-labeled benzaldehydes. The relative intensities of the corresponding peaks in all of the spectra agree reasonably well. [The spectrum for C_6H_5 CDO deviates somewhat; this has been attributed to isotope effects in the underlying reactions (47).] The ratio $I_{p^+}/I_{(p-H)^+}$ is essentially constant in C_6H_5CHO, *o*-C_6H_4DCHO, and *m*-C_6H_4DCHO, indicating that the hydrogen atom removed from $C_6H_5CHO^+$, forming $C_7H_5O^+$, is lost from the formyl group and not from the aromatic ring system. The ratio $I_{p^+}/I_{(p-D)^+}$ from C_6H_5CDO is nearly the same and gives added weight to this conclusion. Consistent with the loss of CO from $C_7H_5O^+$ to give $C_6H_5^+$, the structure of $C_7H_5O^+$ may be written as $C_6H_5CO^+$. Also, the CHO^+ ion has 100% retention of the deuterium label from $C_6H_5CDO^+$ and has no deuterium incorporated into it from the ring positions of *o*-C_6H_4DCHO and *m*-C_6H_4DCHO.

Both fragmentation schemes given above for $C_6H_4CHO^+$ satisfy the experimental facts stated thus far. However, the more general scheme appears better in that the very small metastable peak at 76.0 indicates that at least a small amount of $C_6H_5^+$ arises from $C_6H_6^+$ through loss of a hydrogen atom. This also may be seen from the small retention of the deuterium label in $C_6H_5^+$ formed from C_6H_5CDO. The question remains, may $C_6H_5^+$

also arise directly from $C_6H_5CHO^+$ through loss of CHO? The appearance potentials of the $C_6H_5^+$, CHO^+, and $C_6H_5CO^+$ ions from benzaldehyde have been interpreted (48) as representing the energy requirements for the reactions

$$C_6H_5CHO \longrightarrow C_6H_5CO^+ + H,$$

$$C_6H_5CHO \longrightarrow C_6H_5^+ + CHO,$$

$$C_6H_5CHO \longrightarrow CHO^+ + C_6H_5,$$

which indicates that at least in the region of the threshold for the production of $C_6H_5^+$, the $C_6H_5^+$ results from the decomposition of $C_6H_5CHO^+$. Also, the deuterium-label retention in $C_6H_5^+$ from the four benzaldehydes shown in Table 11–1 are consistent with this process. Thus, it appears that the general fragmentation scheme given earlier best represents the fragmentation processes occurring in benzaldehyde under electron impact.

We have seen in the discussion of the fragmentation of benzaldehyde how four of the five types of experiments for proposing and testing mechanistic pathways are utilized. The fifth type of experiment involves the application of the quasi-equilibrium theory to a given mechanism in an attempt

TABLE 11–1. PARTIAL MASS SPECTRA OF BENZALDEHYDE AND THREE MONODEUTEROBENZALDEHYDES [AFTER (47)]

m/e	C_6H_5CHO	C_6H_5CDO	*o*-C_6H_4DCHO	*m*-C_6H_4DCHO
29	13.1	0.7	13.0	13.3
30	—	17.2	—	—
56.6m	0.3	0.4	—	—
57.4m	—	—	0.4	0.4
76.0m	small	—	—	—
77	100.0	100.0	4.9	5.1
78	13.2	7.0	100.0	100.0
79	0.1	18.0	17.1	17.9
103.0m	—	0.7	—	—
104	} 1.5	0.1	0.1	0.1
104.0m		—	—	—
105	90.9	100.0	} 1.5	} 1.2
105.0m	—	—		
106	85.4	0.7	91.8	91.1
107	—	99.8	85.8	85.6

Metastable Transitions Observed:

56.5m ($C_6H_5CO^+ \longrightarrow C_6H_5^+ + CO$)
57.4m ($C_6H_4DCO^+ \longrightarrow C_6H_4D^+ + CO$)
76.0m ($C_6H_6^+ \longrightarrow C_6H_5^+ + H$)
103.0m ($C_6H_5CDO^+ \longrightarrow C_6H_5CO^+ + D$)
104.0m ($C_6H_5CHO^+ \longrightarrow C_6H_5CO^+ + H$)
105.0m ($C_6H_4DCHO^+ \longrightarrow C_6H_4DCO^+ + H$)

to calculate the same mass spectra (at other voltages in addition to that at 70 ev) as those observed experimentally. Since this has been discussed in Section 7.3, it need not be repeated here.

These methods of investigating the reaction mechanisms of isolated gaseous ions are quite powerful and have already been of significant interest in understanding the chemistry of gaseous ions. Meyerson and co-workers (47, 49–61) have reported several studies of this nature in a series of papers spanning several years.

Rylander and Meyerson (49) studied by mass spectrometry the cationated cyclopropane ring with both methyl and phenyl substituents, and Meyerson and Hart (58) investigated the phenylated cyclopropane ion formed from 3-phenylpentane. More recently, Meyerson, Nevitt, and Rylander (61) reported a mass spectrometric study of the ionization and dissociation processes in cyclohexane, methylcyclohexane, methylcyclopentane, and ethylcyclopentane in which they found that the ionic decomposition processes were more complex than those of the alkylbenzenes, although some effects of molecular structure were present.

Grubb and Meyerson (62) have reviewed the examinations of the alkylbenzenes. The studies of toluene (50, 52, 60) and xylene (54) have indicated that there are many similarities in the mass spectra and that the hydrogen atoms in the $C_7H_7^+$ ion have lost their identity. Similar results have been found in detailed examinations of the ethylbenzenes (50), cycloheptatriene (52, 60, 63), benzyl chloride (55), benzyl alcohol (55, 57), and bicycloheptadiene (56). Hanuš and co-workers have studied the related compounds spiro [2.4] heptadiene-1,3 (63, 64), 1-ethinylcyclopentene (63), 3-ethinylcyclopentene (65), and methylfulvene and quadricyclene (66, 67), and Kendall, *et al.*, (68) have reported on the mass spectra and correlations of C_5 to C_{10} coda compounds. In all of these studies, the $C_7H_7^+$ ion is found to be a seven-membered cyclic system in which each hydrogen is equivalent to all others. This is the tropylium ion,

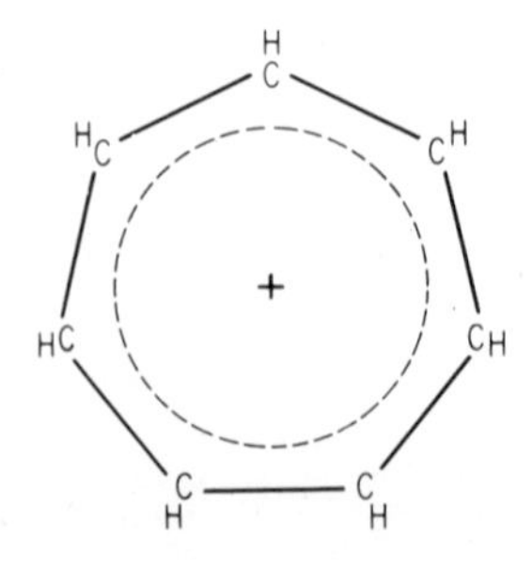

and it is formed in the alkylbenzenes, cyclopentenes, and benzyl compounds by ring expansion. The works cited above provide much evidence against attributing the $C_7H_7^+$ ion in the mass spectra of these compounds to the benzyl ion.

From their mass spectrometric studies of aniline, Rylander, *et al.*, (59) conclude that ring expansion does not play an important role in the dissociation processes which give rise to the mass spectrum. Similar aromatic hydrocarbon ion identities have been examined. Meyerson and Rylander (51) discuss if the $C_6H_5^+$ ion is the phenyl ion and whether or not the $C_6H_7^+$ ion is the benzenium ion. Studies of the structures of these ions and the rearrangements in which they may be involved are important. Recently, Foster and collaborators (69) interpreted some gaseous ions from substituted thiophenes in terms of ring expansion, similar to that for the alkyl benzenes. Because these rearrangements and ring expansions (and possibly even contractions) may be much more common than has been thought, they should be investigated in still greater detail.

McFadden and Wahrhaftig (70) showed in their studies of the mass spectra of deuterated butanes that there is considerable hydrogen atom mobility in paraffin ions, and McCollum and Meyerson (71) have reported briefly about hydrogen migrations in gaseous organic cations. Studies such as these are the bases for the comments on rearrangements in Section 6.5. Through such studies we can hope to learn more of the rearrangements which ions can undergo.

McFadden, Lounsbury, and Wahrhaftig (72) in their study of the mass spectra of deuterium-labeled *n*-butanols pointed out that the loss of a β-hydrogen atom does not accompany the ejection of a water molecule from these alcohols under electron impact. Eliel and Prosser (73) also studied the mass spectra of several unlabeled and monodeuterated butyl alcohols, and recently McFadden, Black, and Corse (74) extended this work with a study of the mass spectra of two monodeuterated 1-butanols. In the latter study, the 3- and 4-positions were labeled, and it was shown that the transfer of a hydrogen atom from position 4 (possibly through the formation of a cyclic intermediate) was quite specific in the rearrangement in which water is lost and the $C_4H_8^+$ ion is formed. In another investigation (75), the mass spectra of a series of normal aliphatic (*n*-butyl to *n*-heptyl) alcohols with a CD_2 group in consecutive positions (positions 1 through 5) from the OH group indicated that the water eliminated in forming the $(p - 18)^+$ ion draws upon a hydrogen atom at position 4 to the extent of about 90% (elimination of water from *t*-alcohols is less specific). Saunders and Williams (76) show the high-resolution mass spectra of seven alcohols containing from two to five carbon atoms and indicate that the results very largely confirm the correlations of the mass spectra of alcohols made by Friedel, Shultz, and Sharkey (77).

Sharkey, Shultz, and Friedel (78) have also reported a mass spectral correlation of a series of esters, and the high-resolution spectra of many esters have been given by Beynon, Saunders, and Williams (79). McLafferty

(80), Godbole and Kebarle (81), and Colomb, *et al.*, (82) have used deuterated compounds to study dissociation and rearrangement processes. A cyclic intermediate was proposed by Ryhage and Stenhagen (83) and by Guriev, Tikhomirov, and Tunitskii (84) to indicate the loss of a hydrocarbon fragment from the center of the ester ion. And Dinh-Nguyen, *et al.*, (85) showed that the group most frequently lost came from the position next to the carbonyl group. Recently, Black, McFadden, and Corse (86) examined the mass spectra of deuterated 1-butyl acetates, 2-butyl acetates, and 1-butyl propionates and found that there is a selective transfer of the hydrogen atom on the carbon atom delta to the carbonyl group, followed by a random selection of the second hydrogen atom from the other hydrogens available in the alcohol moiety, in the formation of the $CH_3COOH_2^+$ ion. Benz and Biemann (75), in studying the loss of acetic acid from *n*-alkyl acetates, found that the hydrogen atoms come approximately 50% each from the C-2 and the C-3 positions. Munson and Franklin (147) and Weber (148) report on the energetics of several of these gaseous oxygenated organic ions.

From the brief remarks in this section it can be seen that studies of mass spectra that lead to suggested reaction mechanisms for ion decomposition are important because they relate to fundamental processes in the chemistry of isolated gaseous ions. Although some excellent work has been done in this relatively young field, much remains to be understood. In light of the known rearrangements and structural changes in the ions during decomposition, it has become obvious that mass spectra cannot safely be interpreted simply in terms of individual bond ruptures in the original parent-molecule ion. Many other factors may enter in, possibly some as yet undiscovered, and studies that lead to the elucidation of these factors will be significant to the whole of mass spectrometry.

11.4 HIGH ENERGY STUDIES

The manner in which energy interacts with matter to produce chemical changes commands much of a scientist's attention. The energies involved in such studies may vary over wide ranges, from a few kilocalories to many million electron volts, and may be delivered into a system in small or large amounts. Such studies include radiation chemistry, photochemistry, flame investigations, and experiments concerned with chemical changes in electric discharges. It will not be possible to discuss each of these in great detail here, but a few samples of current frontiers and the role that mass spectrometry plays in these investigations will be presented.

A number of different studies involving mass spectrometry and electrical discharges were noted and discussed briefly in Section 11.2. Investigations of the flames of hydrocarbon fuels will be discussed in the following section in conjunction with the very interesting chemi-ionization reactions. We shall take note briefly here only of the studies using laser sources and of the particle bombardment, "shake-off," and recoil investigations.

In Section 3.12 it was indicated that laser sources are being developed for mass spectrometers, and that interesting studies are just beginning to result from this mating of the laser and the mass spectrometer. Photolyses of inorganic materials, in which laser beams are employed, are among the first studies being made with this instrumentation. Only recently Honig and Woolston (87–89) reported on the use of lasers in conection with a mass spectrometer.

Honig and Woolston (87, 89) have reported that in the irradiation of conductors, semiconductors, and insulators with a focused beam from a pulsed ruby laser, intense pulses of positive ions and very intense pulses of electrons were obtained. A single pulse delivered about 0.2 joules to the target under study. This caused the removal by vaporization of approximately 2×10^{17} atoms from the target. Using an AEI MS-7 double-focusing mass spectrograph, the positive ions produced were selected according to mass, analyzed according to mass, and recorded on a photographic plate (a good detector for a short, single pulse). Interestingly, no multiply charged ions produced directly by the laser action on the targets were found, although thermal Cu^+, Mo^+, Ta^+, W^+, and $Al_2O_3^+$ ions were formed from Cu, Mo, Ta, W, and Al_2O_3, respectively. Singly charged ions also were observed from graphite and stainless steel. No thermal Ge^+ and SiC^+ ions were observed from Ge and SiC semiconductors. By applying an electron accelerating potential in the source region, a low-voltage arc discharge was formed, causing the production of large ion currents by means of electron impact ionization of vaporized neutrals. In the latter method, significant singly and multiply charged ions typical of the target (and background gases) were produced.

These first studies were followed by a report by Berkowitz and Chupka (90) in which a ruby laser delivered pulses of approximately 1 joule/pulse to targets in the ion source of an electromagnetic mass spectrometer. The vaporized material ejected from the target was collimated into a molecular beam and was ionized by an electron beam of controlled energy. With targets of graphite, boron, and magnesium, they estimated that the temperature corresponded to about 4000° K if thermodynamic equilibrium was assumed. [From the rotational population of the 0,1 CN violet band, Howe (91) estimated a temperature of 4500° K.] This temperature is based on the vapor cloud sampled after expansion and is certainly lower than the heated spot on the target [which is of the order of 10,000° K (89)]. Cavities in the target of approximately 0.005-in. diameter and 0.003-in. depth have been reported (89, 90, 92).

In ruby laser irradiations of bituminous coal samples in sealed bottles,

Sharkey, Shultz, and Friedel (92) noted that about 20% of the material is ejected from the crater as solids and about 80% is vaporized, and that there are attendant difficulties in obtaining representative samples. These workers found by mass spectrometric analyses of the products that there is little liquid or tar formation and that the products differ from those obtained in flash photolyses and high-temperature (about 900° C) pyrolyses. Under the conditions employed, the products were largely simple C_1 and C_2 hydrocarbons and provided little information about the structure of coal.

In addition to the positive ions and the electrons that are emitted by the laser beam action on the target, photons are apparently emitted also from the heated target (93). The effect this photoemission might have on mass spectrometric studies of the laser interaction with matter has not yet been investigated, but it does merit further consideration and study. The action of lasers on other materials, including organic compounds, still remains to be examined. We can look forward confidently to much interesting activity in this area, as well as in the area of impurity analyses, in the next few years.

In 1959, Melton and Rudolph (94) reported the use of Po^{208} α-particles for bombardment (rather than electrons) in the ion source of a mass spectrometer. By working at acetylene pressures of 0.01 to 0.1 mm, they observed (95) a large number of ionic species with even-numbered carbon atoms formed from the $C_2H_2^+$ ion by ion-molecule reactions. Melton and Rudolph (96) extended these studies to ethylene and observed ions containing two to six carbon atoms. It was found that the secondary $C_3H_5^+$ ion was nearly twice the intensity of the $C_2H_5^+$ primary ion, and that a tertiary ion $C_5H_9^+$, was also formed. Kebarle and Godbole (97) found that there were a large number of ion peaks from the Po α-radiolysis of ethylene at 200 Torr, that there were no fragment ions, and that most of the more intense ions contained odd numbers of hydrogen atoms, much as Field (98) found in his high-pressure (0.2 Torr) mass spectrometric study of ethylene. It can be seen that these ion-molecule reaction studies are intimately related to radiation chemistry, and to the "cluster theory" proposed by Lind (99). Stevenson and Schissler (100) have commented on the relations of mass spectrometry and radiation chemistry in an excellent review.

In an attempt to study a consequence of the Born approximation, namely, the conclusion that the fragmentation of a molecule ionized and excited by a massive ion is the same as for electron impact if the velocities are the same and are sufficiently high, Wexler and Hess (101) have studied the bombardment of acetylene with 2.25 Mev protons from a Van de Graaff electrostatic generator. Similar experiments have been carried out by Schuler and Stuber (101) and Wexler (149).

Snell and Pleasonton (102) have studied some of the atomic and molecular consequences of radioactive decay by using a mass spectrometer (without an electron beam) in which the ions formed upon decay of radioactive atoms alone or chemically combined are determined. They showed that if the decay process is electron capture or internal conversion, vacancy cascades develop which lead to ions having multiple charges, and that the distribution of the charge has a maximum. On the other hand, when a charged particle is emitted by the nucleus, the charge on the nucleus is changed and the rapid escape of the charged particle causes an abrupt perturbation in the electrostatic environment; this is felt by all of the extranuclear electrons. This leads to excitation and ionization, with the probability for ionization or "shaking-off" of electrons from outer electronic shells being greater than that from inner electronic shells. Thus, the charge distribution is expected to decrease monotonically with increasing charge. Argon-37 (electron capture) gives a charge distribution up to 8+, with a maximum at 3+. Krypton-85 (beta-minus decay) gives a monotonically decreasing charge distribution. Xenon-131m (isomeric transition) gives a peaked charge distribution. Snell and Pleasonton also examined the molecular dissociation following radioactive decay in HT and found the most abundant ion to be formed was $(He^3H)^+$. From this case, and from their study of dissociation in $C^{14}O_2$, Snell and Pleasonton also briefly studied the CH_3T molecule, related to the studies of Wexler, Anderson, Hess, and Singer (103–106), which we shall discuss next. Other studies have also been made (107–110) using mass spectrometric techniques.

As an example of recoil studies we shall choose the report by Wexler and Anderson (103) on the dissociation of methyl bromide by the isomeric transition of Br^{80m}. Earlier, Wexler (104) found that the average positive charge formed on $C_2H_5Br^{80}$ by the internal conversions and the Auger effect was 10 ± 2 electron units. With such a high charge, a molecule would dissociate by coulombic repulsion if the charge were distributed over the molecule before the C—Br bond ruptured from the loss of bonding electrons. The ions produced from the radioactive decay traveled through the apex of the source cone and were accelerated through 6000 volts, toward the 60°-sector magnetic mass analyzer. It was found that multiply charged Br^{n+} species were observed up to $n = 13$, and that the average charge was $n = 6.4$. These results indicated that the average positive charge developed on the CH_3Br^{80} molecule as a result of internal conversion and vacancy cascades is $\geqslant 6.8$. No multiply charged molecules were observed, implying that these ions dissociate readily (in a time shorter than about 10^{-5} sec). CH_3^+ was found to be the major fragment ion, and its presence suggested that coulombic repulsion after the internal transfer of a single electron is the principal mechanism by which the multiply charged molecule ions fragment. If the C—Br bond (1.9 Å) in CH_3Br is taken as the distance of separation of the two charges in CH_3Br^{2+}, the coulomb repulsion is 7.6 ev, and the C—Br bond energy is certainly less than this. For CH_3Br^{13+}, the coulomb repulsion is 99 ev; clearly, coulombic repulsion plays an important role in the fragmentation of multiply charged molecular ions. Probably polyatomic species with multiple charges are unstable in gases at high pressures or in condensed media. The work of Newton *et al.*, discussed briefly in Sections 6.3 and 6.6, is related to these studies.

In an earlier study of the ions formed following β-decay of C_2H_5T and 1,2-$C_2H_4BrBr^{82}$, Wexler and Hess (105) discussed the observed results for C_2H_5T in terms of the quasi-equilibrium theory of unimolecular decompositions, and surprisingly good agreement was found. This might suggest that the energy given to the molecule from this nuclear decay is similar to that given up by the impacting electron in the ion source, and that the subsequent chemistry of the gaseous ions remains essentially the same.

It is interesting to note that Carlson and White (108) studied the nuclear decay of CH_3I^{131} and observed that a very large intensity ($\sim$ 70%) of CH_3—Xe^+ ions were formed, quite in contrast to the study of the decay of CH_3T, in which the organic-helium ion complexes are not stable. But the carbon -xenon bond remained intact in 70% of the decays, and Carlson and White attributed this to the inherent greater stability of the CH_3Xe^+ ion. As Carlson and White explained, other work had shown already that Xe, Kr and Ar could form complex ions with methane, and that Xe was the only noble gas to form complex ions with acetylene. All of these facts were noted before the discovery of the xenon fluorides or the xenon hexafluoroplatinate.

There still remain many unanswered questions about the interaction of energy with molecules, and several approaches are possible for their solution. One nagging question is whether or not energy is given up to molecules in relatively small increments (10–40 ev, order of magnitude), regardless of the energy of the agent. Possibly only the energy distributions vary (and may be dependent upon the type or energy of the agent.) These areas of study shall probably continue to attract investigators, and mass spectrometry can be expected to continue to play a principal role in the studies.

11.5 CHEMI-IONIZATION REACTIONS

The energy released in a chemical reaction may be sufficient to form an ionic product. This primary process is termed *chemi-ionization* and is frequently found in combustion reactions. It has been noted (111) that the majority of the ionization produced in the flames of hydrocarbon fuels is apparently attributable to chemi-ionization processes.

Probably the chemi-ionization process involving hydrocarbon species that has been studied most is the reaction of a CH radical with an oxygen atom, both apparently in their ground states (112). This reaction yields the formyl ion

$$CH + O \longrightarrow CHO^+ + e, \qquad (11\text{-}14)$$

for which $\Delta H_{\text{reaction}} = 0$. The heat of formation of the oxygen atom is 59 kcal/mole and that of the CH radical is 144 kcal/mole. $\Delta H_f(CHO) = -3$ kcal/mole, so that ΔH for the reaction

$$CH + O \longrightarrow CHO \qquad (11\text{-}15)$$

is simply $-3 - 59 - 144 = -206$ kcal/mole. Since $\Delta H_f(CHO^+) = 203$ kcal/mole (113), the reaction given by Equation (11–14) is seen to have $\Delta H = 0$. This same chemi-ionization has also been observed behind shock-waves in O_2-C_2H_2 mixtures (114) and in H_2-O_2-N_2 flames to which C_2H_2 has been added (115).

It is quite improbable that the ionic product of a chemi-ionization process would be doubly-charged, since the excess energy of chemical reactions is too small to provide the additional energy needed. Similarly, it is not very likely that the ionic product would be formed in an excited state.

But this is not necessarily the only possible chemi-ionization reaction occurring in the flames of hydrocarbon fuels. Kistiakowsky and Michael (116) found no CHO^+ in oxidations of CH_4 and C_2H_2, but they did observe an ion at $m/e = 39$ (using C_2D_2, this ion was observed at $m/e = 42$ rather than at $m/e = 39$). They suggest that the reaction

$$CH + C_2H_2 \longrightarrow C_3H_3^+ + e \qquad (11\text{-}16)$$

occurs, but with an excited CH radical:

$$CH(A^2\Delta) + C_2H_2 \longrightarrow C_3H_3^+ + e, \qquad (11\text{-}17)$$

since reaction (11–16) is endothermic by about 3.2 ev, based on $\Delta H_f(C_3H_3^+) = 274$ kcal/mole (117). But since $CH(A^2\Delta)$ lies 23,150 cm^{-1} (2.87 ev) above the $X^2\Pi$ ground state of the CH radical (118), reaction (11–17) is only endothermic by 0.5 ev. Using the value of $\Delta H_f(\text{cyclo-}C_3H_3^+)$ given by Wiberg, *et al.*, (119) reaction (11–17) would be endothermic by only 0.3 ev, and Kistiakowsky and Michael (116) suggest that $\Delta H_f(\text{cyclo-}C_3H_3^+) < 11.7$ ev so that reaction (11–17) is actually exothermic.

But reactions involving the excited states of atoms with other atoms or molecules are known, and they are properly considered chemi-ionization reactions. In fact, the formation of diatomic noble gas ions involves chemi-ionization. The existence of diatomic noble gas ions was demonstrated by Tüxen (120) more than 25 years ago (using a parabola mass spectrograph), but Hornbeck and Molnar (121) first indicated that the diatomic ions were formed by the reaction of an excited noble gas atom. In recent years, several workers have been actively exploring this interesting area of study (122–128), and very recently, Munson, Franklin, and Field (129) have indicated that chemi-ionization reactions lead to heteronuclear as well as homonuclear noble-gas molecule-ions. And, interestingly, it has been found (130) that the dominant ionization process in shock-heated xenon is a chemi-ionization process:

$$Xe^* + Xe \longrightarrow Xe_2^+ + e. \tag{11–18}$$

Because many of these studies have indicated that the chemistry of excited atoms of noble gases is more extensive than had been anticipated previously, studies have continued. As a result, information has been gained concerning the reaction of excited atoms of noble gases with molecules. Two examples of these types of reactions are (131, 132)

$$Ar^* + N_2 \longrightarrow ArN_2^+ + e \tag{11–19}$$

and

$$Kr^* + CO \longrightarrow KrCO^+ + e. \tag{11–20}$$

Actually, these studies are just beginning. Because chemi-ionization reactions are not completely understood, they present fascinating possibilities for future study. One reaction of hydrocarbon species was cited above, in which the reactant species were in their ground states. The question might well be asked, are there other similar reactions that we might find, and that might help us understand the processes of combustion? And, further more, might there not be important chemi-ionization processes involving excited atoms and molecules of hydrocarbon species? Gatz, Young, and Sharpless (133) recently reported the chemi-ionization reactions

$$N_2^* + NO^* \longrightarrow N_2 + NO^+ + e \tag{11–21}$$

and

$$N + N + NO^* \longrightarrow N_2 + NO^+ + e \tag{11–22}$$

to occur in atomic oxygen and nitrogen mixtures, and Spokes and Evans (12) have suggested chemi-ionization reactions in the pink afterglow of nitrogen. Certainly, we can anticipate seeing many additional studies of chemi-ionization reactions in the future. Possibly some of them shall contain other atoms, e.g., fluorine, in the molecules and excited molecules, atoms, and negative ions. The recent study by Miller and Calcote (150) of negative-ion formation in hydrocarbon flames suggests several additional interesting studies.

11.6 MOLECULAR STRUCTURES OF GASEOUS IONS

Very little information is available on the structure, vibrational and rotational frequencies, moments of inertia, and bond distances in gaseous ionic species, and the information that is available is limited to diatomic species. [See, for example, data for vibrational energy levels in the NO^+ ion (134, 135).] Obviously, it is desirable that information of this nature be obtained for polyatomic as well as diatomic ions, for such data would allow us to better understand the molecular structures of and the bonding forces in ions. Further more, this would allow us to extrapolate and to predict properties of other ionic species. In the following paragraphs are described the basic ideas and suggested experimental approaches to studying gaseous ionic species, as proposed by this author in collaboration with C. E. Meloan.

Basically, the experiments involve the production of ions in the ion source of the mass spectrometer, the mass analysis of these ions, and the study of the infrared absorption of the separated ion beams. From the infrared spectra, vibrational and rotational frequencies in these ions can be determined, the moments of inertia and bond distances can be deduced, and therefore the structure of the ions can be determined. Furthermore, from the *P*, *Q*, and *R*-branches observed in the infrared spectra, knowledge of the vibrational and rotational energy levels of the ions can be obtained.

It is imperative that large, mass-separated ion beam currents be obtained, and this requirement dictates that an isotope separator capable of producing ion beam currents of the order of several amperes be employed in both the ion production and mass analyses. Such equipment is likely to be found only in production isotope separators.

The quadrupole mass spectrometer, described in Section 4.9, has received careful consideration for use as an isotope separator (136, 137), and would be very useful in these suggested studies of gaseous ionic structures. Also, the quadrupole instrument would make the process of mating the infrared spectrometer to the isotope separator an easier task.

By use of beam attenuation and multiple-pass techniques in the infrared spectroscopic measurements, sufficient ions will be intercepted by the infrared radiation at a point just beyond the entrance slit to the collector of the isotope separator (note that the entrance slit to the collector region is not necessary if a quadrupole instrument is used) to enable one to obtain measurable absorption of the infrared radiation. The infrared beam from a glowbar or mercury lamp source would intercept the ion beam at approximately right angles. By varying the wavelength of the infrared radiation, the infrared spectra of the various ions selected by the mass analyzer may be obtained in the region of 50 to 5000 cm^{-1} by using grating interchanges with commercially available equipment.

It is not necessary to restrict the experimental structure studies to only those using infrared absorption spectroscopy. Certainly it should also be possible to perform Raman studies on the mass-separated ion beams, as well as electron diffraction structure studies. In fact, the Raman studies might well be made by employing various lasers to provide the excitation.

If it is too difficult to obtain sufficient absorption, it might be necessary to resort to emission spectroscopy. Recently, Nicholson (134) has determined the various vibrational levels in the NO^+ ion by photoionization and compares his results to those of Miescher (135). Distinct vibrational levels from $v = 0$ to $v = 6$ were reported. Thus, photoionization also may provide some information about the structures of ions.

Using Linnett's modification (138) of the Lewis-Langmuir octet rule (139, 140), it is predicted that the XeF_3^+ ion, abundant in the mass spectrum of XeF_4 (141–143), would be planar; that the $XeOF_3^+$ ion, quite abundant in the $XeOF_4$ mass spectrum (142), would have a distorted tetrahedral structure; and that the XeF_5^+ ion, reasonably intense in the XeF_6 mass spectrum (142), would be square pyramidal. This last ion could be contrasted to the CH_5^+ ion, formed in ion-molecule reactions in methane (144–145), which is expected to be trigonal bipyramidal with the equatorial C—H bonds shorter than the polar C—H bonds. It is anticipated that the Xe—F bond lengths in each of the above noble gas compounds would be very nearly the same, about 1.9 to 2.0 Å. Recently, Svec and Flesch (143) have reported appearance potential data for XeF_2 and XeF_4, from which bond strengths may be calculated.

Of course, many more predictions of structures of various ions could be made. What now would be of significant interest, as already suggested above, would be to determine experimentally these structures and bond lengths in order to judge the correctness of these predictions.

Other techniques and applications are suggested by the aforementioned approach, but in answer to other questions. Consider the question, do the $m/e = 30$ ions with the formula of CH_2O^+ have the structure of CH_2O^+ or $CHOH^+$? High resolution mass spectrometry can not answer this question. Appearance potential studies give some help. But a novel solution might be to perform an electron-spin resonance experiment with mass-analyzed ion beams of $m/e = 30$. The great sensitivity of electron-spin resonance would also be of significant aid in reducing somewhat the demands placed upon the necessary ion beam current.

It is seen that in all of these studies, rather intense ion beam currents must be available. In a few specific cases of *A-B* type molecules, such as for CO, infrared spectroscopy together with plasmas or gaseous discharge sources might be employed without involving mass analysis, providing the discharge, for example, is maintained at a very low pressure. However, even here the analytical tools employed for the structure studies might give complicated spectra due to the possible presence of excited molecular species. Thus, in order to obtain the desired specific information about the molecular structures of gaseous polyatomic ions, mass analyses must be made.

Certainly these studies are of great importance, and we can expect mass spectrometry to play a significant role in the next few years.

11.7 SUMMARY

It may be seen from the discussions above, and from those presented in the preceding ten chapters, that mass spectrometry has an almost overwhelming past record of accomplishments and that this field is one of very active and productive scientific research. There is no question in the author's mind that still greater advances will be made in the future. There are still so many questions unanswered, so many techniques to be developed, so many new ideas to be contributed, that one cannot but be confident that studies in mass spectrometry offer many fine opportunities for further interesting research.

REFERENCES

1. D. M. Yost, "A New Epoch in Chemistry," in *Noble-Gas Compounds*, H. H. Hyman (ed.), University of Chicago Press, Chicago, 1963, pp. 21–22.
2. H. H. Claassen, H. Selig, and J. G. Malm, *J. Am. Chem. Soc.*, **84**, 3593 (1962).
3. C. L. Chernick, H. H. Claassen, P. R. Fields, H. H. Hyman, J. G. Malm, W. M. Manning, M. S. Matheson, L. A. Quarterman, F. Schreiner, H. H. Selig, I. Sheft, S. Siegel, E. N. Sloth, L. Stein, M. H. Studier, J. L. Weeks, and M. H. Zirin, *Science*, **138**, 136 (1962).
4. M. H. Studier and E. N. Sloth, *J. Phys. Chem.*, **67**, 925 (1963).
5. M. H. Studier and E. N. Sloth, "Mass Spectrometric Studies of Noble-Gas Compounds," in *Noble-Gas Compounds*, H. H. Hyman, (ed.), University of Chicago Press, Chicago, 1963, pp. 47–49.
6. W. W. Hunt, Jr., R. E. Huffman, and K. E. McGee, *Rev. Sci. Instr.*, **35**, 82 (1964); W. W. Hunt, Jr., R. E. Huffman, J. Saari, G. Wassel, J. F. Betts, E. H. Paufve, W. Wyess, and R. A. Fluegge, *Rev. Sci. Instr.*, **35**, 88 (1964); W. W. Hunt, Jr. and K. E. McGee, *J. Chem. Phys.*, **41**, 2709 (1964).
7. R. E. Ferguson, K. E. McCulloh, and H. M. Rosenstock, "Observations of the Products of Collision Processes and Ion Decompositions in a Linear, Pulsed Time-of-Flight Mass Spectrometer," 10th annual meeting of the ASTM Committee E-14 on Mass Spectrometry, New Orleans, La., June 3–8, 1962; see also, *J. Chem. Phys.*, **42**, 100 (1965).
8. F. W. McLafferty, "Ion Decomposition Mechanisms," 12th annual meeting of the ASTM Committee E-14 on Mass Spectrometry, Montreal, Canada, June 7–12, 1964.
9. D. S. Jackson and H. I. Schiff, *J. Chem. Phys.*, **21**, 2233 (1953).
10. D. S. Jackson and H. I. Schiff, *J. Chem. Phys.*, **23**, 2333 (1955).
11. J. Berkowitz, W. A. Chupka, and G. B. Kistiakowsky, *J. Chem. Phys.*, **25**, 457 (1956).
12. G. N. Spokes and B. E. Evans, "A Study of the Ions Present in Active Nitro-

gen Using a Quadrupole Mass Spectrometer," 11th annual meeting of the ASTM Committee E-14 on Mass Spectrometry, San Francisco, Calif., May 19–24, 1963.

13. S. N. Foner and R. L. Hudson, *J. Chem. Phys.*, **37**, 1662 (1962).
14. J. T. Herron, J. L. Franklin, and P. Bradt, *Can. J. Chem.*, **37**, 579 (1959).
15. S. N. Foner and R. L. Hudson, *J. Chem. Phys.*, **28**, 719 (1958).
16. S. N. Foner and R. L. Hudson, *J. Chem. Phys.*, **29**, 442 (1958).
17. A. N. Terenin, B. L. Kurbatov, and F. I. Vilesov, *Trudy po Khim. i Khim. Tekhnol.*, **1**, 181 (1961).
18. R. W. Diesen, *J. Chem. Phys.*, **39**, 2121 (1963).
19. S. N. Foner, *Science*, **143**, 441 (1964).
20. J. T. Herron and H. I. Schiff, *J. Chem. Phys.*, **24**, 1266 (1956).
21. J. T. Herron and H. I. Schiff, *Can. J. Chem.*, **36**, 1159 (1958); F. S. Klein and J. T. Herron, *J. Chem. Phys.*, **41**, 1285 (1964).
22. G. B Kistiakowsky and P. H. Kydd, *J. Am. Chem. Soc.*, **79**, 4825 (1957).
23. S. W. Benson, *J. Chem. Phys.*, **38**, 1251 (1963).
24. M. A. A. Clyne and B. A. Thrush, *Trans. Faraday Soc.*, **58**, 511 (1962).
25. A. J. B. Robertson, *Chem. Ind.* (*London*), **1954**, 1485.
26. S. N. Foner and R. L. Hudson, *J. Chem. Phys.*, **21**, 1374 (1953); **23**, 1364 and 1974 (1955).
27. S. N. Foner and R. L. Hudson, *J. Chem. Phys.*, **21**, 1608 (1953).
28. S. N. Foner and R. L. Hudson, *J. Chem. Phys.*, **36**, 2681 (1962).
29. F. P. Lossing, K. U. Ingold, and A. W. Tickner, *Trans. Faraday Soc.*, **14**, 34 (1953).
30. E. J. Gallegos, "Mass Spectroscopic Investigation of Saturated Heterocyclics," *Doctoral Dissertation*, Kansas State University, 1962, pp. 130–32.
31. F. P. Lossing, K. U. Ingold, and I. H. S. Henderson, in *Applied Mass Spectrometry*, The Institute of Petroleum, London, 1954, p. 102.
32. F. P. Lossing, *Ind. Chim. Belge*, **19**, 613 (1954).
33. K. U. Ingold and F. P. Lossing, *Can. J. Chem.*, **31**, 30 (1953).
34. K. U. Ingold and F. P. Lossing, *J. Chem. Phys.*, **21**, 1135 (1954).
35. K. U. Ingold, I. H. S. Henderson, and F. P. Lossing, *J. Chem. Phys.*, **21**, 2239 (1953).
36. J. B. Farmer, F. P. Lossing, D. G. H. Marsden, and E. W. R. Steacie, *J. Chem. Phys.*, **23**, 1169 (1955).
37. P. Kebarle and F. P. Lossing, *Can. J. Chem.*, **37**, 389 (1959).
38. F. P. Lossing, D. G. H. Marsden, and J. B. Farmer, *Can. J. Chem.*, **34**, 701 (1956).

39. A. G. Harrison and F. P. Lossing, *Can. J. Chem.*, **37**, 1478 (1959).

40. A. G. Harrison and F. P. Lossing, *Can. J. Chem.*, **37**, 1696 (1959).

41. F. I. Vilesov, B. L. Kurbatov, and A. N. Terenin. *Dokl. Akad. Nauk S. S. S. R.*, **122**, 94 (1958).

42. J. N. Bradley and G. B. Kistiakowsky, *J. Chem. Phys.*, **35**, 256 (1961).

43. R. W. Diesen and W. J. Felmlee, *J. Chem. Phys.*, **39**, 2115 (1963).

44. T. W. Martin and R. E. Rummel, *Science*, **143**, 797 (1964).

45. F. T. Greene and T. A. Milne, *J. Chem. Phys.*, **39**, 3150 (1963).

46. F. T. Greene, J. Brewer, and T. A. Milne, *J. Chem. Phys.*, **40**, 1488 (1964).

47. J. D. McCollum and S. Meyerson, *J. Am. Chem. Soc.*, **85**, 1739 (1963).

48. R. I. Reed and M. B. Thornley, *Trans. Faraday Soc.*, **54**, 949 (1958).

49. P. N. Rylander and S. Meyerson, *J. Am. Chem. Soc.*, **78**, 5799 (1956).

50. P. N. Rylander, S. Meyerson, and H. M. Grubb, *J. Am. Chem. Soc.*, **79**, 842 (1957).

51. S. Meyerson and P. N. Rylander, *J. Am. Chem. Soc.*, **79**, 1058 (1957).

52. S. Meyerson and P. N. Rylander, *J. Chem. Phys.*, **27**, 901 (1957).

53. P. N. Rylander and S. Meyerson, *J. Chem. Phys.*, **27**, 1116 (1957).

54. S. Meyerson and P. N. Rylander, *J. Phys. Chem.*, **62**, 2 (1958).

55. S. Meyerson, P. N. Rylander, E. L. Eliel, and J. D. McCollum, *J. Am. Chem. Soc.*, **81**, 2606 (1959).

56. S. Meyerson, J. D. McCollum, and P. N. Rylander, *J. Am. Chem. Soc.*, **83**, 1401 (1961).

57. E. L. Eliel, J. D. McCollum, S. Meyerson, and P. N. Rylander, *J. Am. Chem Soc.*, **83**, 2481 (1961).

58. S. Meyerson and H. Hart, *J. Am. Chem. Soc.*, **85**, 2358 (1963).

59. P. N. Rylander, S. Meyerson, E. L. Eliel, and J. D. McCollum, *J. Am. Chem. Soc.*, **85**, 2723 (1963).

60. S. Meyerson, *J. Am. Chem. Soc.*, **85**, 3340 (1963).

61. S. Meyerson, T. D. Nevitt, and P. N. Rylander, "Ionization-Dissociation of Some Cycloalkanes under Electron Impact," in *Advances in Mass Spectrometry*, Vol. 2, R. M. Elliott (ed.), Pergamon Press, Oxford, England, 1963, pp. 313–36.

62. H. M. Grubb and S. Meyerson, "Mass Spectra of Alkylbenzenes," in *Mass Spectrometry of Organic Ions*, F. W. McLafferty (ed.), Academic Press, Inc., New York, 1963, pp. 453–527.

63. V. Hanuš and Z. Dolejšek, *Kernenergie*, **3**, 836 (1960).

64. V. Hanuš, *Nature*, **184**, 1796 (1959).

65. V. Hanuš and Z. Dolejšek, *Jaderna Energie*, **6**, 350 (1960).

66. V. Hanuš and Z. Dolejšek, *Collection Czech. Chem. Commun.*, **28**, 652 (1963).

67. Z. Dolejšek, V. Hanuš, and H. Prinzbach, *Angew. Chem.*, **74**, 902 (1962).

68. R. F. Kendall, F. O. Cotton, N. G. Foster, and B. H. Eccleston, "The Mass Spectra and Analytical Correlations of C_5 through C_{10} Coda Compounds," 10th annual meeting of the ASTM Committee E-14 on Mass Spectrometry, New Orleans, La., June 3–8, 1962.

69. N. G. Foster, D. E. Hirsch, R. F. Kendall, and B. H. Eccleston, "Mass Spectrometry of Sulfur Compounds. IV. Studies of the Mass Spectra of 2-*t*-Butyl-, 3-*t*-Butyl-, and 2,5-Di-*t*-Butylthiophenes," 10th annual meeting of the ASTM Committee E-14 on Mass Spectrometry, New Orleans, La., June 3–8, 1962.

70. W. H. McFadden and A. L. Wahrhaftig, *J. Am. Chem. Soc.*, **78**, 1572 (1956).

71. J. D. McCollum and S. Meyerson, *J. Am. Chem. Soc.*, **81**, 4116 (1959).

72. W. H. McFadden, M. Lounsbury, and A. L. Wahrhaftig, *Can. J. Chem.*, **36**, 990 (1958).

73. E. L. Eliel and T. J. Prosser, *J. Am. Chem. Soc.*, **78**, 4045 (1956).

74. W. H. McFadden, D. R. Black, and J. W. Corse, *J. Phys. Chem.*, **67**, 1517 (1963).

75. W. Benz and K. Biemann, *J. Am. Chem. Soc.*, **86**, 2375 (1964).

76. R. A. Saunders and A. E. Williams, "High Resolution Mass Spectrometry," in *Mass Spectrometry of Organic Ions*, F. W. McLafferty (ed.), Academic Press, Inc., New York, 1963, pp. 343–97.

77. R. A. Friedel, J. L. Shultz, and A. G. Sharkey, *Anal. Chem.*, **28**, 926 (1956).

78. A. G. Sharkey, Jr., J. L. Shultz, and R. A. Friedel, *Anal. Chem.*, **31**, 87 (1959).

79. J. H. Beynon, R. A. Saunders, and A. E. Williams, *Anal. Chem.*, **33**, 221 (1961).

80. F. W. McLafferty, *Anal. Chem.*, **31**, 82 (1959).

81. E. W. Godbole and P. Kebarle, *Trans. Faraday Soc.*, **58**, 1897 (1962).

82. H. O. Colomb, Jr., B. D. Fulks, and V. A. Yarborough, "Rearrangement Ions of Aliphatic Esters as Observed in the Mass Spectrometer," 10th annual meeting of the ASTM Committee E-14 on Mass Spectrometry, New Orleans, La., June 3–8, 1962.

83. R. Ryhage and E. Stenhagen, *Arkiv Kemi*, **13**, 523 (1959); **15**, 291 and 332 (1960).

84. M. V. Guriev and M. V. Tikhomirov, *Zh. Fiz. Khim.*, **32**, 2731 (1957); M. V. Guriev, M. V. Tikhomirov, and N. N. Tunitskii, *Dokl. Akad. Nauk S.S.S.R.* **123**, 120 (1958).

85. N. Dinh-Nguyen, R. Ryhage, S. Ställberg-Stenhagen, and E. Stenhagen, *Arkiv Kemi*, **18**, 393 (1962).

86. D. R. Black, W. H. McFadden and J. W. Corse, *J. Phys. Chem.*, **68**, 1237 (1964).

87. R. E. Honig and J. R. Woolston, *Appl. Phys. Letters*, **2**, 138 (1963).

88. R. E. Honig, *Appl. Phys. Letters*, **3**, 8 (1963).

89. R. E. Honig, "On the Production of Positive Ions from Solids," 12th annual meeting of the ASTM Committee E-14 on Mass Spectrometry, Montreal, Canada, June 7–12, 1964.

90. J. Berkowitz and W. A. Chupka, *J. Chem. Phys.*, **40**, 2735 (1964).

91. J. A. Howe, *J. Chem. Phys.*, **39**, 1362 (1963).

92. A. G. Sharkey, Jr., J. L. Shultz, and R. A. Friedel, "Mass Spectrometric Investigation of Gases from Flash and Laser Irradiation of Coal," 12th annual meeting of the ASTM Committee E-14 on Mass Spectrometry, Montreal, Canada, June 7–12, 1964.

93. D. Lichtman and J. F. Ready, *Phys. Rev. Letters*, **10**, 342 (1963); *Appl. Phys. Letters*, **3**, 115 (1963).

94. C. E. Melton and P. S. Rudolph, *J. Chem. Phys.*, **30**, 847 (1959).

95. P. S. Rudolph and C. E. Melton, *J. Phys. Chem.*, **63**, 916 (1959).

96. C. E. Melton and P. S. Rudolph, *J. Chem. Phys.*, **32**, 1128 (1960).

97. P. Kebarle and E. W. Godbole, *J. Chem. Phys.*, **39**, 1131 (1963).

98. F. H. Field, *J. Am. Chem. Soc.*, **83**, 1523 (1961).

99. S. C. Lind, *The Chemical Effects of Alpha Particles and Electrons*, second edition, Chemical Catalog Co., New York, 1929; S. C. Lind, *Radiation Chemistry of Gases*, A. C. S. Monograph Series No. 151, Reinhold Publishing Corporation, New York, 1961.

100. D. P. Stevenson and D. O. Schissler, "Mass Spectrometry and Radiation Chemistry," in *Actions Chimiques et Biologiques des Radiations*, Cinquieme Serie, M. Haissinsky (ed.), Masson et Cie, Edituers, Paris, 1961, pp. 167–271.

101. S. Wexler and D. C. Hess, *J. Chem. Phys.*, **38**, 2308 (1963); R. H. Schuler and F. A. Stuber, *J. Chem. Phys.*, **40**, 2035 and **41**, 901 (1964).

102. A. H. Snell and F. Pleasonton, *J. Phys. Chem.*, **62**, 1377 (1958).

103. S. Wexler and G. R. Anderson, *J. Chem. Phys.*, **33**, 850 (1960).

104. S. Wexler, *Phys. Rev.*, **93**, 182 (1954).

105. S. Wexler and D. C. Hess, *J. Phys. Chem.*, **62**, 1382 (1958).

106. S. Wexler, G. R. Anderson, and L. A. Singer, *J. Chem. Phys.*, **32**, 417 (1960).

107. T. A. Carlson, *J. Chem. Phys.*, **32**, 1234 (1960).

108. T. A. Carlson and R. M. White, *J. Chem. Phys.*, **36**, 2883 (1962).

109. S. Wexler, *J. Chem. Phys.*, **36**, 1992 (1962).

110. T. A. Carlson and R. M. White, *J. Chem. Phys.*, **38**, 2930 (1963).

111. H. F. Calcote, *Combustion and Flame*, **1**, 385 (1957).

112. A. Fontijn and G. L. Baughman, *J. Chem. Phys.*, **38**, 1784 (1963).

113. F. H. Field and J. L. Franklin, *Electron Impact Phenomena and the Properties of Gaseous Ions*, Academic Press, Inc., Publishers, New York, 1957, p. 281.

114. C. W. Hand and G. B. Kistiakowsky, *J. Chem. Phys.*, **37**, 1239 (1962).

115. K. N. Bascombe, J. A. Green, and T. M. Sugden, "The Ionization Produced by Addition of Acetylene to a Hydrogen-Oxygen-Nitrogen Flame," in *Advances in Mass Spectrometry*, Vol. 2, R. M. Elliott (ed.), Pergamon Press, Oxford, England, 1963, pp. 66–86.

116. G. B. Kistiakowsky and J. V. Michael, *J. Chem. Phys.*, **40**, 1447 (1964).

117. F. H. Field and J. L. Franklin, *loc. cit.*, p. 256.

118. G. Herzberg, *Molecular Spectra and Molecular Structure*. I. *Spectra of Diatomic Molecules*, second edition, D. Van Nostrand Co., Inc., New York, 1950, pp. 518–19.

119. K. B. Wiberg, W. J. Bartley, and F. P. Lossing, *J. Am. Chem. Soc.*, **84**, 3980 (1962).

120. O. Tüxen, *Z. Physik*, **103**, 463 (1936).

121. J. A. Hornbeck and J. P. Molnar, *Phys. Rev.*, **84**, 621 (1951).

122. M. Pahl, *Z. Naturforsch.*, **14A**, 239 (1959).

123. R. Fuchs and W. Kaul, *Z. Naturforsch.*, **15A**, 108 and 326 (1960).

124. C. E. Melton and P. S. Rudolph, *J. Chem. Phys.*, **33**, 1594 (1960).

125. A. Henglein and G. A. Muccini, *Angew. Chem.*, **72**, 630 (1960).

126. F. H. Field and J. L. Franklin, *J. Am. Chem. Soc.*, **83**, 4509 (1961).

127. W. Kaul and R. Taubert, *Z. Naturforsch.*, **17A**, 88 (1962).

128. P. N. Reagan, J. C. Browne, and F. A. Matsen, *Phys. Rev.*, **132**, 304 (1963).

129. M. S. B. Munson, J. L. Franklin, and F. H. Field, *J. Phys. Chem.*, **67**, 1542 (1963).

130. D. S. Hacker and H. Bloomberg, *J. Chem. Phys.*, **39**, 3263 (1963).

131. J. S. Dahler, J. L. Franklin, M. S. B. Munson, and F. H. Field, *J. Chem. Phys.*, **36**, 3332 (1962).

132. M. S. B Munson, F. H. Field, and J. L. Franklin, *J. Chem. Phys.*, **37**, 1790 (1962).

133. C. R. Gatz, R. A. Young, and R. L. Sharpless, *J. Chem. Phys.*, **39**, 1235 (1963),

134. A. J. C. Nicholson, *J. Chem. Phys.*, **39**, 954 (1963).

135. E. Miescher, *Helv. Phys. Acta*, **29**, 135 (1956).

136. W. Paul, H. P. Reinhard, and U. von Zahn, *Z. Physik*, **152**, 143 (1958).

137. W. Paul and H. P. Reinhard, "Electric Mass Spectrometer for Isotope Separation," *Proc. Intern. Symposium Isotope Separation*, Amsterdam, 1957 (published 1958), pp. 640–52.

138. J. W. Linnett, *J. Am. Chem. Soc.*, **83**, 2643 (1961); "The Electronic Structure

of Molecules," Methuen and Co., Ltd., London, 1964; *Am. Scientist*, **52**, 459 (1964).

139. G. N. Lewis, *J. Am. Chem. Soc.*, **38**, 762 (1916).

140. I. Langmuir, *J. Am. Chem. Soc.*, **38**, 2221 (1916).

141. M. H. Studier and E. N. Sloth, *J. Phys. Chem.*, **67**, 925 (1963).

142. M. H. Studier and E. N. Sloth, "Mass Spectrometric Studies of Noble Gas Compounds," 11th annual meeting of the ASTM Committee E-14 on Mass Spectrometry, San Francisco, Calif, May 19–24, 1963.

143. H. J. Svec and G. D. Flesch, *Science*, **142**, 954 (1963).

144. V. L. Tal'roze and A. K. Lyubimova, *Doklady Akad. Nauk S.S.S.R.*, **86**, 909 (1952).

145. F. H. Field, J. L. Franklin, and F. W. Lampe, *J. Am. Chem. Soc.*, **79**, 2419 (1957).

146. A. Maschke, B. S. Shapiro and F. W. Lampe, *J. Am. Chem. Soc.*, **85**, 1876 (1963); *ibid.*, **86**, 1929 (1964).

147. M. S. B. Munson and J. L. Franklin, *J. Phys. Chem.*, **68**, 3191 (1964).

148. J. H. Weber, "Mass Spectrometric Investigations of Low Molecular Weight Esters," *Doctoral Dissertation*, Kansas State University, Manhattan, Kansas, 1965.

149. S. Wexler, *J. Chem. Phys.*, **41**, 2781 (1964).

150. W. J. Miller and H. F. Calcote, *J. Chem. Phys.*, **41**, 4001 (1964).

APPENDIX I

TABLE OF NUCLIDIC MASSES AND ISOTOPE RELATIVE ABUNDANCES FOR NATURALLY OCCURING ISOTOPES

Atomic weights are based on the carbon-12 = 12.000000 scale, as reported by A. E. Cameron and E. Wichers, *J. Am. Chem. Soc.*, **84**, 4175 (1962). Many of the nuclidic masses are based on the carbon-12 = 12.000000 scale from the paper by F. Everling, L. A. König, J. H. E. Mattauch, and A.H. Wapstra, *Nuclear Physics*, **18**, 529 (1960); however, some are from the paper by V. B. Bhanot, W. H. Johnson, Jr., and A. O. Nier, *Phys. Rev.*, **120**, 235 (1960), and a few (Tm, Yb, and Lu) of the masses are based on the recent paper by R. A. Demirkhanov, V. V. Dorokhov, and M. I. Dzkuya, *Doklady Akad. Nauk S.S.S.R.*, **146**, 72 (1962). The data for the nuclidic masses of Ga through Xe are from the recent paper by R. R. Ries, R. A. Damerow, and W. H. Johnson, Jr., *Phys. Rev.*, **132**, 1662 and 1673 (1963). Isotopic abundances are based upon many different and varied reports in the literature, but are commonly those referred to in the report by Cameron and Wichers, referred to above.

Element	Symbol	Atomic Weight	Atomic Number	Mass Number	Nuclidic Mass	Relative Abundance
Hydrogen	H	1.00797	1	1	1.007825	99.9855
				2	2.014102	0.0145
Helium	He	4.0026	2	3	3.016030	(tr)
				4	4.002604	≐100.
Lithium	Li	6.939	3	6	6.015126	7.50
				7	7.016005	92.50
Beryllium	Be	9.0122	4	9	9.012186	100.
Boron	B	10.811	5	10	10.012939	19.91
				11	11.009305	80.09
Carbon	C	12.01115	6	12	12.000000(Standard)	98.888
				13	13.003355	1.112
Nitrogen	N	14.0067	7	14	14.003073	99.633
				15	15.000108	0.367
Oxygen	O	15.9994	8	16	15.994914	99.759
				17	16.999134	0.0374
				18	17.999160	0.2039
Fluorine	F	18.9984	9	19	18.998405	100.
Neon	Ne	20.183	10	20	19.992440	90.92
				21	20.993849	0.257
				22	21.991384	8.82
Sodium	Na	22.9898	11	23	22.989773	100.
Magnesium	Mg	24.312	12	24	23.985045	78.80
				25	24.985840	10.15
				26	25.982591	11.05
Aluminum	Al	26.9815	13	27	26.981535	100.
Silicon	Si	28.086	14	28	27.976927	92.21
				29	28.976491	4.70
				30	29.973761	3.09
Phosphorus	P	30.9738	15	31	30.973768	100.
Sulfur	S	32.064	16	32	31.972074	95.018
				33	32.971460	0.750
				34	33.967864	4.215
				36	35.967091	0.017
Chlorine	Cl	35.453	17	35	34.968853	75.7705
				37	36.965903	24.2295
Argon	Ar	39.948	18	36	35.967548	0.337
				38	37.962724	0.063
				40	39.962384	99.600
Potassium	K	39.102	19	39	38.963714	93.083
				40	39.964008	0.012
				41	40.961835	6.905
Calcium	Ca	40.08	20	40	39.962589	96.97
				42	41.958628	0.64
				43	42.958780	0.145
				44	43.955490	2.06
				46	45.953689	0.003
				48	47.952519	0.185

Element	Symbol	Atomic Weight	Atomic Number	Mass Number	Nuclidic Mass	Relative Abundance
Scandium	Sc	44.956	21	45	44.955919	≐100.
Titantium	Ti	47.90	22	46	45.952633	7.99
				47	46.951758	7.32
				48	47.947948	73.98
				49	48.947867	5.46
				50	49.944789	5.25
Vanadium	V	50.942	23	50	49.947165	0.24
				51	50.943978	99.76
Chromium	Cr	51.996	24	50	49.946051	4.352
				52	51.940514	83.764
				53	52.940651	9.509
				54	53.938879	2.375
Manganese	Mn	54.9380	25	55	54.938054	100.
Iron	Fe	55.847	26	54	53.939621	5.82
				56	55.934932	91.66
				57	56.935394	2.19
				58	57.933272	0.33
Cobalt	Co	58.9332	27	59	58.933189	100.
Nickel	Ni	58.71	28	58	57.935342	67.77
				60	59.930783	26.16
				61	60.931049	1.25
				62	61.928345	3.66
				64	63.927959	1.16
Copper	Cu	63.54	29	63	62.929594	69.1
				65	64.927786	30.9
Zinc	Zn	65.37	30	64	63.929145	48.89
				66	65.926048	27.81
				67	66.927149	4.11
				68	67.924865	18.57
				70	69.925348	0.62
Gallium	Ga	69.72	31	69	68.925569	60.16
				71	70.924701	39.84
Germanium	Ge	72.59	32	70	69.924247	20.51
				72	71.922075	27.40
				73	72.923457	7.76
				74	73.921177	36.56
				76	75.921402	7.77
Arsenic	As	74.9216	33	75	74.921591	100.
Selenium	Se	78.96	34	74	73.922476	0.87
				76	75.919199	9.02
				77	76.919912	7.58
				78	77.917305	23.52
				80	79.916529	49.82
				82	81.916702	9.19

Element	Symbol	Atomic Weight	Atomic Number	Mass Number	Nuclidic Mass	Relative Abundance
Bromine	Br	79.909	35	79	78.918328	50.537
				81	80.916287	49.463
Krypton	Kr	83.80	36	78	77.920364	0.354
				80	79.916372	2.27
				82	81.913477	11.56
				83	82.914125	11.55
				84	83.911497	56.90
				86	85.910609	17.37
Rubidium	Rb	85.47	37	85	84.911793	72.15
				87	86.909183	27.85
Strontium	Sr	87.62	38	84	83.913425	0.560
				86	85.909278	9.870
				87	86.908882	7.035
				88	87.905634	82.535
Yttrium	Y	88.905	39	89	88.905876	100.
Zirconium	Zr	91.22	40	90	89.904696	51.46
				91	90.905631	11.23
				92	91.905028	17.11
				94	93.906317	17.40
				96	95.908268	2.80
Niobium	Nb	92.906	41	93	92.906375	100.
Molybdenum	Mo	95.94	42	92	91.906807	15.86
				94	93.905086	9.12
				95	94.905835	15.70
				96	95.904670	16.50
				97	96.906014	9.45
				98	97.905401	23.75
				100	99.907464	9.62
Ruthenium	Ru	101.07	44	96	95.907592	5.51
				98	97.905282	1.87
				99	98.905928	12.72
				100	99.904210	12.62
				101	100.905572	17.07
				102	101.904343	31.63
				104	103.905426	18.58
Rhodium	Rh	102.905	45	103	102.905509	100.
Palladium	Pd	106.4	46	102	101.905624	0.96
				104	103.903985	10.97
				105	104.905066	22.23
				106	105.903483	27.33
				108	107.903883	26.70
				110	109.905157	11.81
Silver	Ag	107.870	47	107	106.905085	51.817
				109	108.904749	48.183

Element	Symbol	Atomic Weight	Atomic Number	Mass Number	Nuclidic Mass	Relative Abundance
Cadmium	Cd	112.40	48	106	105.906458	1.215
				108	107.904181	0.875
				110	109.902998	12.39
				111	110.904184	12.75
				112	111.902752	24.07
				113	112.904401	12.26
				114	113.903357	28.86
				116	115.904760	7.58
Indium	In	114.82	49	113	112.904108	4.28
				115	114.903863	95.72
Tin	Sn	118.69	50	112	111.904812	0.95
				114	113.902763	0.65
				115	114.903349	0.34
				116	115.901737	14.24
				117	116.902944	7.57
				118	117.901601	24.01
				119	118.903298	8.58
				120	119.902186	32.97
				122	121.903428	4.71
				124	123.905264	5.98
Antimony	Sb	121.75	51	121	120.903811	57.25
				123	122.904214	42.75
Tellurium	Te	127.60	52	120	119.904017	0.089
				122	121.903045	2.46
				123	122.904256	0.87
				124	123.902814	4.61
				125	124.904438	6.99
				126	125.903326	18.71
				128	127.904486	31.79
				130	129.906225	34.48
Iodine	I	126.9044	53	127	126.904471	100.
Xenon	Xe	131.30	54	124	123.906120	0.096
				126	125.904303	0.090
				128	127.903529	1.919
				129	128.904779	26.44
				130	129.903503	4.08
				131	130.905080	21.18
				132	131.904156	26.89
				134	133.905390	10.44
				136	135.907213	8.87
Cesium	Cs	132.905	55	133	132.905090	100.
Barium	Ba	137.34	56	130	129.906247	0.101
				132	131.905120	0.097
				134	133.904310	2.42
				135	134.905570	6.59
				136	135.904360	7.81
				137	136.905560	11.32
				138	137.905010	71.66

Element	Symbol	Atomic Weight	Atomic Number	Mass Number	Nuclidic Mass	Relative Abundance
Lanthanum	La	138.91	57	138	137.906810	0.089
				139	138.906060	99.911
Cerium	Ce	140.12	58	136	135.907100	0.193
				138	137.905720	0.250
				140	139.905280	88.48
				142	141.909040	11.07
Praseodymium	Pr	140.907	59	141	140.907390	100.
Neodymium	Nd	144.24	60	142	141.907478	27.11
				143	142.909620	12.17
				144	143.909900	23.85
				145	144.912160	8.30
				146	145.912690	17.22
				148	147.916480	5.73
				150	149.920710	5.62
Samarium	Sm	150.35	62	144	143.911660	3.15
				147	146.914490	15.09
				148	147.914425	11.35
				149	148.916810	13.96
				150	149.916910	7.47
				152	151.919370	26.55
				154	153.921940	22.43
Europium	Eu	151.96	63	151	150.919550	47.82
				153	152.920980	52.18
Gadolinium	Gd	157.25	64	152	151.919430	0.205
				154	153.920540	2.23
				155	154.922320	15.1
				156	155.921850	20.6
				157	156.923690	15.7
				158	157.923840	24.5
				160	159.926830	21.6
Terbium	Tb	158.924	65	159	158.924300	100.
Dysprosium	Dy	162.50	66	156	155.923820	0.052
				158	157.924020	0.090
				160	159.924880	2.294
				161	160.926610	18.88
				162	161.926450	25.53
				163	162.928350	24.97
				164	163.928780	28.18
Holmium	Ho	164.930	67	165	164.930270	100.
Erbium	Er	167.26	68	162	161.928740	0.136
				164	163.929240	1.56
				166	165.930400	33.41
				167	166.932140	22.94
				168	167.932460	27.07
				170	169.935580	14.88
Thulium	Tm	168.934	69	169	168.934220	100.

Element	Symbol	Atomic Weight	Atomic Number	Mass Number	Nuclidic Mass	Relative Abundance
Ytterbium	Yb	173.04	70	168	167.934100	0.135
				170	169.935030	3.03
				171	170.936275	14.31
				172	171.936400	21.82
				173	172.938200	16.135
				174	173.938830	31.84
				176	175.942690	12.73
Lutetium	Lu	174.97	71	175	174.940760	97.41
				176	175.942740	2.59
Hafnium	Hf	178.49	72	174	173.940300	0.18
				176	175.941790	5.20
				177	176.943630	18.50
				178	177.944122	27.13
				179	178.946230	13.75
				180	179.947000	35.24
Tantalum	Ta	180.948	73	180	179.947440	0.012
				181	180.947865	99.988
Tungsten	W	183.85	74	180	179.946660	0.14
				182	181.948160	26.29
				183	182.950130	14.31
				184	183.950780	30.66
				186	185.954130	28.60
Rhenium	Re	186.2	75	185	184.952600	37.07
				187	186.955335	62.93
Osmium	Os	190.2	76	184	183.952080	0.02
				186	185.953460	1.59
				187	186.955280	1.64
				188	187.955285	13.3
				189	188.957510	16.1
				190	189.957725	26.4
				192	191.960575	41.0
Iridium	Ir	192.2	77	191	190.960480	38.5
				193	192.962845	61.5
Platinum	Pt	195.09	78	190	189.959680	0.013
				192	191.960995	0.78
				194	193.962535	32.9
				195	194.964660	33.8
				196	195.964820	25.2
				198	197.967800	7.19
Gold	Au	196.967	79	197	196.966610	100.
Mercury	Hg	200.59	80	196	195.965829	0.146
				198	197.966769	10.02
				199	198.968256	16.84
				200	199.968344	23.13
				201	200.970315	13.22
				202	201.970630	29.80
				204	203.973482	6.85

Element	Symbol	Atomic Weight	Atomic Number	Mass Number	Nuclidic Mass	Relative Abundance
Thallium	Tl	204.37	81	203	202.972331	29.50
				205	204.974462	70.50
Lead	Pb	207.19	82	204	204.973079	1.40
				206	205.974462	25.2
				207	206.975898	21.7
				208	207.976644	51.7
Bismuth	Bi	208.980	83	209	208.980417	100.
Thorium	Th	232.038	90	232	232.038138	100.
Uranium	U	238.03	92	234	234.040875	0.0056
				235	235.043900	0.7205
				238	238.050734	99.274

APPENDIX II

NOMOGRAMS OF METASTABLE TRANSITIONS

This nomogram represents Equation (6–10), $m^* = m^2/m_0$, where m^* is the apparent mass observed due to the metastable transition of m_0 to give m near the exit of the ion accelerating region. In the illustration, *n*-butane parent ions ($m/e = 58$) undergo a metastable transition to give $m/e = 42$ ions, and this is observed by a broad, low-intensity peak at an apparent mass of

$$m^* = (42)^2/(58) = 30.4 \text{ amu}$$

in the mass spectrum of *n*-butane.

The construction of the nomogram is simple. Use semi-logarithmic graph paper (linear abscissa, logarithmic ordinate) and draw three vertical lines. The distance between the first and second lines is the same as the distance between the second and third lines. The line at the left is m_0, the center is m, and the line at the right is m^*. A straight line through m_0 and m^* will determine the product ion of the metastable transition. Choice of the scale on the semi-logarithmic paper allows one to expand or contract the nomogram to suit any particular study.

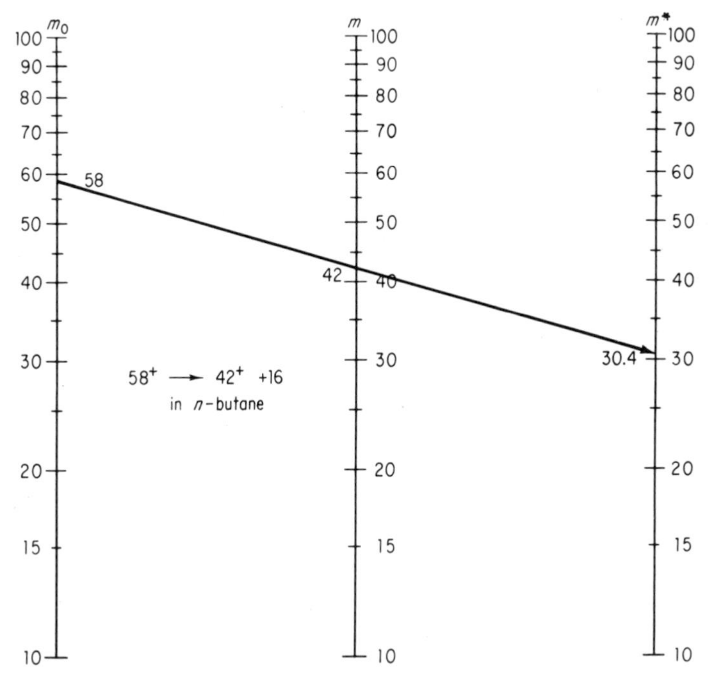

Nomogram of metastable transitions.

APPENDIX III

TOTAL IONIZATION CROSS SECTIONS

TOTAL IONIZATION CROSS SECTIONS FOR 75 ev ELECTRONS, ${}_{75}Q_i$ (IN UNITS OF 10^{-16} cm^2)[a]

Substance	Q_i	Substance	Q_i	Substance	Q_i
He	0.38	C_3H_6	9.73	C_7H_{16}	30.0
Ne	0.62	Cyclo-C_3H_6	10.8	CH_3Cl	9.46
Ar	3.52	C_3H_8	11.1	C_2H_5Cl	12.3
Kr	5.29	*i*-C_4H_8	12.9	CH_3Br	11.2
Xe	7.31	*i*-C_4H_{10}	14.4	CH_3I	12.9
Hg	4.00	*n*-C_4H_{10}	14.1	$\underline{CH_2CH_2O}$	7.55
H_2	1.01	*i*-C_5H_{10}	17.5	CH_3CHO	7.95
N_2	2.75	Cyclo-C_5H_{10}	17.3	C_3H_6O	11.7
O_2	2.55	*n*-C_5H_{12}	18.6	$(CH_3)_2O$	12.8
NO	3.06	*i*-C_5H_{12}	18.0	$(CH_3)_2CO$	12.1
CO	2.99	*neo*-C_5H_{12}	16.9	NH_3	3.54
CO_2	4.31	C_6H_6	16.9	PH_3	11.3
H_2O	2.96	Cyclo-C_6H_8	17.9	H_2S	5.42
N_2O	6.45	Cyclo-C_6H_{10}	19.1	HCl	4.30
CH_4	4.30	1,5-C_6H_{10}	15.8	HCN	6.80
C_2H_2	4.98	Cyclo-C_6H_{12}	23.6	$(CN)_2$	10.8
C_2H_4	6.66	1-C_6H_{12}	20.0	CS_2	14.0
C_2H_6	8.35	*n*-C_6H_{14}	22.3		

[a] J. W. Otvos and D. P. Stevenson, *J. Am. Chem. Soc.*, **78**, 546 (1956); F. W. Lampe, J. L. Franklin, and F. H. Field, *J. Am. Chem. Soc.*, **79**, 6129 (1957); H. S. W. Massey and E. H. S. Burhop, *Electronic and Ionic Impact Phenomenon*, Oxford at the University Press, London, 1952. See also G. DeMaria, G. Balducci, and L. Malaspina, *Ann. Chim.* (*Rome*), **53** (7), 1039 (1963).

APPENDIX IV

IONIZATION POTENTIALS

Ionization potentials for many different atoms, molecules, and radicals are summarized in this appendix. The values listed are believed to be the most reliable values presently available. They have been drawn from an examination of over 800 original literature reports. Several methods of measurement have been employed by the original workers, and for the convenience of the readers, the specific method used for a given compound is listed after the chosen value of the ionization potential (in electron volts) for that molecule. The abbreviations used to indicate the method employed are as follows:

E.I. = Electron impact, most commonly with mass analysis,
P.I. = Photoionization, in some cases with mass analysis,
S. = Vacuum ultraviolet spectroscopy,
S.I. = Surface ionization, mass spectrometric, and
U.V. = Ultraviolet charge transfer spectra.

There are numerous molecules for which ionization potentials have been calculated theoretically (but for which there are yet no experimental determinations) in the literature. These calculated values have not been included in this tabulation, although in some instances they were used to guide the author in his choice of the "best" experimental value.

It is beyond the intended scope of this book to list in this appendix all of the determinations of ionization potentials made on the various molecules. These tables do not include literature references. For those who might wish to critically examine any given value, the entire literature should be studied. The author's *Tables of Ionization Potentials* and Field and Franklin's book provides starting points for such a study.

A. ATOMIC IONIZATION POTENTIALS

Atom	Stage	I.P.	Ref.
Actinium	(I)	6.9	S.
	(II)	12.1	S.
	(III)	20.	S.
Aluminum	(I)	5.984	S.
	(II)	18.823	S.
	(III)	28.44	S.
	(IV)	119.96	S.
	(V)	153.77	S.
	(VI)	190.42	S.
	(VII)	241.38	S.
	(VIII)	284.53	S.
	(IX)	330.1	S.
	(X)	398.5	S.
	(XI)	441.9	S.
	(XII)	2085.5	S.
Americium	(I)	6.0	S.
Antimony	(I)	8.639	S.
	(II)	16.5	S.
	(III)	25.3	S.
	(IV)	44.1	S.
	(V)	56.	S.
	(VI)	108.	S.
Argon	(I)	15.755	S.
	(II)	27.62	S.
	(III)	40.90	S.
	(IV)	59.79	S.
	(V)	75.0	S.
	(VI)	91.3	S.
	(VII)	124.0	S.
	(VIII)	143.46	S.
	(IX)	422.6	S.
Arsenic	(I)	9.81	S.
	(II)	18.63	S.
	(III)	28.34	S.
	(IV)	50.1	S.
	(V)	62.6	S.
	(VI)	127.5	S.
Astatine	(I)	9.5	S.
Barium	(I)	5.210	S.
	(II)	10.001	S.
	(III)	35.5	S.
Beryllium	(I)	9.320	S.
	(II)	18.206	S.
	(III)	153.850	S.
	(IV)	217.657	S.
Bismuth	(I)	7.287	S.
	(II)	16.68	S.
	(III)	25.56	S.
	(IV)	45.3	S.
	(V)	56.0	S.
	(VI)	88.3	S.
Boron	(I)	8.296	S.
	(II)	25.149	S.
	(III)	37.920	S.
	(IV)	259.298	S.
	(V)	340.127	S.
Bromine	(I)	11.84	S.
	(II)	21.6	S.
	(III)	35.9	S.
	(IV)	47.3	S.
	(V)	59.7	S.
	(VI)	88.6	S.
	(VII)	103.	S.
	(VIII)	193.	S.
Cadmium	(I)	8.991	S.
	(II)	16.904	S.
	(III)	37.47	S.
Calcium	(I)	6.111	S.
	(II)	11.868	S.
	(III)	51.21	S.
	(IV)	67.	S.
	(V)	84.39	S.
	(VI)	109.	S.
	(VII)	128.	S.
	(VIII)	143.3	S.
	(IX)	188.	S.
	(X)	211.3	S.
	(XI)	591.8	S.
	(XII)	655.	S.

A. ATOMIC IONIZATION POTENTIALS (CONT.)

Carbon (I)	11.256	S.
(II)	24.376	S.
(III)	47.871	S.
(IV)	64.476	S.
(V)	391.986	S.
(VI)	489.84	S.
Cerium (I)	5.60	S.I.
(II)	12.3	S.
(III)	20.	S.
(IV)	33.3	S.
Cesium (I)	3.893	S.
(II)	25.1	S.
(III)	35.	S.
Chlorine (I)	13.01	S.
(II)	23.80	S.
(III)	39.90	S.
(IV)	53.5	S.
(V)	67.80	S.
(VI)	96.7	S.
(VII)	114.27	S.
(VIII)	348.3	S.
(IX)	400.7	S.
(X)	455.3	S.
(XI)	530.9	S.
Chromium (I)	6.764	S.
(II)	16.49	S.
(III)	30.95	S.
(IV)	50.	S.
(V)	73.	S.
(VI)	91.	S.
(VII)	161.	S.
(VIII)	185.	S.
(IX)	210.	S.
(X)	243.	S.
(XIII)	355.	S.
(XIV)	384.	S.
(XV)	1013.	S.
Cobalt (I)	7.86	S.
(II)	17.05	S.
(III)	33.49	S.
(IV)	83.1	S.
(XI)	305.	S.
(XVI)	512.	S.
(XVII)	547.	S.
(XVIII)	1403.	S.
Copper (I)	7.724	S.
(II)	20.29	S.
(III)	36.83	S.
(XIX)	671.	S.
Dysprosium (I)	6.8	S.
Erbium (I)	6.08	S.I.
Europium (I)	5.67	S.
(II)	11.24	S.
Fluorine (I)	17.418	S.
(II)	34.98	S.
(III)	62.646	S.
(IV)	87.14	S.
(V)	114.214	S.
(VI)	157.117	S.
(VII)	185.139	S.
(VIII)	953.60	S.
Francium (I)	4.0	S.
Gadolinium (I)	6.16	S.
(II)	12.	S.
Gallium (I)	6.00	S.
(II)	20.57	S.
(III)	30.70	S.
(IV)	64.2	S.
Germanium (I)	7.88	S.
(II)	15.93	S.
(III)	34.21	S.
(IV)	44.7	S.
(V)	93.4	S.
Gold (I)	9.22	S.
(II)	20.5	S.
Hafnium (I)	7.	S.
(II)	14.9	S.
(III)	23.2	S.
(IV)	33.30	S.
Helium (I)	24.481	S.
(II)	54.403	S.
Hydrogen (I)	13.595	S.
Indium (I)	5.785	S.
(II)	18.86	S.
(III)	28.03	S.
(IV)	54.4	S.
Iodine (I)	10.454	S.
(II)	19.13	S.
(VIII)	170.	S.
Iridium (I)	9.	S.

A. ATOMIC IONIZATION POTENTIALS (CONT.)

Element	Value	Method
Iron (I)	7.87	S.
(II)	16.18	S.
(III)	30.643	S.
(IV)	56.8	S.
(VIII)	151.	S.
(IX)	235.	S.
(X)	262.	S.
(XI)	290.	S.
(XIII)	355.	S.
(XIV)	390.	S.
(XV)	457.	S.
(XVI)	489.	S.
(XVII)	1266.	S.
Krypton (I)	13.996	S.
(II)	24.56	S.
(III)	36.9	S.
(IV)	43.5	E.I.
(V)	63.	E.I.
(VI)	94.	E.I.
Lanthanum (I)	5.61	S.
(II)	11.43	S.
(III)	19.17	S.
Lead (I)	7.415	S.
(II)	15.028	S.
(III)	31.93	S.
(IV)	42.31	S.
(V)	68.8	S.
Lithium (I)	5.390	S.
(II)	75.619	S.
(III)	122.419	S.
Lutetium (II)	14.7	S.
Magnesium (I)	7.644	S.
(II)	15.031	S.
(III)	80.14	S.
(IV)	109.29	S.
(V)	141.23	S.
(VI)	186.49	S.
(VII)	224.90	S.
(VIII)	265.957	S.
(IX)	327.90	S.
(X)	367.36	S.
(XI)	1761.2	S.
Manganese (I)	7.432	S.
(II)	15.636	S.
(III)	33.69	S.
(IV)	52.	S.
(V)	76.	S.
(VII)	119.	S.
(VIII)	196.	S.
(IX)	222.	S.
(X)	248.	S.
(XI)	284.	S.
(XIV)	404.	S.
(XV)	435.	S.
(XVI)	1136.	S.
Mercury (I)	10.43	S.
(II)	18.751	S.
(III)	34.2	S.
(IV)	49.5	E.I.
(V)	45. (?)	E.I.
(VI)	67.	E.I.
Molybdenum (I)	7.10	S.
(II)	16.15	S.
(III)	27.13	S.
(IV)	46.4	S.
(V)	61.2	S.
(VI)	68.	S.
(VII)	126.	S.
(VIII)	153.	S.
Neodymium (I)	5.51	S.I.
Neon (I)	21.559	S.
(II)	41.07	S.
(III)	63.5	S.
(IV)	97.02	S.
(V)	126.3	S.
(VI)	157.91	S.
Nickel (I)	7.633	S.
(II)	18.15	S.
(III)	35.16	S.
(XII)	350.	S.
(XV)	455.	S.
(XVIII)	607.	S.
Niobium (I)	6.88	S.
(II)	14.32	S.
(III)	25.04	S.
(IV)	38.3	S.
(V)	50.	S.
(VI)	103.	S.
(VII)	125.	S.
Nitrogen (I)	14.53	S.
(II)	29.593	S.
(III)	47.426	S.

A. ATOMIC IONIZATION POTENTIALS (CONT.)

Element	Ion	Potential	Ref.
	(IV)	77.450	S.
	(V)	97.863	S.
	(VI)	551.925	S.
	(VII)	666.83	S.
Osmium	(I)	8.5	S.
	(II)	17.	S.
Oxygen	(I)	13.614	S.
	(II)	35.108	S.
	(III)	54.886	S.
	(IV)	77.394	S.
	(V)	113.873	S.
	(VI)	138.080	S.
	(VII)	739.114	S.
	(VIII)	871.12	S.
Palladium	(I)	8.33	S.
	(II)	19.42	S.
	(III)	32.92	S.
Phosphorus	(I)	10.484	S.
	(II)	19.72	S.
	(III)	30.156	S.
	(IV)	51.354	S.
	(V)	65.007	S.
	(VI)	220.414	S.
	(VII)	263.31	S.
	(VIII)	309.26	S.
	(IX)	371.6	S.
	(X)	424.3	S.
	(XI)	479.4	S.
	(XII)	560.3	S.
	(XIII)	611.4	S.
Platinum	(I)	9.0	S.
	(II)	18.56	S.
Plutonium	(I)	5.1	S.
Polonium	(I)	8.43	S.
Potassium	(I)	4.339	S.
	(II)	31.81	S.
	(III)	46.	S.
	(IV)	60.90	S.
	(V)	82.6	S.
	(VI)	99.7	S.
	(VII)	118.	S.
	(VIII)	155.	S.
	(IX)	175.94	S.
	(X)	503.8	S.
Praesodymium	(I)	5.46	S.I.
Radium	(I)	5.277	S.
	(II)	10.144	S.
Radon	(I)	10.746	S.
Rhenium	(I)	7.87	S.
	(II)	16.6	S.
Rhodium	(I)	7.46	S.
	(II)	18.07	S.
	(III)	31.05	S.
Rubidium	(I)	4.176	S.
	(II)	27.5	S.
	(III)	40.	S.
	(X)	277.	S.
Ruthenium	(I)	7.364	S.
	(II)	16.76	S.
	(III)	28.46	S.
Samarium	(I)	5.6	S.
	(II)	11.2	S.
Scandium	(I)	6.54	S.
	(II)	12.80	S.
	(III)	24.75	S.
	(IV)	73.9	S.
	(V)	92.	S.
	(VI)	111.	S.
	(VII)	139.	S.
	(VIII)	159.	S.
	(IX)	180.	S.
	(X)	226.	S.
	(XI)	250.	S.
	(XII)	687.	S.
Selenium	(I)	9.75	S.
	(II)	21.5	S.
	(III)	32.	S.
	(IV)	43.	S.
	(V)	68.	S.
	(VI)	82.	S.
	(VII)	155.	S.
Silicon	(I)	8.149	S.
	(II)	16.34	S.
	(III)	33.488	S.
	(IV)	45.13	S.
	(V)	166.73	S.
	(VI)	205.11	S.
	(VII)	246.41	S.
	(VIII)	303.07	S.
	(IX)	350.96	S.

A. ATOMIC IONIZATION POTENTIALS (CONT.)

Element		
(X)	401.3	S.
(XI)	476.0	S.
(XII)	523.2	S.
Silver (I)	7.574	S.
(II)	21.48	S.
(III)	34.82	S.
Sodium (I)	5.138	S.
(II)	47.29	S.
(III)	71.715	S.
(IV)	98.88	S.
(V)	138.37	S.
(VI)	172.09	S.
(VII)	208.444	S.
(VIII)	264.155	S.
(IX)	299.78	S.
Strontium (I)	5.692	S.
(II)	11.027	S.
(IV)	57.	S.
(XI)	324.	S.
Sulfur (I)	10.357	S.
(II)	23.4	S.
(III)	35.0	S.
(IV)	47.29	S.
(V)	72.5	S.
(VI)	88.029	S.
(VII)	280.99	S.
(VIII)	328.80	S.
(IX)	378.95	S.
(X)	447.	S.
Tantalum (I)	7.88	S.
(II)	16.2	S.
Technetium (I)	7.28	S.
(II)	15.26	S.
(III)	29.54	S.
Tellurium (I)	9.01	S.
(II)	18.6	S.
(III)	31.	S.
(IV)	38.	S.
(V)	60.	S.
(VI)	72.	S.
(VII)	137.	S.
Terbium (I)	5.98	S.I.
Thallium (I)	6.106	S.
(II)	20.42	S.
(III)	29.8	S.
(IV)	50.7	S.
Thorium (I)	6.95	S.I.
(IV)	29.38	S.
Thulium (I)	5.81	S.
Tin (I)	7.342	S.
(II)	14.628	S.
(III)	30.49	S.
(IV)	40.72	S.
(V)	72.3	S.
Titantium (I)	6.82	S.
(II)	13.57	S.
(III)	27.47	S.
(IV)	43.24	S.
(V)	99.8	S.
(VI)	120.	S.
(VII)	141.	S.
(VIII)	172.	S.
(IX)	193.	S.
(X)	217.	S.
(XI)	266.	S.
(XII)	291.	S.
(XIII)	788.	S.
Tungsten (I)	7.98	S.
(II)	17.7	S.
Uranium (I)	6.08	S.I.
Vanadium (I)	6.74	S.
(II)	14.65	S.
(III)	29.31	S.
(IV)	48.	S.
(V)	65.	S.
(VI)	129.	S.
(VII)	151.	S.
(VIII)	174.	S.
(IX)	205.	S.
(XII)	309.	S.
(XIII)	336.	S.
(XIV)	897.	S.
Xenon (I)	12.127	S.
(II)	21.2	E.I.
(III)	31.3	E.I.
(IV)	42.	E.I.
(V)	53.	E.I.
(VI)	58.	E.I.
(VII)	135.	E.I.
Ytterbium (I)	6.2	S.
(II)	12.10	S.
Yttrium (I)	6.38	S.

A. ATOMIC IONIZATION POTENTIALS (CONT.)

(II)	12.23	S.
(III)	20.5	S.
(V)	77.	S.
(XII)	374.	S.
Zinc (I)	9.391	S.
(II)	17.96	S.
(III)	39.70	S.
Zirconium (I)	6.84	S.
(II)	13.13	S.
(III)	22.98	S.
(IV)	34.33	S.
(VI)	99.	S.

B. MOLECULAR IONIZATION POTENTIALS

Acetamide	9.71	P.I.
Acetic acid	10.35	P.I.
Acetic acid-d_3	10.71	E.I.
Acetophenone	9.27	P.I.
Acetyl bromide	10.55	P.I.
Acetyl chloride	11.02	P.I.
Acridine	7.78	P.I.
Acrylonitrile	10.91	P.I.
Allyl alcohol	9.67	P.I.
Allylamine	9.6	E.I.
Aluminum monofluoride	9.5	E.I.
Aluminum monoxide	9.5	E.I.
Aluminum tribromide	12.2	E.I.
Aluminum trichloride	12.8	E.I.
α-aminonaphthalene	7.30	P.I.
β-aminonaphthalene	7.25	P.I.
4-aminopyridine	8.97	E.I.
2-aminotropone	9.43	E.I.
Ammonia (I)	10.154	P.I.
(II)	23.5	E.I.
Ammonia-d_2	11.47	E.I.
Ammonia-d_3	11.52	E.I.
Ammonium hydroxide	10.8	E.I.
i-amylamine	9.5	E.I.
N-*n*-amylaniline	7.5	U.V.
Anabasine	8.70	E.I.
Aniline	7.70	P.I.
p-anisidine	7.82	E.I.
Anisole	8.22	P.I.
Anthracene	7.23	S.
Anthraquinone	9.34	P.I.
Antimony (Sb_2)	9.5	E.I.
Antimony (Sb_4)	9.1	E.I.
Antimony monochloride	10.9	E.I.
Antimony trichloride	11.4	E.I.
Arsenic (As_2)	11.0	E.I.
Arsenic (As_3)	10.8	E.I.
Arsenic (As_4)	8.9	E.I.
Arsenic dichloride	8.4	E.I.
Arsenic trichloride	11.7	E.I.
Arsenic trimethyl	8.3	E.I.
Arsenic triphosphide	10.3	E.I.
Arsine	10.6	E.I.
Azacyclobutane	8.9	E.I.
Barium oxide	6.0	E.I.
Benzaldehyde	9.53	P.I.
Benz(a)anthracene	7.53	E.I.
Benzene	9.245	P.I.
Benzene-d_1 (I)	9.44	E.I.
(II)	16.6	E.I.
(III)	18.	E.I.
Benzene-d_6	9.251	S.
Benzonitrile	9.71	P.I.
Benzo(c)phenanthrene	8.40	E.I.
Benzophenone	9.45	P.I.
Benzoyl chloride	10.6	E.I.
Benzoyl fluoride	10.6	E.I.
Benzylamine	7.56	P.I.
Benzylmethyl ether	8.85	P.I.
Benzyne	9.75	E.I.
Bicyclo(2.2.1)-heptadiene	8.60	E.I.
Bis-(*n*-butyl) amine	7.69	P.I.
Bis-(2-chloroethyl) ether	9.85	P.I.
Biscyclopentadienyl chromium	6.91	E.I.
Biscyclopentadienyl cobalt	6.2	E.I.
Biscyclopentadienyl iron	7.05	E.I.
Biscyclopentadienyl manganese	7.25	E.I.
Biscyclopentadienyl nickel	7.06	E.I.
Biscyclopentadienyl vanadium	7.56	E.I.
Bis(*p*-methylphenyl) amine	7.8	E.I.
Bismuth (Bi_2)	8.	E.I.
Bismuth monosulfide	8.	E.I.
Bis-(*n*-propyl) amine	7.84	P.I.
Bis-(*i*-propyl) amine	7.73	P.I.
Bis(trifluoromethyl) arsine	10.9	E.I.
Bis(trifluoromethyl) chloroarsine	11.0	E.I.
Bis(trifluoromethyl) methylarsine	10.5	E.I.
Borazine	10.2	E.I.
Boric oxide	13.2	E.I.
Borine	10.5	E.I.
Boron (B_2)	12.06	E.I.
Boron dibromide	7.06	E.I.
Boron dichloride	7.20	E.I.
Boron diethyl	5.98	E.I.
Boron dihydride	8.12	E.I.
Boron diiodide	7.13	E.I.
Boron dimethyl	6.44	E.I.
Boron monobromide	9.25	E.I.
Boron monochloride	10.44	E.I.
Boron monoethyl	8.73	E.I.
Boron monohydride	10.06	E.I.
Boron monoiodide	8.96	E.I.

B. MOLECULAR IONIZATION POTENTIALS (CONT.)

Boron monomethyl	9.28	E.I.
Boron monoxide	7.0	S.
Boron tribromide	9.7	E.I.
Boron trichloride	12.0	E.I.
Boron triethyl	9.0	E.I.
Boron trifluoride	15.5	E.I.
Boron triiodide	9.0	E.I.
Boron trimethyl	8.8	E.I.
Boroxine	13.5	E.I.
Bromine (I)	10.55	P.I.
(II)	19.5	E.I.
Bromine difluoride	11.2	E.I.
Bromine trifluoride	12.9	E.I.
Bromine tetrafluoride	15.6	E.I.
Bromine monochloride	11.1	E.I.
Bromobenzene	8.98	P.I.
1-bromo-bicyclo-(2.2.1)-heptane	9.90	E.I.
1-bromo-bicyclo-(2.2.2)-octane	9.76	E.I.
1-bromobutane	10.13	P.I.
2-bromobutane	9.98	P.I.
1-bromobutanone	9.54	P.I.
1-bromo-2-chloroethane	10.63	P.I.
Bromochloromethane	10.77	P.I.
Bromodichloromethane	10.88	E.I.
Bromodifluoromethane	12.0	E.I.
Bromodurene	8.0	E.I.
Bromoethane	10.24	P.I.
Bromoethene	9.8	P.I.
1-bromo-4-fluorobenzene	8.99	P.I.
Bromoform	10.51	P.I.
1-bromo-3-hexanone	9.26	P.I.
Bromomethane	10.53	P.I.
Bromomethyl ethyl ether	10.08	P.I.
2-(bromomethyl)-propane	10.15	E.I.
1-bromo-2-methyl propane	10.09	P.I.
2-bromo-2-methylpropane	9.89	P.I.
1-bromopentane	10.10	P.I.
p-bromophenol	9.04	E.I.
1-bromopropane	10.18	P.I.
2-bromopropane	10.08	P.I.
1-bromopropene	9.30	P.I.
3-bromopropene	9.7	P.I.
1-bromopropyne	10.1	E.I.
2-bromopyridine	9.65	E.I.
4-bromopyridine	9.94	E.I.
2-bromothiophene	8.63	P.I.
o-bromotoluene	8.78	P.I.
m-bromotoluene	8.81	P.I.
p-bromotoluene	8.67	P.I.
Bromotrifluoromethane	11.78	P.I.
1,2-butadiene	9.57	E.I.
1,3-butadiene (*cis*)	9.07	P.I.
1,3-butadiene (*trans*)	9.07	P.I.
1,3-butadiyne	10.74	S.
n-butanal	9.86	P.I.
n-butane	10.63	P.I.
2,3-butanedione	9.23	P.I.
n-butanoic acid	10.16	P.I.
1-butanol	10.04	P.I.
2-butanol	10.1	P.I.
Butanone	9.53	P.I.
2-butenal	9.73	P.I.
1-butene	9.58	P.I.
2-butene (*cis*)	9.13	P.I.
2-butene (*trans*)	9.13	P.I.
Buteneone	9.91	E.I.
n-butylamine	8.71	P.I.
i-butylamine	8.70	P.I.
sec-butylamine	8.70	P.I.
t-butylamine	8.64	P.I.
N-*n*-butylaniline	7.5	U.V.
n-butylbenzene	8.69	P.I.
i-butylbenzene	8.69	P.I.
sec-butylbenzene	8.68	P.I.
t-butylbenzene	8.68	P.I.
n-butyl ethanoate	10.00	P.I.
i-butyl ethanoate	9.95	P.I.
sec-butyl ethanoate	9.91	P.I.
n-butyl methanoate	10.50	P.I.
i-butyl methanoate	10.46	P.I.
n-butyl pentanoate	9.57	P.I.
2-butylthiophene	8.5	E.I.
1-butyne	10.18	P.I.
2-butyne	9.85	P.I.
1-butyne-3-ene	9.87	E.I.
Calcium monofluoride	5.5	E.I.
Carbon (C_2)	12.0	E.I.
Carbon (C_3)	12.6	E.I.
Carbon (C_4)	12.6	E.I.
Carbon (C_5)	12.5	E.I.
Carbon tetrachloride	11.47	P.I.
Carbon tetrafluoride	<15.0	E.I.
Carbon dioxide (I)	13.79	P.I.
(II)	22.6	E.I.

B. MOLECULAR IONIZATION POTENTIALS (CONT.)

Carbon disulfide	10.076	P.I.
Carbon monoxide (I)	14.01	P.I.
(II)	27.7	E.I.
Carbon monosulfide	11.8	E.I.
Carbon suboxide	10.8	E.I.
Carbonyl sulfide	11.17	E.I.
Chlorine (I)	11.48	P.I.
(II)	21.0	E.I.
Chlorine difluoride	11.0	E.I.
Chlorine dioxide	11.1	E.I.
Chlorine monoxide	10.4	E.I.
Chlorine trifluoride	13.0	E.I.
Chlorine trioxide	11.7	E.I.
o-chloroaniline	7.9	U.V.
Chlorobenzene	9.07	P.I.
1-chloro-2-bromoethane	10.63	P.I.
Chlorobromomethane	10.77	P.I.
2-chloro-1,3-butadiene	8.79	S.
1-chlorobutane	10.67	P.I.
2-chlorobutane	10.65	P.I.
1-chlorobutanone	9.54	P.I.
Chlorocyanomethane	12.2	P.I.
Chlorocyclopropane	10.10	E.I.
Chlorodibromomethane	10.59	P.I.
1-chloro-1,1-difluoroethane	11.98	P.I.
Chlorodifluoromethane	12.45	P.I.
Chloroethane	10.97	P.I.
Chloroethene	10.00	P.I.
1-chloro-2-fluorobenzene	9.155	P.I.
1-chloro-3-fluorobenzene	9.21	P.I.
1-chloro-2-fluoroethene (*cis*)	9.87	P.I.
1-chloro-2-fluoroethene (*trans*)	9.87	P.I.
Chloroform	11.42	P.I.
o-chloroiodobenzene	8.35	P.I.
Chloromethane	11.28	P.I.
Chloromethyl ethyl ether	10.08	P.I.
Chloromethylmethyl ether	10.25	P.I.
1-chloro-2-methylpropane	10.66	P.I.
2-chloro-2-methylpropane	10.2	S.
o-chlorophenol	9.28	E.I.
p-chlorophenol	9.07	E.I.
Chloroprene	8.8	S.
1-chloropropane	10.82	P.I.
2-chloropropane	10.78	P.I.
1-chloropropanone	9.71	P.I.
3-chloropropene	10.04	P.I.
1-chloropropyne	9.9	E.I.
2-chloropyridine	9.91	E.I.
4-chloropyridine	10.15	E.I.
2-chlorothiophene	8.68	E.I.
o-chlorotoluene	8.83	P.I.
m-chlorotoluene	8.83	P.I.
p-chlorotoluene	8.69	P.I.
Chlorotrifluoroethene	10.4	E.I.
Chlorotrifluoromethane	12.8	P.I.
Chromium hexacarbonyl	8.03	P.I.
Chromium monoxide	8.2	E.I.
Chromyl chloride	12.6	E.I.
Chromyl fluoride	14.0	E.I.
Chrysene	7.75	U.V.
Coronene	7.6	U.V.
o-cresol	8.93	E.I.
m-cresol	8.98	E.I.
p-cresol	8.97	E.I.
Cyanoethane	11.84	P.I.
Cyanoethene	10.91	P.I.
Cyanoethyne	11.6	E.I.
Cyanogen	13.57	E.I.
Cyanogen bromide	11.95	E.I.
Cyanogen chloride	12.49	E.I.
Cyanogen iodide	10.98	E.I.
Cyanomethane	12.22	P.I.
1-cyanopropane	11.67	P.I.
3-cyanopropene	10.39	P.I.
Cyclobutane	10.50	P.I.
Cycloheptatriene	8.55	E.I.
N-cycloheptylaniline	7.45	U.V.
Cyclohexadiene	8.40	S.
Cyclohexane	9.88	P.I.
Cyclohexanone	9.14	P.I.
Cyclohexene	8.95	P.I.
N-cyclohexylaniline	7.45	U.V.
Cyclooctatetraene	7.99	P.I.
Cyclopentadiene	8.58	S.
Cyclopentane	10.52	P.I.
Cyclopentanone	9.26	P.I.
Cyclopentene	9.01	P.I.
N-cyclopentylaniline	7.45	U.V.
Cyclopropane	11.06	P.I.

B. MOLECULAR IONIZATION POTENTIALS (CONT.)

Cyclopropene	9.95	E.I.
Cyclopropyl chloride	10.10	E.I.
Cyclopropyl cyanide	11.2	E.I.
Decaborane	10.7	E.I.
Decafluorocyclohexene	11.3	E.I.
Decafluoro-*o*-xylene	10.6	E.I.
n-decane	10.19	E.I.
2-decanone	9.40	P.I.
1-decene	9.51	E.I.
N-*n*-decylaniline	7.5	U.V.
Deuterium	15.457	S.
Dialuminum monoxide	7.7	E.I.
N, N-di-*n*-amylaniline	7.1	U.V.
Diazirine	10.18	E.I.
Diazomethane	9.00	S.
Diborane	11.9	E.I.
Diborane-d_6	12.0	E.I.
Diboron dihydride	11.36	E.I.
Diboron dihydride-d_2	11.50	E.I.
Diboron dioxide	13.3	E.I.
Diboron monodeuteride	8.7–11.7	E.I.
Diboron monohydride	10.62	E.I.
Diboron pentahydride	7.86	E.I.
Diboron pentahydride-d_5	8.01	E.I.
Diboron tetrahydride	10.93	E.I.
Diboron tetrahydride-d_4	10.90	E.I.
Diboron trihydride	8.79	E.I.
Diboron trihydride-d_3	8.81	E.I.
1, 4-dibromobutane	10.28	E.I.
Dibromochloromethane	10.59	P.I.
Dibromodifluoromethane	11.07	P.I.
1,1-dibromoethane	10.19	P.I.
1,2-dibromoethane	10.30	E.I.
1,2-dibromoethene (*cis*)	9.45	P.I.
1,2-dibromoethene (*trans*)	9.46	P.I.
Dibromomethane	10.49	P.I.
1,3-dibromopropane	10.07	P.I.
N,N-di-*n*-butylaniline	7.15	U.V.
Di-*n*-butyl ether	9.18	P.I.
o-Dichlorobenzene	9.07	P.I.
m-dichlorobenzene	9.12	P.I.
p-dichlorobenzene	8.94	P.I.
1,2-dichloro-1,2-bis (trifluoromethyl)-ethene	10.36	P.I.
Dichlorobromomethane	10.88	E.I.
Dichlorocyanomethane	12.9	E.I.
1,1-dichlorocyclopropane	10.30	E.I.
Dichlorodifluoromethane	12.31	P.I.
Dichlorodifluoroethene	10.0	E.I.
1,2-dichloroethane	11.12	P.I.
1,1-dichloroethene	9.46	S.
1,2-dichloroethene (*cis*)	9.66	P.I.
1,2-dichloroethene (*trans*)	9.96	P.I.
Dichloroethyne	13.	E.I.
Dichlorofluoromethane	12.39	E.I.
Dichloromethane	11.35	P.I.
Dichloromethyl methyl ether	10.25	P.I.
1,2-dichloropropane	10.87	P.I.
1,3-dichloropropane	10.85	P.I.
1,1-dichloropropanone	9.71	P.I.
2,3-dichloropropene	9.82	P.I.
Dicyanoacetylene	11.4	E.I.
Dicyanodiacetylene	11.4	E.I.
N,N-di-*n*-decylaniline	7.1	U.V.
Diethoxymethane	9.70	P.I.
N,N-diethylacetamide	8.60	P.I.
Diethylamine	8.01	P.I.
N,N-diethylaniline	7.15	U.V.
Diethylbenzene	8.88	E.I.
1,2-diethylbenzene	8.91	E.I.
1,3-diethylbenzene	8.99	E.I.
1,4-diethylbenzene	8.93	E.I.
Diethyl ether	9.53	P.I.
N,N-diethyl formamide	8.89	P.I.
Diethyl sulfide	8.43	P.I.
Diethyl sulfite	9.68	P.I.
o-difluorobenzene	9.31	P.I.
p-difluorobenzene	9.15	P.I.
1,1-difluoro-1-chloroethane	11.98	P.I.
Difluorochloromethane	12.45	P.I.
Difluorocyanomethane	12.4	E.I.
1,1-difluoro-1,2-dibromoethane	10.83	P.I.
1,1-difluoroethene	10.30	P.I.
Difluorodibromomethane	11.07	P.I.
Difluorodichloroethene	10.0	E.I.
Difluorodichloromethane	12.31	P.I.
Difluoromethane	12.55	S.
Difluoromethylbenzene	9.45	P.I.

B. MOLECULAR IONIZATION POTENTIALS (CONT.)

N,N-di-*n*-hexylaniline	7.1	U.V.
Dihydropyran	8.34	P.I.
Diimide	9.85	E.I.
Diiodomethane	9.34	P.I.
Diketene	9.4	E.I.
Dilithium iodide	8.75	E.I.
Dilithium oxide	6.8	E.I.
Dimethoxyborine	4.46	E.I.
1,1-dimethoxyethane	9.65	P.I.
Dimethoxymethane	10.00	P.I.
N,N-dimethylacetamide	8.81	P.I.
Dimethylamine	8.24	P.I.
N,N-dimethylaniline	7.14	P.I.
Dimethylarsine	9.0	E.I.
2,3-dimethylbutadiene	8.72	P.I.
2,2-dimethylbutane	10.05	P.I.
2,3-dimethylbutane	10.01	P.I.
3,3-dimethylbutanone	9.17	P.I.
2,3-dimethyl-2-butene	8.30	P.I.
Dimethyl chloroarsine	9.9	E.I.
Dimethyl disulfide	8.46	P.I.
Dimethyl ether	10.00	P.I.
N,N-dimethylformamide	9.12	P.I.
2,3-dimethylfuran	8.01	E.I.
3,5-dimethyl-4-heptanone	9.04	P.I.
1,1-dimethylhydrazine	8.12	E.I.
1,2-dimethylhydrazine	7.75	E.I.
Dimethyl mercury	8.90	E.I.
2,2-dimethyl-3-pentanone	8.98	P.I.
2,2-dimethylpropane	10.35	P.I.
Dimethyl sulfide	8.69	P.I.
Dimethyl sulfoxide	8.85	P.I.
Dimethyltrifluoromethyl arsine	9.2	E.I.
Dimethyl zinc	8.86	E.I.
Dinitrogen difluoride	13.1	E.I.
Dinitrogen tetrafluoride	12.0	E.I.
N,N-di-*n*-octylaniline	7.1	U.V.
1,3-dioxane	10.15	E.I.
1,4-dioxane	9.13	P.I.
Diphenyl	8.27	P.I.
Diphenylamine	7.4	U.V.
Diphenylbutadiene	7.75	U.V.
Diphenyldecapentaene	7.4	U.V.
Diphenylhexadiene	8.2	U.V.
Diphenylhexatriene	7.6	U.V.
Diphenyloctatetraene	7.5	U.V.
Diphosphine	8.7	E.I.
Diphosphorusdiarsenide	10.3	E.I.
Diphosphorus tetrachloride	9.36	E.I.
N,N-di-*n*-propylaniline	7.15	U.V.
Di-*n*-propyl disulfide	8.27	P.I.
Di-*n*-propyl ether	9.27	P.I.
Di-*i*-propyl ether	9.20	P.I.
Di-*n*-propyl sulfide	8.30	P.I.
Disilicon dioxide	10.0	E.I.
Disulfur monoxide	10.3	E.I.
2,3-dithiabutane	8.46	P.I.
3,4-dithiahexane	8.27	P.I.
N-*n*-dodecylaniline	7.5	U.V.
Durene	8.03	P.I.
3,4-epoxy-1-butene	9.7	E.I.
1,2-epoxypropane	9.81	E.I.
Ethanal	10.21	P.I.
Ethane	11.65	P.I.
Ethane-d_1	11.70	E.I.
Ethanoic acid	10.35	P.I.
Ethanoic acid-d_3	10.71	E.I.
Ethanol	10.48	P.I.
Ethanol-d_1(OD)	10.45	E.I.
Ethene	10.51	P.I.
Ethene-d_4	10.52	S.
Ethylamine	8.86	P.I.
N-ethylaniline	7.5	U.V.
Ethylbenzene	8.76	P.I.
Ethyl boron difluoride	11.8	E.I.
Ethyl bromide	10.29	P.I.
Ethyl bromoacetate	10.13	P.I.
Ethyl ω-bromobutanoate	9.85	P.I.
2-ethyl-1-butene	9.21	E.I.
Ethyl chloride	10.97	P.I.
Ethyl chloroacetate	10.20	P.I.
Ethyl decaborane	9.0	E.I.
Ethyl disulfane	9.4	E.I.
Ethyleneimine	9.94	E.I.
Ethylene oxide	10.565	P.I.
Ethyl ethanoate	10.10	P.I.
Ethyl hexanoate	9.67	P.I.
Ethyl iodide	9.33	P.I.
Ethyl isothiocyanate	9.10	P.I.
Ethyl mercaptan	9.29	P.I.
Ethyl methanoate	10.61	P.I.
Ethyl nitrate	11.22	P.I.
Ethyl propanoate	10.00	P.I.
2-ethylthiophene	8.8	E.I.
Ethyl thiocyanate	9.89	P.I.

B. MOLECULAR IONIZATION POTENTIALS (CONT.)

Molecule	I.P.	Method
Ethyl trichloroacetate	10.44	P.I.
Ethyne	11.41	P.I.
Ethyne-d_2	11.39	E.I.
Ethynylbenzene	8.82	P.I.
Ferrous chloride (monomer)	11.5	E.I.
Ferrous chloride (dimer)	10.5	E.I.
Fluorene	8.63	E.I.
Fluorine	15.7	P.I.
o-fluoroaniline	7.95	P.I.
m-fluoroaniline	7.90	P.I.
p-fluoroaniline	7.82	P.I.
Fluorobenzene	9.20	P.I.
Fluorocyanomethane	13.0	E.I.
1-fluoro-1, 2-dibromoethane	10.75	P.I.
Fluoroethane	12.00	E.I.
Fluoroethene	10.37	P.I.
Fluoroform	13.84	S.
Fluoromethanal	11.4	P.I.
Fluoromethane	12.80	S.
o-fluorophenol	8.66	P.I.
o-fluorotoluene	8.91	P.I.
m-fluorotoluene	8.91	P.I.
p-fluorotoluene	8.78	P.I.
Fluorotribromomethane	10.67	P.I.
Fluorotrichloromethane	11.77	P.I.
Fluorotrifluoromethylbenzene	9.12	P.I.
Formamide	10.20	P.I.
Formic acid	11.05	P.I.
Formic acid-d_1	11.57	E.I.
Furan	8.89	P.I.
Furfural	9.21	P.I.
d-galactose	9.1	E.I.
Germane	12.3	E.I.
Germanium tetrachloride	11.90	E.I.
Germanium tetramethyl	9.2	E.I.
d-glucose	8.8	E.I.
Glycine	9.5	E.I.
n-heptane	10.07	P.I.
2-heptanone	9.33	P.I.
4-heptanone	9.12	P.I.
1-heptene	9.54	E.I.
N-*n*-heptylaniline	7.5	U.V.
1,5-hexadiene	9.51	E.I.
2,4-hexadiyne	10.65	S.
Hexafluoroacetone	11.81	S.
Hexafluorobenzene	9.39	S.
Hexafluoropropene	10.3	E.I.
Hexamethylbenzene	7.85	P.I.
Hexamethyleneimine	8.76	E.I.
n-hexane	10.17	P.I.
2-hexanone	9.34	P.I.
1,3,5-hexatriene	8.26	S.
1-hexene	9.46	P.I.
2-hexene (*trans*)	9.16	E.I.
3-hexene (*trans*)	9.12	E.I.
3-hexene-1,5-diyne	9.46	E.I.
N-*n*-hexylaniline	7.5	U.V.
Hydrazine	9.00	E.I.
Hydrazoic acid	10.3	E.I.
Hydrogen	15.427	S.
Hydrogen bromide (I)	11.62	P.I.
(II)	21.6	E.I.
Hydrogen chloride (I)	12.74	P.I.
(II)	22.9	E.I.
Hydrogen cyanide (I)	13.73	E.I.
(II)	26.3	E.I.
Hydrogen disulfide	10.2	E.I.
Hydrogen fluoride	15.77	P.I.
Hydrogen iodide (I)	10.38	P.I.
(II)	19.6	E.I.
Hydrogen peroxide	10.92	E.I.
Hydrogen selenide	9.88	P.I.
Hydrogen selenide-d_2	9.88	P.I.
Hydrogen sulfide	10.46	P.I.
Hydrogen sulfide-d_2	10.47	P.I.
Hydrogen telluride	9.138	P.I.
Hydrogen telluride-d_2	9.14	P.I.
4-hydroxypyridine	9.70	E.I.
Indene	8.81	E.I.
Iodine	9.28	P.I.
Iodine difluoride	10.7	E.I.
Iodine monobromide	9.98	E.I.
Iodine monochloride	10.31	E.I.
Iodine pentafluoride	13.5	E.I.
Iodine tetrafluoride	14.5	E.I.
Iodine trifluoride	9.7	E.I.
Iodobenzene	8.73	P.I.
1-iodobutane	9.21	P.I.
2-iodobutane	9.09	P.I.
Iodoethane	9.33	P.I.
Iodomethane	9.54	P.I.
1-iodo-2-methylpropane	9.18	P.I.
2-iodo-2-methylpropane	9.02	P.I.

B. MOLECULAR IONIZATION POTENTIALS (CONT.)

Iodopentaborane	11.1	E.I.
1-iodopentane	9.19	P.I.
1-iodopropane	9.26	P.I.
2-iodopropane	9.17	P.I.
o-iodotoluene	8.62	P.I.
m-iodotoluene	8.61	P.I.
p-iodotoluene	8.50	P.I.
Iron pentacarbonyl	7.95	P.I.
Isoleucine	9.5	E.I.
Isoprene	8.845	P.I.
Isothiocyanic acid	10.4	E.I.
Ketene	9.61	S.
Lanthanum monoxide	4.8	E.I.
Lead tetramethyl	8.0	E.I.
Lithium (diatomic)	4.96	S.
Lithium iodide	8.55	E.I.
Lithium oxide	6.8	E.I.
2,3-lutidine	8.85	P.I.
2,4-lutidine	8.85	P.I.
2,6-lutidine	8.85	P.I.
Magnesium dicyclo-pentadienide	7.76	E.I.
Maleic anhydride	9.9	P.I.
Mercuric chloride	12.1	E.I.
Mercury dimethyl	8.90	E.I.
Metaboric acid	12.6	E.I.
Methanal	10.87	E.I.
Methanal-d_2	10.83	E.I.
Methanal dimer	10.51	P.I.
Methane	12.98	P.I.
Methane-d_1	13.12	E.I.
Methane-d_2	13.14	E.I.
Methane-d_3	13.18	E.I.
Methane-d_4	13.19	E.I.
Methanoic acid	11.05	P.I.
Methanoic acid-d_1	11.57	E.I.
Methanol	10.85	P.I.
Methanol-d_1(OD)	11.04	E.I.
Methionine	9.5	E.I.
N-methylacetamide	8.90	P.I.
N-methylaniline	7.35	P.I.
Methylamine	8.97	P.I.
p-methylaniline	8.14	E.I.
Methylarsine	9.7	E.I.
Methyl azide	9.5	E.I.
Methyl benzoate	10.0	E.I.
Methyl boron difluoride	12.54	E.I.
Methyl bromide	10.53	P.I.
2-methyl-1,3-butadiene	8.85	P.I.
2-methylbutanal	9.71	P.I.
3-methylbutanal	9.92	E.I.
2-methylbutane	10.31	P.I.
Methyl *n*-butanoate	10.07	P.I.
Methyl *i*-butanoate	9.98	P.I.
3-methyl-2-butanone	9.32	P.I.
2-methyl-1-butene	9.12	P.I.
3-methyl-1-butane	9.51	P.I.
2-methyl-2-butene	8.68	P.I.
3-methyl-1-butyne	10.35	E.I.
Methyl chloride	11.28	P.I.
Methyl chloroacetate	10.35	P.I.
Methylcyclohexane	9.85	P.I.
4-methylcyclohexene	8.91	P.I.
Methylcyclopentane	10.45	E.I.
Methylcyclopropane	9.88	E.I.
Methyl dichloroacetate	10.44	P.I.
Methyldichloroarsine	10.4	E.I.
Methyl disulfane	8.8	E.I.
Methylene chloride	11.35	P.I.
Methyl ethanoate	10.27	P.I.
Methyl ethyl ether	9.81	E.I.
Methyl ethyl sulfide	8.55	P.I.
Methyl fluoride	12.80	S.
N-methylformamide	9.25	P.I.
2-methylfuran	8.39	P.I.
Methyl iodide	9.54	P.I.
Methyl isothiocyanate	9.13	E.I.
Methyl mercaptan	9.44	P.I.
Methyl methanoate	10.82	P.I.
α-methylnaphthalene	7.96	P.I.
β-methylnaphthalene	7.955	P.I.
Methyl nitrite	10.7	E.I.
2-methylpentane	10.11	P.I.
3-methylpentane	10.07	P.I.
Methyl pentanoate	9.87	P.I.
4-Methyl-2-pentanone	9.30	P.I.
2-methyl-2-pentene-4-one	9.08	E.I.
p-methylphenylamine	8.2	E.I.
2-methylpropane	10.56	P.I.
2-methylpropanal	9.74	P.I.
Methyl propanoate	10.15	P.I.
2-methylpropanoic acid	10.02	P.I.
2-methyl-2-propanol	9.7	P.I.
2-methylpropene	9.23	P.I.
Methyl *i*-propyl sulfide	8.7	E.I.
Methyl *n*-propyl sulfide	8.80	E.I.

B. MOLECULAR IONIZATION POTENTIALS (CONT.)

N-methylpyrrolidine	8.06	E.I.
α-methylstyrene	8.35	P.I.
3-methyl-2-thiabutane	8.7	E.I.
Methyl thiocyanate	10.065	P.I.
Molybdenum dioxide	9.4	E.I.
Molybdenum hexacarbonyl	8.12	P.I.
Molybdenum monoxide	8.0	E.I.
Molybdenum trioxide	12.0	E.I.
Monoaluminum oxide	9.5	E.I.
Monobromobenzene	8.98	P.I.
Monobromodifluoromethane	12.0	E.I.
Monobromoethane	10.29	P.I.
Monobromoethene	9.80	P.I.
Monobromomethane	10.53	P.I.
Monobromotrifluoromethane	11.78	P.I.
Monochlorobenzene	9.07	P.I.
Monochlorocyclopropane	10.10	E.I.
Monochloroethane	10.97	P.I.
Monochloroethene	10.00	P.I.
Monochloromethane	11.28	P.I.
Monochlorotrifluoromethane	12.8	P.I.
Monofluorobenzene	9.20	P.I.
Monofluorodichloromethane	13.06	E.I.
Monofluoroethane	12.00	E.I.
Monofluoroethene	10.37	P.I.
Monofluoromethane	12.80	S.
Monoiodobenzene	8.73	P.I.
Monoiodoethane	9.33	P.I.
Monoiodomethane	9.54	P.I.
Monolithium oxide	9.0	E.I.
Monomethylarsine	9.7	E.I.
Monomethylhydrazine	8.63	E.I.
Naphthalene (I)	8.12	P.I.
(II)	14.7	E.I.
(III)	17.2	E.I.
1-naphthylamine	7.30	P.I.
2-naphthylamine	7.25	P.I.
Nickel chloride	11.2	E.I.
Nickel tetracarbonyl	8.28	P.I.
Nicotine	8.01	E.I.
Nitric oxide (I)	9.25	P.I.
(II)	30.6	E.I.
Nitric sulfide	8.8	P.I.

Nitritomethane	10.7	E.I.
o-nitroaniline	8.68	E.I.
m-nitroaniline	8.80	E.I.
p-nitroaniline	8.85	E.I.
Nitrobenzene	9.92	P.I.
Nitroethane	10.88	P.I.
Nitrogen (I)	15.576	S.
(II)	27.8	E.I.
Nitrogen difluoride	11.4	E.I.
Nitrogen dioxide	9.78	P.I.
Nitrogen monofluoride	12.0	E.I.
Nitrogen trifluoride	12.9	S.
Nitromethane	11.08	P.I.
p-nitrophenol	9.52	E.I.
1-nitropropane	10.81	P.I.
2-nitropropane	10.71	P.I.
p-nitrotoluene	9.82	E.I.
Nitrous oxide	12.89	P.I.
n-nonane	10.21	E.I.
5-nonanone	9.10	P.I.
N-*n*-nonylaniline	7.5	U.V.
Nornicotine	9.30	E.I.
Octafluoroacetophenone	11.25	E.I.
Octafluorotoluene	10.4	E.I.
n-octane	10.24	E.I.
3-octanone	9.19	P.I.
4-octanone	9.10	P.I.
1,3,5,7-octatetraene	7.8	S.
1-octene	9.52	P.I.
2-octene	9.11	E.I.
N-*n*-octylaniline	7.5	U.V.
Osmium tetroxide	12.6	E.I.
Osmium trioxide	12.3	E.I.
Oxacyclobutane	9.85	E.I.
Oxygen	12.075	P.I.
Oxygen difluoride	13.7	E.I.
Ozone	12.80	P.I.
Pentaborane	10.8	E.I.
1,2-pentadiene	9.42	E.I.
1,3-pentadiene	8.68	E.I.
1,4-pentadiene	9.58	E.I.
2,3-pentadiene	9.26	E.I.
Pentafluorobenzene	9.84	P.I.
Pentamethylbenzene	7.92	P.I.
n-pentanal	9.82	P.I.
n-pentane	10.34	P.I.
2,4-pentanedione	8.87	P.I.
n-pentanoic acid	10.12	P.I.

B. MOLECULAR IONIZATION POTENTIALS (CONT.)

2-pentanone	9.39	P.I.
3-pentanone	9.32	P.I.
1-pentene	9.50	P.I.
2-pentene (*cis*)	9.11	E.I.
2-pentene (*trans*)	9.06	E.I.
n-pentyl ethanoate	9.92	P.I.
1-pentyne	10.39	E.I.
Perchloryl fluoride	13.6	E.I.
Perfluoroheptane	12.5	E.I.
Perfluoro-1-heptene	10.48	P.I.
(*n*-perfluoropropyl)-chloromethane	11.84	P.I.
n-perfluoropropyl iodide	10.36	P.I.
(*n*-perfluoropropyl)-iodomethane	9.96	P.I.
(*n*-perfluoropropyl)-methyl ketone	10.58	P.I.
Perylene	7.15	U.V.
Phenanthrene	7.8	S.
Phenetole	8.13	P.I.
Phenol	8.50	P.I.
Phenylacetylene	8.82	P.I.
o-Phenylenediamine	8.00	E.I.
m-Phenylenediamine	7.96	E.I.
p-Phenylenediamine	7.58	E.I.
Phenylhydrazine	7.64	P.I.
Phenyl isocyanete	8.77	P.I.
Phenyl isothiocyanate	8.52	P.I.
Phosgene	11.78	S.
Phosphine	10.1	E.I.
Phosphorous acid	12.6	E.I.
Phosphorus (P_2)	11.1	E.I.
Phosphorus (P_3)	11.2	E.I.
Phosphorus (P_4)	9.0	E.I.
Phosphorus arsenide	11.2	E.I.
Phosphorus dichloride	9.0	E.I.
Phosphorus monoarsenide	11.2	E.I.
Phosphorus monochloride	9.6	E.I.
Phosphorus triarsenide	10.0	E.I.
Phosphorus trichloride	10.75	E.I.
2-picoline	9.02	P.I.
3-picoline	9.04	P.I.
4-picoline	9.04	P.I.
Piperidine	8.49	E.I.
Polymethylene	10.15	E.I.
Potassium (K_2)	4.09	S.
Potassium iodide	8.3	E.I.
Propanal	9.98	P.I.
Propane	11.07	P.I.
Propadiene	10.19	P.I.
Propanoic acid	10.24	P.I.
1-Propanol	10.17	P.I.
2-Propanol	10.17	P.I.
Propanone	9.69	P.I.
Propenal	10.10	P.I.
Propene	9.73	P.I.
Prop-1-ene-2-ol	8.2	P.I.
Prop-2-ene-1-ol	9.67	P.I.
Propenoic acid	10.90	E.I.
Propiolactone	9.70	P.I.
n-propylamine	8.78	P.I.
i-propylamine	8.72	P.I.
N-*n*-propylaniline	7.5	U.V.
N-*i*-propylaniline	7.5	U.V.
1-propylbenzene	8.72	P.I.
2-propylbenzene	8.69	P.I.
Propylene oxide	9.81	E.I.
Propylene sulfide	8.6	E.I.
n-propyl ethanoate	10.04	P.I.
i-propyl ethanoate	9.99	P.I.
i-propyl isothiocyanate	9.4	E.I.
n-propyl methanoate	10.54	P.I.
n-propyl nitrate	11.07	P.I.
2-propyl thiophene	8.6	E.I.
Propyne	10.36	P.I.
Pyrazine	10.00	E.I.
Pyrene	7.72	E.I.
Pyridazine	9.86	E.I.
Pyridine	9.266	S.
2-pyridinecarboxaldehyde	9.75	E.I.
4-pyridinecarboxaldehyde	10.12	E.I.
Pyrimidine	9.91	E.I.
Pyrrole	8.20	P.I.
Quadricyclene	8.70	E.I.
Quinoline	8.30	P.I.
Quinone	9.68	P.I.
Selenium dioxide	11.94	E.I.
Selenium dioxydifluoride	13.15	E.I.
Selenium oxydifluoride	12.50	E.I.
Silane	12.2	E.I.
Silicon carbide	9.3	E.I.
Silicon dichloride	11.8	E.I.
Silicon dioxide	11.7	E.I.
Silicon monofluoride	7.26	P.I.
Silicon monoxide	10.8	E.I.
Silicon tetrachloride	12.06	E.I.

B. MOLECULAR IONIZATION POTENTIALS (CONT.)

Silicon tetrafluoride	15.4	E.I.
Silicon tetramethyl	9.80	E.I.
Sodium (Na_2)	4.87	S.
Sodium azide	11.7	E.I.
Sodium hydroxide	9.	E.I.
Sodium iodide	8.8	E.I.
Stannane	11.7	E.I.
Stibine	9.58	P.I.
Stilbene	7.95	U.V.
Styrene	8.47	P.I.
Sulfur (S_2)	9.9	E.I.
Sulfur (S_3)	10.5	E.I.
Sulfur (S_4)	10.4	E.I.
Sulfur (S_5)	9.9	E.I.
Sulfur (S_6)	9.4	E.I.
Sulfur (S_7)	9.2	E.I.
Sulfur (S_8)	8.9	E.I.
Sulfur dioxide	12.34	S.
Sulfur hexafluoride	19.3	E.I.
Sulfur monoxide	12.1	E.I.
Tetracene	6.88	P.I.
1,1,2,2-tetrachloroethane	11.10	E.I.
Tetrachloroethene	9.32	P.I.
Tetrachloromethane	11.47	P.I.
1,2,3,4-tetrafluoro-benzene	9.61	P.I.
1,2,3,5-tetrafluoro-benzene	9.55	P.I.
1,2,4,5-tetrafluoro-benzene	9.39	P.I.
Tetrafluoroethene	10.12	P.I.
Tetrafluoromethane	$<$15.0	E.I.
Tetrahydrofuran	9.45	E.I.
Tetrahydropyran	9.26	P.I.
Tetrahydropyrrole	8.60	E.I.
2,3,5,6-tetramethyl-aniline	7.7	E.I.
1,2,4,5-tetramethyl-benzene	8.03	P.I.
2,2,3,3-tetramethyl-butane	9.79	E.I.
Tetramethyl germanium	9.2	E.I.
Tetramethyl hydrazine	7.76	E.I.
Tetramethyl lead	8.0	E.I.
2,2,4,4-tetramethyl-3-pentanone	8.65	P.I.
Tetramethyl silane	9.80	E.I.
Tetramethyl tin	8.25	E.I.
2-thiabutane	8.55	P.I.
Thiacyclobutane	8.9	E.I.
Thiacyclohexane	8.36	P.I.
Thiacyclopentane	8.48	P.I.
Thiacyclopropane	8.87	E.I.
Thiadioxane	8.50	E.I.
4-thiaheptane	8.30	P.I.
2-thiapentane	8.80	E.I.
3-thiapentane	8.43	P.I.
4-thia-1-pentane	8.70	E.I.
2-thiapropane	8.69	P.I.
Thioanisole	8.9	E.I.
1-thiobutanol	9.14	P.I.
t-thiobutanol	8.79	P.I.
Thioethanoic acid	10.00	P.I.
Thioethanol	9.29	P.I.
Thiomethanol	9.44	P.I.
Thiophene	8.86	P.I.
Thiophenol	8.33	P.I.
1-thiopropanol	9.20	P.I.
Tin tetramethyl	8.25	E.I.
Titantium tetrachloride	11.7	E.I.
Titantium trichloride	13.0	E.I.
Toluene (I)	8.82	P.I.
(II)	15.5	E.I.
(III)	17.5	E.I.
o-toluidine	7.75	U.V.
m-toluidine	7.50	P.I.
p-toluidine	7.50	P.I.
p-tolunitrile	9.76	E.I.
Triazene	9.6	E.I.
s-triazine	10.07	E.I.
Tribromoethene	9.27	P.I.
Tribromofluoromethane	10.67	P.I.
Tribromomethane	10.51	P.I.
1,1,1-trichlorobutanone	9.54	P.I.
Trichlorofluoromethane	11.77	P.I.
Trichloroethene	9.45	P.I.
Trichloromethane	11.42	P.I.
Trichloromethyl ethyl ether	10.08	P.I.
Trichlorovinylsilane	10.79	P.I.
Triethylamine	7.50	P.I.
Triethylphosphine	8.27	E.I.
Trifluoroacetophenone	10.25	E.I.
1,2,4-trifluorobenzene	9.37	P.I.
1,3,5-trifluorobenzene	9.3	P.I.
Trifluorochloromethane	12.91	P.I.
Trifluoroethane	10.4	E.I.
Trifluoroethene	10.14	P.I.

B. MOLECULAR IONIZATION POTENTIALS (CONT.)

1,1,1-trifluoro-2-iodethane	10.00	P.I.
Trifluoroiodomethane	10.40	P.I.
Trifluoromethane	13.84	S.
Trifluoromethylbenzene	9.68	P.I.
Trifluoromethyl-cyclohexane	10.46	P.I.
1,1,1-trifluoropropene	10.9	P.I.
1,1,1-trifluoro-2,2,2-trichloroethane	11.78	P.I.
1,1,2-trifluoro-1,2,2-trichloroethane	11.99	P.I.
Trimethoxyborine	8.9	E.I.
Trimethylamine	7.82	P.I.
2,4,6-trimethylaniline	7.7	E.I.
Trimethyl arsine	8.3	E.I.
1,2,3-trimethylbenzene	8.48	P.I.
1,2,4-trimethylbenzene	8.27	P.I.
1,3,5-trimethylbenzene	8.39	P.I.
2,2,3-trimethylbutane	10.09	E.I.
Trimethylene oxide	9.85	E.I.
Trimethyl hydrazine	7.93	E.I.
2,2,4-trimethylpentane	9.85	P.I.
2,2,4-trimethyl-3-pentanone	8.82	P.I.
Trimethylphosphine	8.60	E.I.
Trimethylsilane	9.8	E.I.
Triphenylamine	7.6	E.I.
Triphenylene	7.8	U.V.
Tris-(*p*-methylphenyl)-amine	7.4	E.I.
Tris-(perfluoroethyl)-amine	11.7	P.I.
Tris(*n*-propyl) amine	7.23	P.I.
Tris (trifluoromethyl)-arsine	11.0	E.I.
Tris(trifluoromethyl)-phosphorus	11.3	E.I.
2,3,4-trithiapentane	8.80	E.I.
Tropolone	9.83	E.I.
Tropone	9.68	E.I.
Tungsten dioxide	9.9	E.I.
Tungsten hexacarbonyl	8.18	P.I.
Tungsten monoxide	9.1	E.I.
Tungsten trioxide	11.7	E.I.
Uranium dioxide	4.3	E.I.
Uranium hexafluoride	15.0	E.I.
Uranium monoxide	4.7	E.I.
Uranium tetrachloride	11.5	E.I.
Uranium trioxide	10.4	E.I.
Vinyl benzene	8.47	P.I.
Vinyl boron difluoride	11.06	E.I.
Vinyl bromide	9.80	P.I.
Vinyl chloride	10.00	P.I.
4-vinylcyclohexene	8.93	P.I.
Vinyl ethanoate	9.19	P.I.
Vinyl fluoride	10.37	P.I.
Vinyl methyl ether	8.93	P.I.
Water (I)	12.59	P.I.
(II)	16.7	S.
(III)	24.2	S.
(IV)	33.4	S.
Water-d_1	12.58	E.I.
Water-d_2	12.60	E.I.
Xenon difluoride	11.5	S.
Xenon tetrafluoride	12.9	E.I.
o-xylene	8.56	P.I.
m-xylene	8.56	P.I.
p-xylene	8.445	P.I.
Zinc chloride	12.9	E.I.
Zinc dimethyl	8.86	E.I.
Zinc phthalocyanine	7.	U.V.

C. RADICAL IONIZATION POTENTIALS

Acetyl	7.90	E.I.
Allyl	8.16	E.I.
Amino	11.3	E.I.
Aminocyclopentadienyl	7.55	E.I.
Anilino	8.26	E.I.
Azido	11.6	E.I.
Benzoyl	7.40	E.I.
Benzyl	7.76	E.I.
Bromocyclopentadienyl	8.85	E.I.
Bromomethynyl	10.43	E.I.
2-buten-1-yl	7.71	E.I.
n-butyl	8.64	E.I.
i-butyl	8.35	E.I.
sec-butyl	7.93	E.I.
t-butyl	7.42	E.I.
p-chlorobenzyl	7.95	E.I.
Chlorodioxy	11.1	E.I.
Chlorocyclopentadienyl	8.78	E.I.
Chloromethynyl	12.9	E.I.
Chlorotrioxy	11.7	E.I.
Chloroxy	10.4	E.I.
m-cyanobenzyl	8.58	E.I.
p-cyanobenzyl	8.36	E.I.
Cyanocyclopentadienyl	9.44	E.I.
1-cyanoethyl	9.76	E.I.
2-cyano-1-ethyl	9.85	E.I.
Cyanomethyl	10.87	E.I.
2-(2-cyanopropyl)	9.15	E.I.
Cyclobutyl	7.88	E.I.
Cycloheptatrienyl	6.24	S.
Cyclohexyl	7.66	E.I.
Cyclopentadienyl	8.69	E.I.
Cyclopentyl	7.79	E.I.
Cyclopropyl	8.05	E.I.
Dibromomethynyl	10.11	E.I.
Dibromomethyl	8.13	E.I.
Dichloromethynyl	13.10	E.I.
Dichloromethyl	8.67	E.I.
Difluoroamino	11.4	E.I.
Difluoromethynyl	13.30	E.I.
Difluoromethyl	9.45	E.I.
Dimethylhydrazyl	5.29	E.I.
Dimethylsilyl	7.1	E.I.
Diphenylmethyl	7.32	E.I.
Dithiomethylperoxy	9.4	E.I.
Ethenyl	9.45	E.I.
Ethoxy	10.30	E.I.
Ethyl	8.30	E.I.
Ethyleniminyl	7.6	E.I.
Fluorenyl	7.07	E.I.
m-fluorobenzyl	8.18	E.I.
p-fluorobenzyl	7.78	E.I.
Fluorocyclopentadienyl	8.82	E.I.
Fluoroimino	12.0	E.I.
Fluoromethynyl	13.81	E.I.
Fluorophenyl	10.86	E.I.
Fluoroxy	13.0	E.I.
Formyl	9.43	E.I.
Formyl-d_1	9.82	E.I.
Hydrazyl	11.53	E.I.
Hydroperoxy	10.50	E.I.
Hydrosulfyl	6.20	E.I.
Hydroxyl	13.53	E.I.
Imino	13.10	E.I.
Indenyl	8.35	E.I.
Isothiocyanato	$\leqslant$10.4	E.I.
Methenyl	10.39	S.
Methoxy	10.7	E.I.
p-methoxybenzyl	6.82	E.I.
Methyl	9.83	S.
Methyl-d_3	9.83	S.
Methylcyclopentadienyl	8.54	E.I.
Methylhydrazyl	5.12	E.I.
Methylnitrosyl	8.2	E.I.
2-methyl-1-propen-1-yl	8.03	E.I.
Methylsilyl	9.3	E.I.
Methynyl	11.13	E.I.
Monobromomethyl	8.34	E.I.
Monochloromethyl	8.70	E.I.
Monofluoromethyl	9.35	E.I.
Nitrile	14.2	E.I.
m-nitrobenzyl	8.56	E.I.
Pentafluorophenyl	10.6	E.I.
2-pentyl	7.73	E.I.
3-pentyl	7.86	E.I.
neo-pentyl	8.33	E.I.
t-pentyl	7.12	E.I.
Phenyl	9.89	E.I.
Propargyl	8.25	E.I.
Propionyl	7.66	E.I.
1-propyl	7.37	P.I.
2-propyl	7.21	P.I.
p-(*i*-propylbenzyl)	7.42	E.I.
2-pyridylmethyl	8.17	E.I.
3-pyridylmethyl	7.92	E.I.

C. RADICAL IONIZATION POTENTIALS (CONT.)

4-pyridylmethyl	8.40	E.I.
Thioethoxy	8.15	E.I.
Thiomethoxy	8.06	E.I.
Thiophenoxy	8.63	E.I.
Trichloromethyl	8.78	E.I.
Trifluoromethyl	10.10	E.I.
Trimethylgermanyl	8.0	E.I.
Trimethylstanyl	7.6	E.I.
Trimethylplumbyl	7.5	E.I.
Trimethylsilyl	7.8	E.I.
Tropylium	6.24	S.
Vinyl	9.45	E.I.
Vinylcyclopentadienyl	8.44	E.I.
o-xylyl	7.61	E.I.
m-xylyl	7.65	E.I.
p-xylyl	7.46	E.I.

APPENDIX V

GENERAL BIBLIOGRAPHY

Applied Mass Spectrometry, Report of a conference organized by the mass spectroscopy panel of the Institute of Petroleum, London, Oct. 29–31, 1953, The Institute of Petroleum, London, 1954, 333 pp.

F. W. Aston, *Mass Spectra and Isotopes*, second edition, Edward Arnold and Company, London, 1942, 276 pp.

G. P. Barnard, *Modern Mass Spectrometry*, The Institute of Physics, London, 1953, 326 pp.

C. E. Berry and J. K. Walker, "Industrial Applications (Mass Spectrometry)," in *Annual Reviews of Nuclear Physics*, Vol. 5, J. G. Beckerley, M. D. Kamen, and L. I. Schiff (eds.), Annual Reviews, Inc., Stanford, Calif., 1955, pp. 197–211.

J. H. Beynon, *Mass Spectrometry and Its Applications to Organic Chemistry*, Elsevier Publishing Company, Amsterdam, 1960, 640 pp.

J. H. Beynon, and A. E. Williams, *Mass and Abundance Tables for Use in Mass Spectrometry*, Elsevier Publishing Company, Amsterdam, 1963, 570 pp.

K. Biemann, *Mass Spectrometry: Applications to Organic Chemistry*, McGraw-Hill Book Company, New York, 1962, 370 pp.

K. Biemann, "Mass Spectrometry," in *Annual Reviews of Biochemistry*, Vol.

32, J. M. Luck, E. E. Snell, F. W. Allen, and G. Mackinney (eds.), Annual Reviews, Inc., Stanford, Calif., 1963, pp. 755–80.

H. Birkenfeld, G. Haase, and H. Zahn, *Massenspektrometrische Isotopenanalyse*, VEB Deutscher Verlag der Wissenschaften, Berlin, 1962, 254 pp.

L. M. Branscomb, "Negative Ions," in *Advances in Electronics and Electron Physics*, Vol. 9, L. Marton (ed.), Academic Press, Inc., New York, 1957, pp. 43–94.

H. Budzikiewicz, C. Djerassi, and D. H. Williams, *Interpretation of Mass Spectra of Organic Compounds*, Holden-Day, Inc., San Francisco, 1964, 271 pp.

A. E. Cameron, "Electromagnetic Separations," in *Physical Methods in Chemical Analysis*, Vol. IV, W. G. Berl (ed.), Academic Press, Inc., New York, 1961, pp. 119–32.

J. D. Craggs and C. A. McDowell, "The Ionization and Dissociation of Complex Molecules by Electron Impact," in *Reports on Progress in Physics*, Vol. 18, A. C. Strickland (ed.), The Physical Society, London, 1955, pp. 374–422.

H. E. Duckworth, *Mass Spectroscopy*, Cambridge at the University Press, London, 1960, 206 pp.

H. E. Duckworth (ed.), *Proceedings of the International Conference on Nuclidic Masses*, University of Toronto Press, Toronto, 1960, 540 pp.

W. J. Dunning, "The Application of Mass Spectrometry to Chemical Problems," *Quart. Revs.*, **11**, 23 (1955).

R. M. Elliott (ed.), *Advances in Mass Spectrometry*, Vol. 2, Pergamon Press, Oxford, England, 1963, 628 pp.

H. Ewald and H. Hintenberger, *Methoden und Anwendungen der Massenspektroskopie*, Verlag Chemie, Gmbh, Weinheim, Germany, 1952, 288 pp.

F. H. Field and J. L. Franklin, *Electron Impact Phenomena and the Properties of Gaseous Ions*, Academic Press, Inc., New York, 1957, 350 pp.

M. J. Higatsberger and F. P. Viehböck, *Electromagnetic Separation of Radioactive Isotopes*, Springer-Verlag, Vienna, 1961, 318 pp.

H. Hintenberger (ed.), *Nuclear Masses and Their Determination*, Pergamon Press, London, 1957.

H. Hintenberger, "High-Sensitivity Mass Spectroscopy in Nuclear Studies," in *Annual Reviews of Nuclear Science*, Vol. 12, E. Segre, G. Friedlander, and W. E. Meyerhof (eds.), Annual Reviews, Inc., Palo Alto, Calif., 1962, pp. 435–506.

R. G. E. Hutter, "The Deflection of Beams of Charged Particles," in *Advances in Electronics*, Vol. 1, L. Marton (ed.), Academic Press, Inc., New York, 1948, pp. 167–218.

M. G. Inghram, "Modern Mass Spectroscopy," in *Advances in Electronics*, Vol. 1, L. Marton (ed.), Academic Press, Inc., New York, 1948, pp. 219–68.

M. G. Inghram and R. J. Hayden, *A Handbook on Mass Spectroscopy*, Nuclear Science Series Report No. 14, National Academy of Sciences, National Research Council Publication 311, Washington, D. C., 1954.

L. Kerwin, "Mass Spectroscopy," in *Advances in Electronics and Electron Physics*, Vol. 8, L. Marton (ed.), Academic Press, Inc., New York, 1956, pp. 187–253.

M. Krauss, A. L. Wahrhaftig, and H. Eyring, "Mass Spectra and the Chemical Species Produced by the Impact of Low Energy Electrons," in *Annual Review of Nuclear Science*, Vol. 5, J. G. Beckerley, M. D. Kamen, and L. I. Schiff (eds.), Annual Reviews, Inc., Stanford, Calif., 1955, pp. 241–68.

F. W. Lampe, J. L. Franklin, and F. H. Field, "Kinetics of the Reactions of Ions with Molecules," in *Progress in Reaction Kinetics*, G. Porter (ed.), Pergamon Press, New York, 1961, pp. 67–103.

L. B. Loeb, *Basic Processes of Gaseous Electronics*, University of California Press, Berkeley, 1955, 1012 pp.

Mass Spectrometry, Report of a conference organized by the mass spectrometry panel of the Institute of Petroleum, Manchester, Apr. 20–21, 1950, The Institute of Petroleum, London, 1952, 105 pp.

Mass Spectroscopy in Physics Research, National Bureau of Standards Circular 522, U.S. Government Printing Office, Washington, D.C., 1953, 273 pp.

H. S. W. Massey, *Negative Ions*, second edition, Cambridge at the University Press, London, 1950, 136 pp.

H. S. W. Massey and E. H. S. Burhop, *Electronic and Ionic Impact Phenomena*, Oxford at the Clarendon Press, London, 1952, 670 pp.

K. I. Mayne, "Mass Spectrometry," in *Reports on Progress in Physics*, Vol. 15, A. C. Strickland (ed.), The Physical Society, London, 1952, pp. 24–48.

E. W. McDaniel, *Collisional Phenomena in Ionized Cases,* John Wiley and Sons, Inc., New York, 1964, 775 pp.

C. A. McDowell (ed.), *Mass Spectrometry*, McGraw-Hill Book Company, New York, 1963, 639 pp.

F. W. McLafferty, *Mass Spectral Correlations*, Advances in Chemistry Series 40, American Chemical Society, Washington, D. C., 1963, 118 pp.

F. W. McLafferty (ed.), *Mass Spectrometry of Organic Ions*, Academic Press, Inc., New York, 1963, 730 pp.

F. W. McLafferty, "Mass Spectrometry," in *Determination of Organic Structures by Physical Methods*, Vol. 2, F. C. Nachod and W. D. Phillips (eds.), Academic Press, Inc., New York, 1962, pp. 93–179.

S. Meyerson and J. D. McCollum, "Mass Spectra of Organic Molecules," in *Advances in Analytical Chemistry and Instrumentation*, Vol. 2, C. N. Reilley (ed.), Interscience Publishers, New York, 1963, pp. 179–218.

N. F. Mott and H. S. W. Massey, *The Theory of Atomic Collisions*, second edition, Oxford at the Clarendon Press, London, 1949, 388 pp.

R. I. Reed, *Ion Production by Electron Impact*, Academic Press, Inc., New York, 1962, 242 pp.

A. J. B. Robertson, *Mass Spectrometry*, Methuen and Company, Ltd., London, 1954, 135 pp.

C. F. Robinson, "Mass Spectrometry," in *Physical Methods in Chemical Analysis*, Vol. 1, second revised edition, W. G. Berl (ed.), Academic Press, Inc., New York, 1960, pp. 473–545.

K. E. Shuler and J. B. Fenn, (eds.), "Ionization in High-Temperature Gases," Vol. 12 of *Progress in Astronautics and Aeronautics*, Academic Press, Inc., New York, 1963., 409 pp.

M. L. Smith (ed.), *Electromagnetically Enriched Isotopes and Mass Spectrometry*, Proceedings of the Harwell Conferences, Sept. 13–16, 1955, Academic Press, Inc., New York, 1956.

D. P. Stevenson and D. O. Schissler, "Mass Spectrometry and Radiation Chemistry," in *Actions Chimiques et Biologiques des Radiations*, Cinquieme Serie, M. Haissinsky (ed.), Masson et Cie, Edituers, Paris, 1961, pp. 167–271.

A. Streitwieser, Jr., "Ionization Potentials in Organic Chemistry," in *Progress in Physical Organic Chemistry*, Vol. 1, S. G. Cohen, A. Streitwieser, Jr., and R. W. Taft (eds.), Interscience Publishers, New York, 1963, pp. 1–30.

H. G. Thode, C. C. McMullen, and K. Fritze, "Mass Spectrometry in Nuclear Chemistry," in *Advances in Inorganic Chemistry and Radiochemistry*, Vol. 2, H. J. Emeleus and A. G. Sharpe (eds.), Academic Press, Inc., New York, 1960, pp. 315–63.

H. G. Thode and R. B. Shields, "Mass Spectrometry," in *Reports on Progress in Physics*, Vol. 12, A. C. Strickland (ed.), The Physical Society, London, 1949, pp. 1–21.

J. J. Thomson, *Rays of Positive Electricity and Their Application to Chemical Analyses*, Longmans, Green and Co., London, 1913.

V. I. Vedeneev, L. V. Gurvich, V. N. Kondrat'ev, V. A. Medvedev, and E. L. Frankevich, *Dissociation Energies of Chemical Bonds. Ionization Potentials and Electron Affinities Handbook*, Academy of Sciences of the U.S.S.R., Chemical Physics Institute, Moscow, 1962, 216 pp.

J. D. Waldron (ed.), *Advances in Mass Spectrometry*, Vol. 1, Pergamon Press, New York, 1959, 704 pp.

H. W. Washburn, "Mass Spectrometry," in *Physical Methods in Chemical Analysis*, Vol. 1, W. G. Berl (ed.), Academic Press, Inc., New York, 1950, pp. 587–639.

S. E. Wiberley and D. A. Aikens, "Mass Spectrometry," *J. Chem. Ed.*, **41**, (2), A75–A91 and (3), A153–A180 (1964).

NAME INDEX

SUBJECT INDEX